A WORLD OF HORSES

Books by Margaret Cabell Self

TEACHING THE YOUNG TO RIDE

HORSES: THEIR SELECTION, CARE AND HANDLING

HORSEMAN'S ENCYCLOPEDIA

FUN ON HORSEBACK

A TREASURY OF HORSE STORIES

RIDING SIMPLIFIED

THE HORSEMAN'S COMPANION

IRISH ADVENTURE

HORSEMASTERSHIP

THE AMERICAN HORSE SHOW

JUMPING SIMPLIFIED

RIDING WITH MARILES

A WORLD OF HORSES

Fiction

THOSE SMITH KIDS

CHITTER-CHAT STORIES

PONIES ON PARADE

COME AWAY

A WORLD
OF
HORSES

AN ANTHOLOGY EDITED BY

Margaret Cabell Self

Illustrated by Harold Breul

McGRAW-HILL BOOK COMPANY, INC.

New York Toronto London

A WORLD OF HORSES

Acknowledgments

"The Summer of the Beautiful White Horse." From *My Name Is Aram*, copyright, 1937, 1938, 1939, 1940, by William Saroyan. Reprinted by permission of Harcourt, Brace & World, Inc. Open market with permission of Harold Matson Company.

"A Money-making Proposition." From *Penrod: His Complete Story*. Doubleday & Company, Inc. Copyright, 1915, 1943 by Booth Tarkington. Reprinted by permission of Brandt & Brandt.

"A Prince and a Cowboy." From *The Autobiography of Lincoln Steffens*, copyright, 1931, by Harcourt, Brace & World, Inc.; renewed, 1959, by Peter Steffens. Reprinted by permission of the publishers.

"The Marriage of Ghazal and the Grey Mare." From *Drinkers of the Wind*, by Carl R. Raswan, copyright © 1942 by Carl R. Raswan. Used by permission of the publishers, Farrar, Straus and Cudahy, Inc., and Sanford J. Greenburger.

"Jumper." Chapter II from *Jumper*, pp. 15–17, by Nicholas Kalashnikoff (Copyright 1944 Charles Scribner's Sons) is reprinted with the permission of Charles Scribner's Sons.

"Red Tobal," by Herbert Ravenel Sass. First published in *The Saturday Evening Post*. Copyright 1929 by The Curtis Publishing Co. Copyright 1935 by Herbert Ravenel Sass. Reprinted with permission of Marion H. Sass.

"Tzagan," by Clement Wood. Copyright 1935 by Clement Wood. Reprinted with the permission of Gloria G. Wood.

"The Ghost Horse." From *Long Lance* by Chief Buffalo Child Long Lance. Copyright 1928, copyright renewed ⓒ 1956 by Holt, Rinehart and Winston, Inc. Reprinted by permission of Holt, Rinehart and Winston, Inc.

"That Colt Pericles," by Henry Herbert Knibbs. First published in *The Saturday Evening Post*. Copyright 1932 by The Curtis Publishing Co. Copyright 1935 by Henry Herbert Knibbs. Reprinted with permission of the Cancer Research Foundation of America, Los Angeles, California.

"County Down." From *Irish Hunting* by Muriel Bowen, first published by The Kerryman, Ltd., 1954. Reprinted with permission of Muriel Bowen and The Kerryman, Ltd.

"A Quiet Bye." From *Handley Cross* by Robert Smith Surtees. Reprinted by permission of The Viking Press, Inc. All rights reserved. Reprinted by permission of George G. Harrap & Company, Limited.

"The Crest of Athelling Hill." From *The Millbeck Hounds* by Gordon Grand (Copyright 1947, Gordon Grand). Published with the permission of Mr. Grand's family.

"Trail's End." From *The Bolinvars* by Marguerite Bayliss. Copyright ⓒ 1937 by The Derrydale Press. Copyright ⓒ 1944 by Marguerite Bayliss. Reprinted by permission of McIntosh and Otis, Inc.

"Some Statistics on Speed and Endurance Records." From *Riders of Many Lands* by Theodore Ayrault Dodge. Reprinted by permission of Houghton Mifflin Company.

"An Endurance Ride in the Year 1704." From *Horses and Americans,* by Phil Stong. Copyright 1939 by Phil Stong. Reprinted with permission of Harold Matson Company.

"A Rugged Ride." From *Tschiffely's Ride* by A. F. Tschiffely. Copyright 1933 by A. F. Tschiffely. Reprinted by permission of the literary executors of the late A. F. Tschiffely.

"A Discovery and a Chase." From *The Pickwick Papers* by Charles Dickens.

"The Hambletonian." From *Drivers Up!* By Dwight Akers. Copyright 1938 by Dwight Akers. Reprinted by permission of G. P. Putnam's Sons, Publishers.

"Overcoat Meeting." From *Overcoat Meeting* by George Agnew Chamberlain. Copyright 1949 by George Agnew Chamberlain. Reprinted by permission of A. S. Barnes and Company, Inc.

"Thomasheen James and the Dangerous Age," by Maurice Walsh. First published in *The Saturday Evening Post*. Copyright 1938 by The Curtis Publishing Company. Reprinted by permission of Brandt & Brandt and W. & R. Chambers Ltd.

"The Broken Link Handicap." From: *Plain Tales from the Hills* by Rudyard Kipling. Reprinted by permission of Mrs. George Bambridge and Doubleday & Company, Inc., and The Macmillan Company of Canada, Ltd.

"The Race." From *National Velvet* by Enid Bagnold. Wm. Morrow & Company, Inc. Copyright, 1935, by Enid Bagnold Jones. Reprinted by permission of Brandt & Brandt and A. M. Heath & Co., Ltd.

viii   *Acknowledgments*

"The Old Hunter." From *Stories of Liam O'Flaherty* by Liam O'Flaherty, copyright and publication in 1956 by The Devin-Adair Co., New York. Published in 1937 by Jonathan Cape Limited. Reprinted with permission of the publishers.

"Carty Carteret's Sister." From *Gallups I* by David Gray. Century Co., 1899. Reprinted with permission of the author.

"The Horse Looked at Him" copyright 1938, by Crowell-Collier Publishing Company; copyright 1938 by MacKinlay Kantor, is reprinted by permission of the World Publishing Company.

"The Story of a Piebald Horse." Reprinted from *Tales of the Pampas* by W. H. Hudson, by permission of Alfred A. Knopf, Inc. Copyright 1916 by Alfred A. Knopf, Inc. Reprinted with permission of The Royal Society for the Protection of Birds, and The Society of Authors.

"Rodney," by Leonard H. Nason. First published in *The Saturday Evening Post*. Copyright 1933 by The Curtis Publishing Co. Reprinted with permission of Leonard H. Nason.

"The Seeing Eye" is reprinted from *Horses I Have Known* by Will James (copyright 1940 Will James) with the permission of Charles Scribner's Sons.

"The Sheikh and His Mare." From *Palestine Caravan* by Moshe Smilansky, first published by Methuen & Co. Ltd., 1935. Reprinted with permission of Methuen & Co. Ltd., Publishers.

"Metzengerstein." From *Prose Tales, Second Series* by Edgar Allan Poe.

"I Ride a Bucking Horse." From *Roughing It* by Mark Twain. Reprinted by permission of Harper & Brothers.

Preface

The horse is, and has been, an inspiring subject for centuries. I have tried here to present a group of stories and excerpts from books which represent the best in writing on this subject and as much diversity as possible in treatment and subject. As is inevitable, some of the selections in this volume will appeal to one reader while others will be more popular with another. There are a few old favorites, and many which are less familiar. May you, the reader, enjoy reading this book as much as I enjoyed the research that went into the preparation of it.

Margaret Cabell Self

Contents

For Speed and Endurance

The Race Run

The Horse as Friend, Servant, and Sometimes Master

Youthful Encounters

The Summer of the Beautiful White Horse

WILLIAM SAROYAN

If one searched throughout the pages of fiction it would be difficult to find two stories with identical themes which are such complete opposites in treatment and style as this story by William Saroyan and the one that follows it by Booth Tarkington. In both stories, the heroes are boys of about twelve who acquire horses by somewhat nefarious means. Yet from this common ground spring two tales completely different in tone, though both are delightful and diverting. Tarkington's nag and boys are the pragmatic sort, while Saroyan's steed and young riders are touched with poetry in this soaring tale. I can think of no happier encounter with which to enter a world of horses.

One day back there in the good old days when I was nine and the world was full of every imaginable kind of magnificence, and life was still a delightful and mysterious dream, my cousin Mourad, who was considered crazy by everybody who knew him except me, came to my house at four in the morning and woke me up by tapping on the window of my room.

Aram, he said.

I jumped out of bed and looked out the window.

I couldn't believe what I saw.

It wasn't morning yet, but it was summer and with daybreak not many minutes around the corner of the world it was light enough for me to know I wasn't dreaming.

My cousin Mourad was sitting on a beautiful white horse.

I stuck my head out of the window and rubbed my eyes.

Yes, he said in Armenian. It's a horse. You're not dreaming. Make it quick if you want to ride.

I knew my cousin Mourad enjoyed being alive more than anybody else who had ever fallen into the world by mistake, but this was more than even I could believe.

In the first place, my earliest memories had been memories of horses and my first longings had been longings to ride.

This was the wonderful part.

In the second place, we were poor.

This was the part that wouldn't permit me to believe what I saw.

We were poor. We had no money. Our whole tribe was poverty-stricken. Every branch of the Garoghlanian family was living in the most amazing and comical poverty in the world. Nobody could understand where we ever got money enough to keep us with food in our bellies, not even the old men of the family. Most important of all, though, we were famous for our honesty. We had been famous for our honesty for something like eleven centuries, even when we had been the wealthiest family in what we liked to think was the world. We were proud first, honest next, and after that we believed in right and wrong. None of us would take advantage of anybody in the world, let alone steal.

Consequently, even though I could *see* the horse, so magnificent; even though I could *smell* it, so lovely; even though I could *hear* it breathing, so exciting; I couldn't *believe* the horse had anything to do with my cousin Mourad or with me or with any of the other members of our family, asleep or awake, because I *knew* my cousin Mourad couldn't have bought the horse, and if he couldn't have bought it he must have *stolen* it, and I refused to believe he had stolen it.

No member of the Garoghlanian family could be a thief.

I stared first at my cousin and then at the horse. There was a pious stillness and humor in each of them which on the one hand delighted me and on the other frightened me.

Mourad, I said, where did you steal this horse?

Leap out of the window, he said, if you want to ride.

It was true, then. He *had* stolen the horse. There was no question about it. He had come to invite me to ride or not, as I chose.

Well, it seemed to me stealing a horse for a ride was not the same thing as stealing something else, such as money. For all I knew, maybe it wasn't stealing at all. If you were crazy about horses the way my cousin Mourad and I were, it wasn't stealing. It wouldn't become stealing until we offered to sell the horse, which of course I knew we would never do.

Let me put on some clothes, I said.

All right, he said, but hurry.

I leaped into my clothes.

I jumped down to the yard from the window and leaped up onto the horse behind my cousin Mourad.

That year we lived at the edge of town, on Walnut Avenue. Behind our house was the country: vineyards, orchards, irrigation ditches, and country roads. In less than three minutes we were on Olive Avenue, and then the horse began to trot. The air was new and lovely to breathe. The feel of the horse running was wonderful. My cousin Mourad, who was considered one of the craziest members of our family, began to sing. I mean, he began to roar.

Every family has a crazy streak in it somewhere, and my cousin Mourad was considered the natural descendant of the crazy streak in our tribe. Before him was our uncle Khosrove, an enormous man with a powerful head of black hair and the largest mustache in the San Joaquin Valley, a man so furious in temper, so irritable, so impatient, that he stopped anyone from talking by roaring, *It is no harm; pay no attention to it.*

That was all, no matter what anybody happened to be talking about. Once it was his own son Arak running eight blocks to the barber shop where his father was having his mustache trimmed to tell him their house was on fire. This man Khosrove sat up in the chair and roared, It is no harm; pay no attention to it. The barber said, But the boy says your house is on fire. So Khosrove roared, Enough, it is no harm, I say.

My cousin Mourad was considered the natural descendant of this man, although Mourad's father was Zorab, who was practical and nothing else. That's how it was in our tribe. A man could be the father of his son's flesh, but that did not mean that he was also the father of his spirit. The distribution of the various kinds of spirit of our tribe had been from the beginning capricious and vagrant.

We rode and my cousin Mourad sang. For all anybody knew

we were still in the old country where, at least according to some of our neighbors, we belonged. We let the horse run as long as it felt like running.

At last my cousin Mourad said, Get down, I want to ride alone.

Will you let me ride alone? I said.

That is up to the horse, my cousin said. Get down.

The *horse* will let me ride, I said.

We shall see, he said. Don't forget that I have a way with a horse.

Well, I said, any way you have with a horse, I have also.

For the sake of your safety, he said, let us hope so. Get down.

All right, I said, but remember you've got to let me try to ride alone.

I got down and my cousin Mourad kicked his heels into the horse and shouted, *Vazire,* run. The horse stood on its hind legs, snorted, and burst into a fury of speed that was the loveliest thing I had ever seen. My cousin Mourad raced the horse across a field of dry grass to an irrigation ditch, crossed the ditch on the horse, and five minutes later returned, dripping wet.

The sun was coming up.

Now it's my turn to ride, I said.

My cousin Mourad got off the horse.

Ride, he said.

I leaped to the back of the horse and for a moment knew the awfulest fear imaginable. The horse did not move.

Kick into his muscles, my cousin Mourad said. What are you waiting for? We've got to take him back before everybody in the world is up and about.

I kicked into the muscles of the horse. Once again it reared and snorted. Then it began to run. I didn't know what to do. Instead of running across the field to the irrigation ditch the horse ran down the road to the vineyard of Dikran Halabian where it began to leap over vines. The horse leaped over seven vines before I fell. Then it continued running.

My cousin Mourad came running down the road.

I'm not worried about you, he shouted. We've got to get that horse. You go this way and I'll go this way. If you come upon him be kindly, I'll be near.

I continued down the road and my cousin Mourad went across the field to the irrigation ditch.

It took him half an hour to find the horse and bring him back.

All right, he said, jump on. The whole world is awake now.

What will we do? I said.

Well, he said, we'll either take him back or hide him until tomorrow morning.

He didn't sound worried and I knew he'd hide him and not take him back. Not for a while, at any rate.

Where will we hide him? I said.

I know a place, he said.

How long ago did you steal this horse? I said.

It suddenly dawned on me that he had been taking these early morning rides for some time and had come for me this morning only because he knew how much I longed to ride.

Who said anything about stealing a horse? he said.

Anyhow, I said, how long ago did you begin riding every morning?

Not until this morning, he said.

Are you telling the truth? I said.

Of course not, he said, but if we are found out, that's what you're to say. I don't want both of us to be liars. All you know is that we started riding this morning.

All right, I said.

He walked the horse quietly to the barn of a deserted vineyard which at one time had been the pride of a farmer named Fetvajian. There were some oats and dry alfalfa in the barn.

We began walking home.

It wasn't easy, he said, to get the horse to behave so nicely. At first it wanted to run wild, but, as I've told you, I have a way with a horse. I can get it to do anything *I* want it to do. Horses understand me.

How do you do it? I said.

I have an understanding with a horse, he said.

Yes, but what sort of an understanding? I said.

A simple and honest one, he said.

Well, I said, I wish I knew how to reach an understanding like that with a horse.

You're still a small boy, he said. When you get to be thirteen you'll know how to do it.

I went home and ate a hearty breakfast.

That afternoon my uncle Khosrove came to our house for coffee and cigarettes. He sat in the parlor, sipping and smoking and remembering the old country. Then another visitor arrived, a farmer named John Byro, an Assyrian who, out of loneliness, had learned to speak Armenian. My mother brought the lonely visitor coffee and tobacco, and he rolled a cigarette and sipped and smoked, and then at last, sighing sadly, he said, My white horse which was stolen last month is still gone. I cannot understand it.

My uncle Khosrove became very irritated and shouted, It's no harm. What is the loss of a horse? Haven't we all lost the homeland? What is this crying over a horse?

That may be all right for you, a city dweller to say, John Byro said, but what of my surrey? What good is a surrey without a horse?

Pay no attention to it, my uncle Khosrove roared.

I walked ten miles to get here, John Byro said.

You have legs, my uncle Khosrove roared.

My left leg pains me, the farmer said.

Pay no attention to it, my uncle shouted.

That horse cost me sixty dollars, the farmer said.

I spit on money, my uncle Khosrove said.

He got up and stalked out of the house, slamming the screen door.

My mother explained.

He has a gentle heart, she said. It is simply that he is homesick, and such a large man.

The farmer went away and I ran over to my cousin Mourad's house.

He was sitting under a peach tree, trying to repair the hurt wing of a young robin which could not fly. He was talking to the bird.

What is it? he said

The farmer, John Byro, I said. He visited our house. He wants his horse. You've had it a month. I want you to promise not to take it back until I learn to ride.

It will take a *year* to learn to ride, my cousin Mourad said.

We could keep the horse a year, I said.

My cousin Mourad leaped to his feet.

What? he roared. Are you inviting a member of the Garoghlanian family to steal? The horse must go back to its true owner.

When? I said.

In six months at the latest, he said.

He threw the bird into the air. The bird tried hard, almost fell twice, but at last flew away, high and straight.

Early every morning for two weeks my cousin Mourad and I took the horse out of the barn of the deserted vineyard where we were hiding it and rode it, and every morning the horse, when it was my turn to ride alone, leaped over grape vines and small trees and threw me and ran away. Nevertheless, I hoped in time to learn to ride the way my cousin Mourad rode.

One morning on the way to Fetvajian's deserted vineyard we ran into the farmer John Byro who was on his way to town.

Let me do the talking, my cousin Mourad said. I have a way with farmers.

Good morning, John Byro, my cousin Mourad said to the farmer.

The farmer studied the horse eagerly.

Good morning, sons of my friends, he said. What is the name of your horse?

My heart, my cousin Mourad said in Armenian.

A lovely name, John Byro said, for a lovely horse. I could swear it is the horse that was stolen from me many weeks ago. May I look into its mouth?

Of course, Mourad said.

The farmer looked into the mouth of the horse.

Tooth for tooth, he said, I would swear it *is* my horse if I didn't know your parents. The fame of your family for honesty is well known to me. Yet the horse is the twin of my horse. A suspicious man would believe his eyes instead of his heart. Good day, my young friends.

Good day, John Byro, my cousin Mourad said.

Early the following morning we took the horse to John Byro's vineyard and put it in the barn. The dogs followed us around without making a sound.

The dogs, I whispered to my cousin Mourad. I thought they would bark.

They would at somebody else, he said. I have a way with dogs.

My cousin Mourad put his arms around the horse, pressed his nose into the horse's nose, patted it, and we went away.

That afternoon John Byro came to our house in his surrey and showed my mother the horse that had been stolen and returned.

I do not know what to think, he said. The horse is stronger than ever. Better-tempered, too. I thank God.

My uncle Khosrove, who was in the parlor, became irritated and shouted, Quiet, man, quiet. Your horse has been returned. Pay no attention to it.

A Money-making Proposition

BOOTH TARKINGTON

*Booth Tarkington, like Mark Twain, is best known and loved
for his exact knowledge of the inmost workings of the mind
of the adolescent male. In these days when the juvenile mind
and its reactions, are constantly being analyzed, and children
are treated like morons one minute and adults the next, it is
refreshing to read an author who wrote before people's opinions were biased by reading the works of experts on psychology and child behavior. Booth Tarkington writes from his own
knowledge and experience, and his characters are as alive and
true today as they were the day he first put pen to paper.
This story, while it concerns a horse, reveals the author's insight into the ability of the boy to adapt his mental reactions
of circumstances and is surely one of the most delightful lessons in psychology ever written.*

Penrod and Sam made a gloomy discovery one morning in mid-
October. All week had seen amiable breezes and fair skies until
Saturday, when, about breakfast-time, the dome of heaven filled
solidly with gray vapour and began to drip. The boys' discovery
was that there was no justice about the weather.

They sat in the carriage-house of the Schofields' empty stable;
the doors upon the alley were open, and Sam and Penrod stared
torpidly at the thin but implacable drizzle which was the more
irritating because there was barely enough of it to interfere with a
number of things they had planned to do.

"Yes; this is *nice!*" Sam said, in a tone of plaintive sarcasm.

"This is a *perty* way to do!" (He was alluding to the personal spite-fulness of the elements.) "I'd like to know what's the sense of it—ole sun pourin' down every day in the week when nobody needs it, then cloud up and rain all Saturday! My father said it's goin' to be a three days' rain."

"Well, nobody with any sense cares if it rains Sunday and Monday," said Penrod. "I wouldn't care if it rained every Sunday as long as I lived; but I just like to know what's the reason it had to go and rain to-day. Got all the days o' the week to choose from and goes and picks on Saturday. That's a fine biz'nuss!"

"Well, in vacation—" Sam began, but at a sound from a source invisible to him he paused. "What's that?" he said, somewhat startled.

It was a curious sound, loud and hollow and unhuman, yet it seemed to be a cough. Both boys rose, and Penrod asked uneasily:

"Where'd that noise come from?"

"It's in the alley," said Sam.

Perhaps if the day had been bright, both of them would have stepped immediately to the alley doors to investigate; but their actual procedure was to move a little distance in the opposite direction. The strange cough sounded again.

"*Say!*" Penrod quavered. "What *is* that?"

Then both boys uttered smothered exclamations and jumped, for the long, gaunt head which appeared in the doorway was entirely unexpected. It was the cavernous and melancholy head of an incredible thin, old, whitish horse. This head waggled slowly from side to side; the nostrils vibrated; the mouth opened, and the hollow cough sounded again.

Recovering themselves, Penrod and Sam underwent the customary human reaction from alarm to indignation.

"What you want, you ole horse, you?" Penrod shouted. "Don't you come coughin' around *me!*"

And Sam, seizing a stick, hurled it at the intruder.

"Get out o' here!" he roared.

The aged horse nervously withdrew his head, turned tail, and made a rickety flight up the alley, while Sam and Penrod, perfectly obedient to inherited impulse, ran out into the drizzle and uproariously pursued. They were but the automatons of instinct, meaning no evil. Certainly they did not know the singular and pathetic history of the old horse who had wandered into the alley and ventured to look through the open door.

This horse, about twice the age of either Penrod or Sam, had lived to find himself in a unique position. He was nude, possessing neither harness nor halter; all he had was a name, Whitey, and he would have answered to it by a slight change of expression if any one had thus properly addressed him. So forlorn was Whitey's case, he was actually an independent horse; he had not even an owner. For two days and a half he had been his own master.

Previous to that period he had been the property of one Abalene Morris, a person of colour, who would have explained himself as engaged in the hauling business. On the contrary, the hauling business was an insignificant side line with Mr. Morris, for he had long ago given himself, as utterly as fortune permitted, to that talent which, early in youth, he had recognized as the greatest of all those surging in his bosom. In his waking thoughts and in his dreams, in health and in sickness Abalene Morris was the dashing and emotional practitioner of an art probably more than Roman in antiquity. Abalene was a crap-shooter. The hauling business was a disguise.

A concentration of events had brought it about that, at one and the same time, Abalene, after a dazzling run of the dice, found the hauling business an actual danger to the preservation of his liberty. He won seventeen dollars and sixty cents, and within the hour found himself in trouble with an officer of the Humane Society on account of an altercation with Whitey. Abalene had been offered four dollars for Whitey some ten days earlier; wherefore he at once drove to the shop of the junk-dealer who had made the offer and announced his acquiescence in the sacrifice.

"*No, suh!*" said the junk-dealer, with emphasis. "I awready done got me a good mule fer my deliv'ry hoss, 'n 'at ole Whitey hoss ain' wuff no fo' dollah nohow! I 'uz a fool when I talk 'bout th'owin' money roun' that a-way. *I* know what you up to, Abalene. Man come by here li'l bit ago tole me all 'bout white man try to 'rest you, ovah on the avvynoo. Yessuh; he say white man goin' to git you yit an' th'ow you in jail 'count o' Whitey. White man tryin' to fine out who you *is*. He say, nemmine, he'll know Whitey ag'in, even if he

don' know you! He say he ketch you by the hoss; so you come roun'
tryin' fix me up with Whitey so white man grab me, th'ow *me* in
jail. G'on 'way f'um hyuh, you Abalene! You cain' sell an' you cain'
give Whitey to no cullud man 'n 'is town. You go an' drowned 'at
ole hoss, 'cause you sutny goin' to jail if you git ketched drivin'
him."

The substance of this advice seemed good to Abalene, especially
as the seventeen dollars and sixty cents in his pocket lent sweet
colours to life out of jail at this time. At dusk he led Whitey to a
broad common at the edge of town, and spoke to him finally.

"G'on, 'bout you biz'nis," said Abalene; "you ain' *my* hoss.
Don' look roun' at me, 'cause *I* ain' got no 'quaintance wif you.
I'm a man o' money, an' I got my own frien's; I'm a-lookin' fer
bigger cities, hoss. You got you' biz'nis an' I got mine. Mista' Hoss,
good-night!"

Whitey found a little frosted grass upon the common and remained there all night. In the morning he sought the shed where Abalene had kept him, but that was across the large and busy town, and Whitey was hopelessly lost. He had but one eye, a feeble one, and his legs were not to be depended upon; but he managed to cover a great deal of ground, to have many painful little adventures, and to get monstrously hungry and thirsty before he happened to look in upon Penrod and Sam.

When the two boys chased him up the alley they had no intention to cause pain. They were no more cruel than Duke, Penrod's little old dog, who followed his own instincts, and, making his appearance hastily through a hole in the back fence, joined the pursuit with sound and fury. A boy will nearly always run after anything that is running, and his first impulse is to throw a stone at it. This is a survival of primeval man, who must take every chance to get his dinner. So, when Penrod and Sam drove the hapless Whitey up the alley, they were really responding to an impulse thousands and thousands of years old—an impulse founded upon the primordial observation that whatever runs is likely to prove edible. Penrod and Sam were not "bad"; they were never that. They were something which was not their fault; they were historic.

At the next corner Whitey turned to the right into the cross-street; thence, turning to the right again and still warmly pursued, he zigzagged down a main thoroughfare until he reached another cross-street, which ran alongside the Schofields' yard and brought him to the foot of the alley he had left behind in his flight. He entered the alley, and there his dim eye fell upon the open door he had previously investigated. No memory of it remained, but the place had a look associated in his mind with hay, and as Sam and Penrod turned the corner of the alley in panting yet still vociferous pursuit, Whitey stumbled up the inclined platform before the open doors, staggered thunderously across the carriage-house and through another door into a stall, an apartment vacant since the occupancy of Mr. Schofield's last horse, now several years deceased.

The two boys shrieked with excitement as they beheld the coincidence of this strange return. They burst into the stable, making almost as much noise as Duke, who had become frantic at the invasion. Sam laid hands on a rake.

"You get out o' here, you ole horse, you!" he bellowed. "I ain't afraid to drive him out. I—"

"Wait a minute!" shouted Penrod, "Wait till I—"

Sam was manfully preparing to enter the stall.

"You hold the doors open," he commanded, "so's they won't blow shut and keep him in here. I'm goin' to hit him with—"

"Quee-*yut*" Penrod shouted, grasping the handle of the rake so that Sam could not use it. "Wait a *minute,* can't you" He turned with ferocious voice and gestures upon Duke. *"Duke!"* And Duke, in spite of his excitement, was so impressed that he prostrated himself in silence, and then unobtrusively withdrew from the stable. Penrod ran to the alley doors and closed them.

"My gracious!" Sam protested. "What you goin' to do?"

"I'm goin' to keep this horse," said Penrod, whose face showed the strain of a great idea.

"What *for?"*

"For the reward," said Penrod simply.

Sam sat down in the wheelbarrow and stared at his friend almost with awe.

"My gracious," he said," I never thought o' that. How—how much do you think we'll get, Penrod?"

Sam's thus admitting himself to a full partnership in the enterprise met no objection from Penrod, who was absorbed in the contemplation of Whitey.

"Well," he said judicially, "we might get more and we might get less."

Sam rose and joined his friend in the doorway opening upon the two stalls. Whitey had preëmpted the nearer, and was hungrily nuzzling the old frayed hollows in the manger.

"Maybe a hundred dollars—or sumpthing?" Sam asked in a low voice.

Penrod maintained his composure and repeated the new-found expression which had sounded well to him a moment before. He recognized it as a symbol of the non-committal attitude that makes people looked up to. "Well"—he made it slow, and frowned—"we might get more and we might get less."

"More'n a hundred *dollars?"* Sam gasped.

"Well," said Penrod, "we might get more and we might get

less." This time, however, he felt the need of adding something. He put a question in an indulgent tone, as though he were inquiring, not to add to his own information, but to discover the extent of Sam's. "How much do you think horses are worth, anyway?"

"I don't know," said Sam frankly, and, unconsciously, he added, "They might be more and they might be less."

"Well, when our ole horse died," said Penrod, "papa said he wouldn't take five hundred dollars for him. That's how much *horses* are worth!"

"My gracious!" Sam exclaimed. Then he had a practical afterthought. "But maybe he was a better horse than this'n. What colour was he?"

"He was bay. Looky here, Sam"—and now Penrod's manner changed from the superior to the eager—"you look what kind of horses they have in the circus, and you bet a circus has the *best* horses, don't it? Well, what kind of horses do they have in a circus? They have some black and white ones but the best they have are white all over. Well, what kind of a horse is this we got here? He's perty near white right now, and I bet if we washed him off and got him fixed up nice he *would* be white. Well, a bay horse is five hundred dollars, because that's what papa said, and this horse—"

Sam interrupted rather timidly.

"He—he's awful bony, Penrod. You don't guess that'd make any—"

Penrod laughed contemptuously.

"Bony! All he needs is a little food and he'll fill right up and look good as ever. You don't know much about horses, Sam, I expect. Why *our* ole horse—"

"Do you expect he's hungry now?" asked Sam, staring at Whitey.

"Let's try him," said Penrod. "Horses like hay and oats the best, but they'll eat most anything."

"I guess they will. He's trying to eat that manger up right now, and I bet it ain't good for him."

"Come on," said Penrod, closing the door that gave entrance to the stalls. "We got to get this horse some drinkin'-water and some good food."

They tried Whitey's appetite first with an autumnal branch which they wrenched from a hardy maple in the yard. They had

seen horses nibble leaves, and they expected Whitey to nibble the
leaves of this branch, but his ravenous condition did not allow him
time for cool discriminations. Sam poked the branch at him from the
passageway, and Whitey, after one backward movement of alarm,
seized it venomously.

"Here! You stop that!" shouted Sam. "You stop that, you ole
horse, you!"

"What's the matter?" called Penrod from the hydrant, where he
was filling a bucket. "What's he doin' now?"

"Doin'! He's eatin' the wood part, too! He's chewin' up sticks
as big as baseball bats! He's crazy!"

Penrod rushed to see the sight, and stood aghast.

"Take it away from him, Sam!" he commanded sharply.

"Go on, take it away from him yourself!" was the prompt retort
of his comrade.

"You had no biz'nuss to give it to him," said Penrod. "Anybody with any sense ought to know it'd make him sick. What'd you
want to go and give it to him for?"

"Well, you didn't say not to."

"Well, what if I didn't? I never said I did, did I? You go on in
that stall and take it away from him."

"*Yes*, I will!" Sam returned bitterly. Then, as Whitey had
dragged the remains of the branch from the manger to the floor of
the stall, Sam scrambled to the top of the manger and looked
over. "There ain't much left to *take* away! He's swallered it all except some splinters. Better give him the water to try and wash it
down with." And, as Penrod complied, "My gracious, look at that
horse *drink!*"

They gave Whitey four buckets of water, and then debated the
question of nourishment. Obviously, this horse could not be trusted
with branches, and, after getting their knees black and their backs
sodden, they gave up trying to pull enough grass to sustain him.
Then Penrod remembered that horses like apples, both "cooking-
apples" and "eating-apples," and Sam mentioned the fact that
every autumn his father received a barrel of "cooking-apples" from
a cousin who owned a farm. That barrel was in the Williams' cellar
now, and the cellar was providentially supplied with "outside
doors," so that it could be visited without going through the house.
Sam and Penrod set forth for the cellar.

They returned to the stable bulging, and, after a discussion of Whitey's digestion (Sam claiming that eating the core and seeds, as Whitey did, would grow trees in his inside), they went back to the cellar for supplies again—and again. They made six trips, carrying each time a capacity cargo of apples, and still Whitey ate in a famished manner. They were afraid to take more apples from the barrel, which began to show conspiciously the result of their raids, wherefore Penrod made an unostentatious visit to the cellar of his own house. From the inside he opened a window and passed vegetables out to Sam, who placed them in a bucket and carried them hurriedly to the stable, while Penrod returned in a casual manner through the house. Of his *sang-froid* under great strain it is sufficient to relate that, in the kitchen, he said suddenly to Della, the cook, "Oh, look behind you!" and by the time Della discovered that there was nothing unusual behind her, Penrod was gone, and a loaf of bread from the kitchen table was gone with him.

Whitey now ate nine turnips, two heads of lettuce, one cabbage, eleven raw potatoes, and the loaf of bread. He ate the loaf of bread last and he was a long time about it; so the boys came to a not unreasonable conclusion.

"Well, sir, I guess we got him filled up at last!" said Penrod. "I bet he wouldn't eat a saucer of ice-cream now, if we'd give it to him!"

"He looks better to me," said Sam, staring critically at Whitey. "I think he's kind of begun to fill out some. I expect he must like us, Penrod; we been doin' a good deal for this horse."

"Well, we got to keep it up," Penrod insisted rather pompously. "Long as *I* got charge o' this horse, he's goin' to get good treatment."

"What we better do now, Penrod?"

Penrod took on the outward signs of deep thought.

"Well, there's plenty to *do*, all right. I got to think."

Sam made several suggestions, which Penrod—maintaining his air of preoccupation—dismissed with mere gestures.

"Oh, *I* know!" Sam cried finally. "We ought to wash him so's he'll look whiter'n he does now. We can turn the hose on him acrost the manger."

"No, not yet," said Penrod. "It's too soon after his meal. You ought to know that yourself. What we got to do is to make up a bed for him—if he wants to lay down or anything."

"Make up a what for him?" Sam echoed, dumfounded. "What you talkin' about? How can—"

"Sawdust," said Penrod. "That's the way the horse we used to have used to have it. We'll make this horse's bed in the other stall, and then he can go in there and lay down whenever he wants to."

"How we goin' to do it?"

"Look, Sam, there's a hole into the sawdust-box! All you got to do is to walk in there with the shovel, stick the shovel in the hole till it gets full of sawdust, and then sprinkle it around on the empty stall."

"All *I* got to do!" Sam cried. "What are you goin' to do?"

"I'm goin' to be right here," Penrod answered reassuringly. "He won't kick or anything, and it isn't goin' to take you half a second to slip around behind him to the other stall."

"What makes you think he won't kick?"

"Well, I *know* he won't, and, besides, you could hit him with the shovel if he tried to. Anyhow, I'll be right here, won't I?"

"I don't care where you are," Sam said earnestly. "What difference would that make if he ki—"

"Why, you were goin' right in the stall," Penrod reminded him. "When he first came in, you were goin' to take the rake and—"

"I don't care if I was," Sam declared. "I was excited then."

"Well, you can get excited now, can't you?" his friend urged. "You can just as easy get—"

He was interrupted by a shout from Sam, who was keeping his eye upon Whitey throughout the discussion.

"Look! Looky there!" And undoubtedly renewing his excitement, Sam pointed at the long, gaunt head beyond the manger. It was disappearing from view. "Look!" Sam shouted. "He's layin' down!"

"Well, then," said Penrod, "I guess he's goin' to take a nap. If he wants to lay down without waitin' for us to get the sawdust fixed for him, that's his lookout, not ours."

On the contrary, Sam perceived a favourable opportunity for action.

"I just as soon go and make his bed up while he's layin' down," he volunteered. "You climb up on the manger and watch him,

Penrod, and I'll sneak in the other stall and fix it all up nice for him, so's he can go in there any time when he wakes up, and lay down again, or anything; and if he starts to get up, you holler and I'll jump out over the other manger."

Accordingly, Penrod established himself in a position to observe the recumbent figure. Whitey's breathing was rather laboured but regular, and, as Sam remarked, he looked "better," even in his slumber. It is not to be doubted that, although Whitey was suffering from a light attack of colic, his feelings were in the main those of contentment. After trouble, he was solaced; after exposure, he was sheltered; after hunger and thirst, he was fed and watered. He slept.

The noon whistles blew before Sam's task was finished, but by the time he departed for lunch there was made a bed of such quality that Whitey must needs have been a born faultfinder if he complained of it. The friends parted, each urging the other to be prompt in returning, but Penrod got into threatening difficulties as soon as he entered the house.

"Penrod," said his mother, "what did you do with that loaf of bread Della says you took from the table?"

"Ma'am? *What* loaf o' bread?"

"I believe I can't let you go outdoors this afternoon," Mrs. Schofield said severely. "If you were hungry, you know perfectly well all you had to do was to—"

"But I wasn't hungry; I—"

"You can explain later," said Mrs. Schofield. "You'll have all afternoon."

Penrod's heart grew cold.

"I *can't* stay in," he protested. "I've asked Sam Williams to come over."

"I'll telephone Mrs. Williams."

"Mamma!" Penrod's voice became agonized. "I *had* to give that bread to a—to a poor ole man. He was starving and so were his children and his wife. They were all just *starving*—and they couldn't wait while I took time to come and ask you, mamma. I *got* to go outdoors this afternoon. I *got* to! Sam's—"

She relented.

In the carriage house, half an hour later, Penrod gave an account of the episode.

"Where'd we been, I'd just like to know," he concluded, "if I hadn't got out here this afternoon?"

"Well, I guess I could of managed him all right," said Sam. "I was in the passageway, a minute ago, takin' a look at him. He's standin' up again. I expect he wants more to eat."

"We got to fixt that," said Penrod. "But what I mean—if I'd had to stay in the house, where would we been about the most important thing in the whole biz'nuss?"

"What you talkin' about?"

"Well, why can't you wait till I tell you?" Penrod's tone had become peevish. For that matter, so had Sam's; they were developing one of the little differences, or quarrels, that composed the very texture of their friendship.

"Well, why don't you tell me, then?"

"Well, how can I?" Penrod demanded. "You keep talkin' every minute."

"I'm not talkin' *now*, am I?" Sam protested. "You can tell me *now*, can't you? I'm not talk—"

"You are, too!" shouted Penrod. "You talk all the time! You—"

He was interrupted by Whitey's peculiar cough. Both boys jumped and forgot their argument.

"He means he wants some more to eat, I bet," said Sam.

"Well, if he does, he's got to wait," Penrod declared. "We got to get the most important thing of all fixed up first."

"What's that, Penrod?"

"The reward," said Penrod mildly. "That's what I was tryin' to tell you about, Sam, if you'd ever give me half a chance."

"Well, I *did* give you a chance. I kept *tellin'* you to tell me, but—"

"You never! You kept sayin'—"

They renewed the discussion, protracting it indefinitely; but as each persisted in clinging to his own interpretation of the facts, the question still remained unsettled. It was abandoned, or rather, it merged into another during the later stages of the debate, this other being concerned with which of the debaters had the least "sense." Each made the plain statement that if he were more deficient than his opponent in that regard, self-destruction would be his only refuge. Each declared that he would "rather die than be talked to death"; and then, as the two approached a point bluntly recriminative, Whitey coughed again, whereupon they were miraculously silent, and went into the passageway in a perfectly amiable manner.

"I got to have a good look at him, for once," said Penrod, as he stared frowningly at Whitey. "We got to fix up about that reward."

"I want to take a good ole look at him myself," said Sam.

After supplying Whitey with another bucket of water, they returned to the carriage-house and seated themselves thoughtfully. In truth, they were something a shade more than thoughtful; the adventure to which they had committed themselves was beginning to be a little overpowering. If Whitey had been a dog, a goat, a fowl, or even a stray calf, they would have felt equal to him; but now that the earlier glow of their wild daring had disappeared, vague apprehensions stirred. Their "good look" at Whitey had not reassured them—he seemed large, Gothic, and unusual.

Whisperings within them began to urge that for boys to undertake an enterprise connected with so huge an animal as an actual horse was perilous. Beneath the surface of their musings, dim but ominous prophecies moved; both boys began to have the feeling that, somehow, this affair was going to get beyond them and that they would be in heavy trouble before it was over—they knew not why. They knew why no more than they knew why they felt it imperative to keep the fact of Whitey's presence in the stable a secret from their respective families, but they did begin to realize that keeping a secret of that size was going to be attended with some difficulty. In brief, their sensations were becoming comparable to those of the man who stole a house.

Nevertheless, after a short period given to unspoken misgivings, they returned to the subject of the reward. The money-value of bay horses, as compared to white, was again discussed, and each announced his certainty that nothing less than "a good ole hundred dollars" would be offered for the return of Whitey.

But immediately after so speaking they fell into another silence, due to sinking feelings. They had spoken loudly and confidently, and yet they knew, somehow, that such things were not to be. According to their knowledge, it was perfectly reasonable to suppose that they would receive this fortune, but they frightened themselves in speaking of it; they knew that they *could* not have a hundred dollars for their own. An oppression, as from something awful and criminal, descended upon them at intervals.

Presently, however, they were warmed to a little cheerfulness again by Penrod's suggestion that they should put a notice in the paper. Neither of them had the slightest idea how to get it there, but such details as that were beyond the horizon; they occupied themselves with the question of what their advertisement ought to "say." Finding that they differed irreconcilably, Penrod went into a cache of his in the sawdust-box and brought two pencils and a supply of paper. He gave one of the pencils and several sheets to Sam; then both boys bent themselves in silence to the labour of practical composition. Penrod produced the briefer paragraph. (See Fig. I.) Sam's was more ample. (See Fig. II.)

Neither Sam nor Penrod showed any interest in what the other had written, but both felt that something praiseworthy had been accomplished. Penrod exhaled a sigh, as of relief, and, in a manner he had observed his father use sometimes, he said;

"Thank goodness, *that's* off my mind, anyway!"

"What we goin' do next, Penrod?" Sam asked deferentially, the borrowed manner having some effect on him.

"I don't know what *you're* goin' to do," Penrod returned, picking up the old cigarbox which had contained the paper and pencils. *"I'm* goin' to put mine in here, so's it'll come in handy when I haf to get at it."

"Well, I guess I'll keep mine there, too," said Sam. Thereupon he deposited his scribbled slip beside Penrod's in the cigarbox, and the box was solemnly returned to the secret place whence it had been taken.

"There, *that's* 'tended to!" said Sam, and, unconsciously imitating his friend's imitation, he gave forth audibly a breath of satisfaction and relief. Both boys felt that the financial side of their great affair had been conscientiously looked to, that the question of the reward was settled, and that everything was proceeding in a businesslike manner. Therefore, they were able to turn their attention to another matter.

This was the question of Whitey's next meal. After their exploits of the morning, and the consequent imperilment of Penrod, they decided that nothing more was to be done in apples, vegetables, or bread; it was evident that Whitey must be fed from the bosom of nature.

"We couldn't pull enough o' that frostbit ole grass in the yard to feed him," Penrod said gloomily. "We could work a week and

FIG I

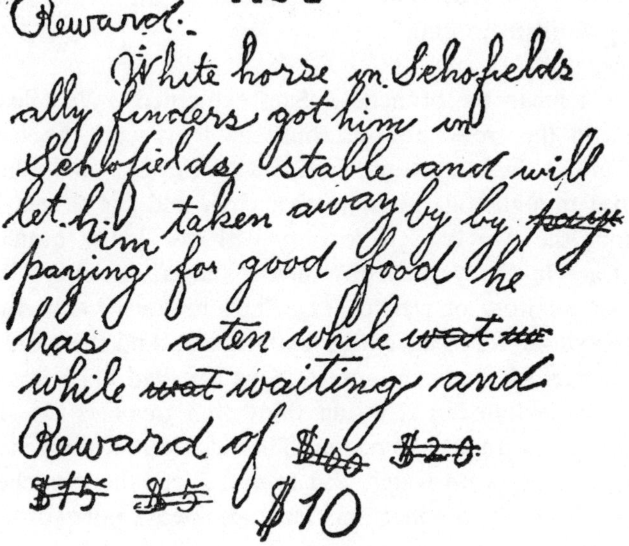

Reward:-
White horse in Schofields
ally finders got him in
Schofields stable and will
let him taken away by by ~~payi~~
paying for good food he
has aten while ~~wat~~ ~~wa~~
while ~~wat~~ waiting and
Reward of ~~$100~~ ~~$20~~
~~$15~~ ~~$5~~ $10

FIG II

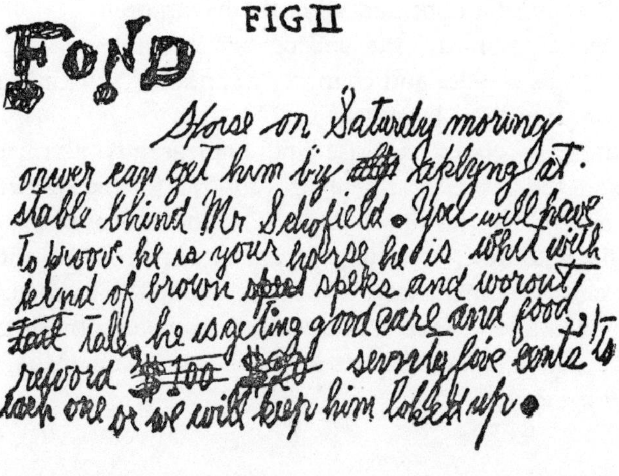

FOND

Horse on Saturdy moring
onwer can get him by ~~ap~~ aplying at
stable bhind Mr Schofield. You will have
To proov he is your horse he is whit with
kind of brown ~~sped~~ spks and worout
~~teat~~ Tale he is geting good care and food
reword ~~$100~~ ~~$50~~ seventy five cents to
teh one or we will keep him lokt up.

not get enough to make him swaller more'n about twice. All we got this morning, he blew most of it away. He'd try to scoop it in toward his teeth with his lip, and then he'd haf to kind of blow out his breath, and after that all the grass that'd be left was just some wet pieces stickin' to the outsides of his face. Well, and you know how he acted about the maple branch. We can't trust him with branches."

Sam jumped up.

"*I* know!" he cried. "There's lots of leaves left on the branches. We can give them to him."

"I just said—"

"I don't mean the branches," Sam explained. "We'll leave the branches on the trees, but just pull the leaves off the branches and put 'em in the bucket and feed 'em to him out of the bucket."

Penrod thought this plan worth trying, and for three-quarters of an hour the two boys were busy with the lower branches of various trees in the yard. Thus they managed to supply Whitey with a fair quantity of wet leaves, which he ate in a perfunctory way, displaying little of his earlier enthusiasm. And the work of his purveyors might have been more tedious if it had been less damp, for a boy is seldom bored by anything that involves his staying-out in the rain without protection. The drizzle had thickened; the leaves were heavy with water, and at every jerk the branches sent fat drops over the two collectors. They attained a noteworthy state of sogginess.

Finally, they were brought to the attention of the authorities indoors, and Della appeared upon the back porch.

"Musther Penrod," she called, "y'r mamma says ye'll c'm in the house this minute and change y'r shoes an' stockin's an' everythun' else ye got on! D'ye hear me?"

Penrod, taken by surprise and unpleasantly alarmed, darted away from the tree he was depleting and ran for the stable.

"You tell her I'm dry as toast!" he shouted over his shoulder.

Della withdrew, wearing the air of a person gratuitously insulted; and a moment later she issued from the kitchen, carrying an umbrella. She opened it and walked resolutely to the stable.

"She says I'm to bring ye in the house," said Della, "an' I'm goin' to bring ye!"

Sam had joined Penrod in the carriage-house, and, with the beginnings of an unnamed terror, the two beheld this grim advance. But they did not stay for its culmination. Without a word to each other they hurriedly tiptoed up the stairs to the gloomy loft, and there they paused, listening.

They heard Della's steps upon the carriage-house floor.

"Ah, there's plenty places t'hide in," they heard her say, "but I'll show ye! She tole me to bring ye, and I'm—"

She was interrupted by a peculiar sound—loud, chilling, dismal, and unmistakably not of human origin. The boys knew it for Whitey's cough, but Della had not their experience. A smothered shriek reached their ears; there was a scurrying noise, and then, with horror, they heard Della's footsteps in the passageway that ran by Whitey's manger. Immediately there came a louder shriek, and even in the anguish of knowing their secret discovered, they were shocked to hear distinctly the words, "O Lard in hivvin!" in the well-known voice of Della. She shrieked again, and they heard the rush of her footfalls across the carriage-house floor. Wild words came from the outer air, and the kitchen door slammed violently. It was all over. She had gone to "tell."

Penrod and Sam plunged down the stairs and out of the stable. They climbed the back fence and fled up the alley. They turned into Sam's yard, and, without consultation, headed for the cellar doors, nor paused till they found themselves in the farthest, darkest, and gloomiest recess of the cellar. There, perspiring, stricken with fear, they sank down upon the earthen floor, with their moist backs against the stone wall.

Thus with boys. The vague apprehensions that had been creeping upon Penrod and Sam all afternoon had become monstrous; the unknown was before them. How great their crime would turn out to be (now that it was in the hands of grown people), they did not know, but, since it concerned a horse, it would undoubtedly be considered of terrible dimensions.

Their plans for a reward, and all the things that had seemed both innocent and practical in the morning, now staggered their minds as manifestations of criminal folly. A new and terrible light seemed to play upon the day's exploits; they had chased a horse belonging to strangers, and it would be said that they deliberately drove him into the stable and there concealed him. They had, in truth, virtually stolen him, and they had stolen food for him. The waning light through the small window above them warned Penrod that his inroads upon the vegetables in his own cellar must soon be discovered. Della, that Nemesis, would seek them in order to prepare them for dinner, and she would find them not. But she would recall his excursion to the cellar, for she had seen him when he came up; and also the truth would be known concerning the loaf of bread. Altogether, Penrod felt that his case was worse than Sam's—until Sam offered a suggestion which roused such horrible possibilities concerning the principal item of their offense that all thought of the smaller indictments disappeared.

"Listen, Penrod," Sam quavered: "What—what if that—what if that ole horse maybe belonged to a—policeman!" Sam's imagination was not of the comforting kind. "'What'd they—do to us, Penrod, if it turned out he was some policeman's horse?"

Penrod was only able to shake his head. He did not reply in words but both boys thenceforth considered it almost inevitable that Whitey *had* belonged to a policeman, and in their sense of so ultimate a disaster, they ceased for a time to brood upon what their parents would probably do to them. The penalty for stealing a policeman's horse would be only a step short of capital, they were sure. They would not be hanged; but the vague, looming sketches of something called the penitentiary began to flicker before them.

It grew darker in the cellar, so that finally they could not see each other.

"I guess they're huntin' for us by now," Sam said, huskily. "I don't—I don't like it much down here, Penrod."

Penrod's hoarse whisper came from the profound gloom:

"Well, who ever said you did?"

"Well—" Sam paused; then he said plaintively, "I wish we'd never *seen* that dern ole horse."

"It was every bit his fault," said Penrod. "*We* didn't do anything. If he hadn't come stickin' his ole head in our stable, it'd never happened at all. Ole fool!" He rose. "I'm goin' to get out of here; I guess I've stood about enough for one day."

"Where—where you goin', Penrod? You aren't goin' *home,* are you?"

"No; I'm not! What you take me for? You think I'm crazy?"

"Well, where *can* we go?"

How far Penrod's desperation actually would have led him is doubtful, but he made this statement:

"I don't know where *you're* goin', but *I'm* goin' to walk straight out in the country till I come to a farmhouse and say my name's George and live there!"

"I'll do it, too," Sam whispered eagerly. "I'll say my name's Henry."

"Well, we better get started," said the executive Penrod. "We got to get away from here, anyway."

But when they came to ascend the steps leading to the "outside doors," they found that those doors had been closed and locked for the night.

"It's no use," Sam lamented, "and we can't bust 'em, 'cause I tried to, once before. Fanny always locks 'em about five o'clock— I forgot. We got to go up the stairway and try to sneak out through the house."

They tiptoed back, and up the inner stairs. They paused at the top, then breathlessly stepped out into a hall which was entirely dark. Sam touched Penrod's sleeve in warning, and bent to listen at a door.

Immediately that door opened, revealing the bright library, where sat Penrod's mother and Sam's father.

It was Sam's mother who had opened the door.

"Come into the library, boys," she said. "Mrs. Schofield is just telling us about it."

And as the two comrades moved dumbly into the lighted room, Penrod's mother rose, and, taking him by the shoulder, urged him close to the fire.

"You stand there and try to dry off a little, while I finish telling Mr. and Mrs. Williams about you and Sam," she said. "You'd better make Sam keep near the fire, too, Mrs. Williams, because they both got wringing wet. Think of their running off just when most people would have wanted to stay! Well, I'll go on with the story, then. Della told me all about it, and what the cook next door said *she'd* seen, how they'd been trying to pull grass and leaves for the poor old thing all day—and all about the apples they carried from *your* cellar, and getting wet and working in the rain as hard as they could—and they'd given him a loaf of bread! Shame on you, Penrod!" She paused to laugh, but there was a little moisture around her eyes, even before she laughed. "And they'd fed him on potatoes and lettuce and cabbage and turnips out of *our* cellar! And I wish you'd seen the sawdust bed they made for him! Well, when I telephoned, and the Humane Society got there, he said it was the most touching thing he ever knew. It seems he *knew* this horse, and had been looking for him. He said ninety-nine boys out of a hundred would have chased the poor old thing away, and he was going to see to it that this case didn't go unnoticed, because the local branch of the society gives little silver medals for special acts like this. And the last thing he said before he led the poor old horse away was that he was sure Penrod and Sam each would be awarded one at the meeting of the society next Thursday night."

. . . On the following Saturday morning a yodel sounded from the sunny sidewalk in front of the Schofields' house, and Penrod, issuing forth, beheld the familiar figure of Samuel Williams in waiting.

Upon Sam's breast there glittered a round bit of silver metal. Upon the breast of Penrod was a decoration precisely similar.

" 'Lo, Penrod," said Sam. "What you goin' to do?"

"Nothin'."

"I got mine on," said Sam.

"I have, too," said Penrod. "I wouldn't take a hundred dollars for mine."

"I wouldn't take two hundred for mine," said Sam.

Each glanced pleasantly at the other's medal. They faced each other without shame. Neither had the slightest sense of hypocrisy either in himself or in his comrade. On the contrary!

Penrod's eyes went from Sam's medal back to his own; thence they wandered, with perhaps a little disappointment, to the lifeless street and to the empty yards and spectatorless windows of the neighbourhood. Then he looked southward toward the busy heart of the town, where multitudes were.

"Let's go down and see what time it is by the court-house clock," said Penrod.

A Prince and a Cowboy

BY LINCOLN STEFFENS

The adolescent dreams of a boy on horseback are beautifully humored in Lincoln Steffens' description of an encounter between a would-be cowboy and the genuine article.

A boy's life is pestered with problems—hard ones, as hard as any adult's. There is the whole world to get into your head. You have to make a picture of it; that's easy, but the picture has to correspond somewhat with the world outside, which keeps changing. You have the sun going fine around the earth, and then all of a sudden you learn something more and the earth starts whirling around the sun. This means a complete readjustment. It happens often. Every time I had everything all right and working harmoniously inside so that I could leave it and mind my own business, some fact would bob up to throw it all out. I remember how, when the earth was flat, I had to put China and the Far East to the west of me, no easy task for a boy; and then when I had that done, I studied a book which made the earth round like an orange. Where was one to put China then?

I consulted some of the other boys about that, and they looked dazed for a moment; but they soon turned to the ball and bats and bade me do likewise.

"Ah, play ball," they said in effect.

Our cook, a Chinaman, was contemptuous. "What for you go lookee see find China? China no lost. Fool boy lost, yes, but China all li."

And this, the construction of the universe as a whole, was only
the main business of life. There were minor problems. It took me
and my crowd days of exploration to discover and map in our
minds the confluence of our two rivers, the American and the
Sacramento. It took longer to make out how the river steamboats
and the railroad trains could start from Sacramento at right angles
and arrive both at the same place, San Francisco. Also there were
the inhabitants of the earth to understand, the grown-ups who do
and say such queer things. They say they love you and yet they
balk you like enemies. They tell you to be good and you'll succeed,
and the next thing you know they will be chuckling about how
dishonest some successful man was. Nor will they explain anything,
not seriously. They laugh at a fellow's questions. Or if they pretend to throw a light, they only cast a shadow that darkens and

complicates the puzzle. They don't seem to realize how painful your need is to find out just where you are at in a mixed-up world. Sometimes it seemed to me almost as if they didn't know where they were at themselves.

As I was leaving the Neely farm that day I was wondering what Jim Neely meant by what he said about Mrs. Neely wanting a boy like me and what Mrs. Neely meant by being so cross with me and then so soft. If she wanted me why couldn't she take me straight as a regular fellow would? I could not make it out. I thought and thought, but the sun was hot over me and the pony was hot under me. I did what I had to do with many, many questions: I gave them up, for the present; I laid them aside and hung on to the thought that anyhow I had a feeding-station seven miles out on the Stockton road. And before I reached home I had another feeding-station still farther out and another problem.

Single-footing along the flaming road, I picked up the track of cattle going my way, and pretty soon there was a cloud of dust ahead. Hurrying as much as I could on such a day, I caught up with a cowboy driving a small herd of big calves and young steers to market. I asked if I might help him.

"You betcher life," he answered. "My horse is about in."

No wonder. It was a small drove, and, as the cowboy said, it's easier to handle a big drove. If there's a mob, cattle will herd like humans. But when they're a few, and of mixed ages, they are like a bunch of shooting stars. "Maybe we can do it together," he said. "I'll drive from behind here and you'll ride along the side of the next cross road, doing the dirty work."

It was dirty work. A calf would bleat and bolt. My pony would spring ahead and cut him off. Then a young steer, smelling water, would bellow and go, with others after him, down the road. I had to race to the front, stop short, and hold them. An open lane on one side was easy; the pony would of himself see and take and hold it, but when there was a cross road, open both sides, we had, us two cowboys, alternately to drive and head. I would shoot up, yelling, along one side, then fall back and drive as he galloped up the other side. By good team work we got by. I was sweating, my pony was in a lather, and the cowboy and his horse were caked with the mud of the damp dust. He was pleased, however, and, to keep me with him, he paid me a compliment (the way grown-ups do).

"You know the cattle game, don't you?" he said.

"No," I answered, "but my pony does, and I'm learning it from him. How long you been on the road?"

"All day," he said. "The ranch is about twenty miles out."

Twenty miles out! Just right. I began fishing for an invitation to visit him, asking him questions. The ranch was not a big one, he said; it was mostly a wheat farm, only part hay and cattle. He was one of five or six hands that worked steady on the place.

"Why don't you ride out and see us sometime?" he invited. "You like to work cattle. We'll let you have all you want of it."

I told him about my gang, and he laughed. "Five or six! All kids? Well, you may all come. Why not? Make a week-end of it." A week-end? What was that? He used lots of funny words, and he spoke them very English. And he suggested a date when there would be work for us to do, cattle work.

I liked the idea, accepted it, and I liked this fellow. I stared at him approvingly till he turned away as if embarrassed, and when he looked back at me, he asked me a diverting question.

"Why no saddle?"

I explained that my father wanted me to learn bareback, and that led to the Comanches. I told him all about them, how they rode, fought, and—I must have become so enthusiastic about those Indians that he suspected me.

"I see," he said, "you are a Comanche Indian chief."

This struck me at first as fresh. I did not like to have anybody walk right into my—my privacy, like that, sit down, and stick his feet up on the table. But my second thought was that maybe he was my kind of a fellow, like the bridge-tender. I decided to see.

"No," I said. "I used to be a Comanche chief's son, but that was long ago; several weeks back. I am—something else now. I'll tell you what I am if you'll tell me first what you are."

"Why," he said, "I am, as you see, a cowboy."

I was disappointed. He did not understand. I said as much. "Of course, I can see you're a cow-puncher, but that's only your job. I don't mean that. What I mean is, what are you really?"

"Really?" he echoed. "What's really? I'm a real cowboy."

"That's funny," I said, "I thought you'd tumble to what I meant, and you didn't."

I was about to give up, and he seemed to sense that. He looked almost ashamed, and I didn't care. If he wasn't my sort, if he didn't belong to our crowd, he didn't matter. We rode along in a silence that could be felt, like the heat, till a steer charged the fence. "Water," I called as my pony charged at the steer, and I was glad that the rest of the herd joined the attack on that fence. It kept us busy for a while. When we could fall back and ride together, the cowboy had decided to talk.

"I'll tell you about myself," he said. "My name, my cattle name, is Duke. That's what the cattlemen call me from Texas to the Pacific, only they pronounce it Dook. And they name me so, not because I am a duke. My father, as it happens, is a lord, but my older brother will inherit his title. I myself, I am nothing, as you see. I'm called by an English title because I am English, but as a matter of fact, I am a plain American cowboy."

I was thrilled. I had read about the English nobility, books on books, and here for the first time I was seeing one.

"Is that what you mean by 'really'?" he inquired.

"Maybe," I answered, and it was his turn to be disappointed. I was sorry now. It was my turn to talk. I told him about me, to explain what I meant.

I had been reading Scott's novels lately, I said, and lots of other English stories about knights and gentlemen and ladies. I knew what a younger son was and had even thought I'd like to be one.

"Really?" he said, only he said it differently from me.

"Yes-s—" I hesitated. But I decided to trust him. "Yes," I confessed. "I wouldn't have minded being the son of a lord, and, as a matter of fact, I was—not exactly that, but I've been something like that for a good while lately."

"But why?" he asked. "You are in the way of being what I wanted to be when I was a boy, and yet here you are—"

"Nothing," I interrupted, and I poured out my woes.

Here I was, a boy, just an ordinary boy. I wasn't a poor boy, like the boys I had read about in stories, the fellows that started with nothing, no father, no mother, no home. They starved in the

streets, picking up now and then a crust of bread to eat, and finding
here and there a dark hallway to sleep in, but they begin by selling
papers and shining shoes; they are smart, industrious, honest, and
brave; so they rise slowly but surely and by and by they are a success.
They own the paper they sold or—whatever it is they are at.

"That's great," I summed up. "They are heroes of books. I'd
like to be the hero of a book."

But, I grieved, I could not be that. My father and mother did
not die when I was young. They are both still living, and they had
a home for me. I didn't have a chance; I could not go out and suffer,
strive, and become a success.

The Duke saw my predicament. He tried to be encouraging.
There were other things I might do.

"What?" I demanded. "I can't be one of those rich men's sons
or the son of a duke and do what they do." There were stories about
them, too. They had boats and rivers they could row on; not like the
Sacramento and the American Rivers: not swift floods or all dried
up. They had snow and ice and parks. They could go sledding, and
skating, and they had places to go riding in, made on purpose for
saddle horses, and grooms to follow them. Not like me. I had to ride
over to the river bottom or out on the plains, always with other boys,
among farmers and—and—

I halted. I had almost said something that might hurt his feelings. He saw my embarrassment, and like a duke, he bridged it
gracefully (the nobility is very graceful, you know).

"And cowboys," he suggested.

"Yes," I said, and to make it easy for him, I explained gracefully that I didn't mean him. I was glad I had met him; I was certainly coming out to his ranch with my crowd to help with his cattle.
I had to do something to fill up my time.

"But you can see, can't you," I said, "that working cattle on a
ranch isn't what a fellow with ambition would choose to do if he
had his choice."

A team was coming toward me. "I'll head 'em," I said, and I
rode up and turned our cattle off to the right side of the road. After
that there were two cross roads in succession; both the Duke and I
were busy, and by that time, the city limit was near. There were
other things to think of.

What butcher were his calves for? When he told me, I told him that all would be well. Loony Louie was that butcher's ranchman; he would be on the look-out for us, with the bars down, and there was a pond in his corral. The cattle would turn in of themselves for the water. And this happened. We had a couple of miles of very hard work. The herd split, and half of them got away up one of the many lanes. My pony brought them back, and—well, we worked the whole tired, famished drove to the butcher's place. There was Louie standing out in the middle of the road with his gate wide open. The cattle rushed in, and our horses followed—one mad rush for the pond, and there they all waded in up to their bellies and sank their heads in up to their eyes. And Louie, closing the gate and running after us to the pond, stood and danced there; he laughed and yelled like a maniac at the sight of the drinking animals.

I saw Duke looking astonished at him.

"What's the matter with that man?" he asked, as we rode up out of the water and headed for town. I saw my chance to explain what I meant by "really."

"Well," I said, "Loony Louie is called crazy, but he isn't. He is all right, only he loves stock. You saw how he was glad when your thirsty calves wallowed in the water and drank their fill? Well, he loves that; he loves to see 'em drink and feed. He'll cry if he sees them slaughtered; sure. That's why they say he's crazy: because he loves animals and goes crazy when he sees them drink when they're thirsty and eat when they're hungry; and—and when they're killed he goes crazy too."

"Poor devil!" the Duke muttered.

"No," I corrected, "Louie was in prison once for stealing cattle and once he was in the insane asylum for the same thing. But I know him, and I knew what he wanted: knew he didn't want to own cattle but only to take good care of them, so I got him a job here to take care of the butcher's cattle. It would have been better to put him on a ranch where cattle aren't killed, but no rancher would take a loco cattle-lover. Only this old German butcher could understand about Louie. He gave him the job of priming up his cattle, and he keeps him away as much as he can from the slaughter house."

"Really!" the cowboy exclaimed, and I answered, "Yes, really. And there you have said it yourself."

But he didn't see it even yet. We rode along the city streets, quietly; all you could hear was the flap of his chaps and the clink of his spurs.

"Come again, kid," he said at last.

"Why, don't you see?" I said. "That butcher's man, who has the job of feeding up cattle to be killed, he is really—he is playing he's the friend of those calves of yours, and he'll take 'em into the barn, feed them a lot, pet them, talk to them, and he will listen to them, and—and—"

"And?" the cowboy boosted, and I told him straight how Louie could sit up on a fence with you and tell you how a young calf feels when it is separated from its mother and what a wild steer would like to be—really.

"He does to me," I said. "He has told me stories that are—real about what the cattle tell him."

"Really?"

"Yes," I said, and I told him about the bridge-tender, whose job was to tend the American River trestle. A good job, and dangerous, and he did it up brown. But he didn't care for it. "He's really a prospector who strikes it rich and goes home where his people live, and the girl that wouldn't marry him, and—and—"

"And—" the cowboy said, and I saw he was understanding, so I went on.

"And I go out there and sit in his cabin, and him and me, we go back home rich and spend the money; he just blows it and he makes his folks proud of him, and—and—"

"And—"

I had to go back and explain that the bridge-tender's troubles all came from a certain preacher in his home town who, because the bridge-tender got to dancing and raising the dust, denounced him to his face in a sermon in the church. The bridge-tender was with his girl, and it so shamed her that she wouldn't have him 'round any more.

"See?" I said, and he saw that much; so I trusted him with the whole truth, how, when the bridge-tender and I are alone on the trestle and there is no train due, we make his pile, we go back east to his home. We walk into that church—everybody's there, the girl, too, of course—and the bridge-tender, who has been the talk of the

town for a week, he walks up the middle aisle of the church, draws
his gun, and makes that preacher come down out of his pulpit, kneel
down, and apologize to the girl.

"And she marries the bridge-tender?" the Duke asked.

"Sometimes," I answered. "Sometimes we take her, and sometimes she begs to be took, but we scorn her."

We had come to the corner where there was a small drovers'
hotel with a stable next door, the Duke's hotel. We stopped; since
the Duke did not seem to see it, I pointed it out to him: "Your
hotel," I said.

"Yes, yes," he said. "But let's finish this. Your butcher's man is
—really—a cattle-lover; your bridge-tender is a rich miner. Any
others like that?"

"Yes," I said. "You know Hank Dobran, the gambler, that
runs this hotel and bar where you are stopping tonight? Well, he
—this is a secret, of course—when Hank has made enough to be
independent—he tells me he is going to turn in and clear up the
dirty politics of this town and make a fine, grand town that all the
other cities all over the world can copy."

"Any more?" he asked after a while, and I looked at him and he
wasn't joshing me. He believed. I answered him, therefore:

"Every fellow I get to really know is that way," I told him.
"Every one of them is playing he is really something else besides
what his job is. And that's what I mean by really," I said, "and—
and that's why I asked you what you were, really."

The Duke did not answer. He just sat there on his horse in front
of the hotel stable. We were so quiet that the stableman came out
and looked at us—and gave us up. But his wonder brought the
Duke to. He spoke.

"I was that way, kid," he said. "I was like you. I read books, as
a boy; I read and I wanted to go and be what I read. Only I read
stories about the far west, Indians, scouts, cowboys. I read about
knights, too, and lords and ladies, kings, queens, and princesses.
Yes, but I saw that sort. I knew them as—as you know cowboys. So
I didn't want to be a prince or the son of a—duke. I played I was
a cowboy. I could ride; I had horses, yes, and—but I hated to ride
on our silly little saddles on bridle paths in our fancy parks with a
groom behind me—and my sister. I wanted to go west and be a

cowboy among cowboys—and really ride—really. And—well—as you see—I did. That's what I am now and have been for ten years. It isn't what I imagined it to be. It is no more what it is cracked up to be than a lord is or the son of a lord. But no matter, here I am, Dook the cowboy—really a cow-puncher."

He seemed to be sad about it, and his sadness put up a problem to me, the hardest puzzle of that day.

"Funny!" I said. "You're a cowboy really—and I—I don't know what to be now, but for a long time lately—weeks—when I rode up to you, I was a prince, the son of a lord, the Black Prince in the Middle Ages."

The Duke didn't laugh the way some men would. He thought and thought, and at last he looked as if he was going to say something. He didn't. He changed his mind, I guess. For all he did was to put out his hand, take mine, and shake it hard, once.

"Good-by, Prince," he said. "It's time to go home. It's time for both of us to go home—really."

"Good-by, Duke," I said, and I rode off home puzzling and puzzling.

As a Horse Sees It

The Marriage of Ghazal and the Grey Mare

CARL RASWAN

Most horsemen are familiar with Carl Raswan's adventures in Arabia, where he went seeking evidence that the horses of the Parthenon were descended from pure Arabian stock. There he lived in the tents with the Bedouins, was accepted and helped by them in his search. This beautiful description of the love act between a mare and stallion is typical of the book.

Before dawn I awoke to the melodious chant of the Muezzin. Making the round on the high balcony of the minaret, he called to the four winds: "God alone is great. I testify there is no god but God! I confess that Mohammed is His Prophet! Come to prayer! Prayer is better than sleep!"

Life stirred as the morning call to prayer drifted over Amrieh. Lights appeared in many windows. At the edge of the desert men arose from coffee fires in Bedouin tents. Prayer rugs were spread out. Men turned their faces toward the east, to Mecca, where the first brightness of day appeared like a dim, distant silver breach in the night.

"Allah Akbar! Ahadu Anla, Illa'llah . . ."

Down below me, in a narrow lane, a dark bundle also came to life—a blind beggar who had spent the night there rolled up in rags. He spread his tattered covers before him like a precious prayer rug and standing upon them, he called out the Tabkir and the Fatlah: "Exalt thy God, O my soul! Exalt the perfection of my Lord the most high!" With hands outspread upon his thighs he dropped to his knees and inclined his head, first to the right and then to the left, in greeting to the unseen guardians of his soul.

Before joining Marzuki at the Greek café, I walked over to the paddock to greet Ghazal, but the enclosure was empty! The cross-bar of the gate had been lifted, and the bolt hung neatly by its leather thong. Someone familiar with the place must have opened the gate and taken Ghazal away.

I tried to find the watchman, but he, too, had disappeared. His bedstead with its mattress and blankets was still in place, barring the street entrance to the yard. But on both sides of the keeper's bed I found imprints of Ghazal's hoofs, a definite proof that my stallion, in one leap, had cleared the sleeping watchman. The question of how Ghazal had lifted the crossbar to open the gate remained to be solved. But first I must find him.

I called Marzuki and walked over with him to the enclosure to examine the evidence. There we found remains of munched hay and marks of Ghazal's teeth on the wooden bolt; also hairs from his mane, clinging to the rough edge of the crossbar. Ghazal could not have crawled under it, for a horse will never do that, but he had used the top of his head to work the bar upward until it fell over against the wall.

Marzuki ordered horses saddled for us, and we set off down the avenue leading from Amrieh to the hills, where we encountered a group of Bedouins who told us that they had seen a chestnut horse pursued by two riders.

Within half a mile from Amrieh we turned off into the desert and soon came across Arab herdsmen with their pasturing camels. They also had seen the horse.

"How far away?" we asked the herdsmen.

They pointed to the hill. "On the uplands just beyond."

We rode on, over the hill into a wide plain. At a little distance we saw two riderless horses, tails flying high over their backs, one a chestnut stallion, and the other a dapple-grey mare. Two men following them were trying in vain to separate the chestnut and his companion, for they were plunging and kicking vigorously.

Marzuki and I closed in from the opposite side. The chestnut—

and undoubtedly it was Ghazal—still ran at full speed behind the grey mare. She turned upon him, squealing and kicking in an attempt to fight him off. And again both ran away, manes and tails high.

They led us toward the edge of the plain, with the sun behind us. The wind blew hard across the gravel tableland. Hills rose to the south, and a gradual slope to the north.

The grey mare was no less fleet-footed than Ghazal, though more compact and rounded of line. They capered with the verve of two giddy foals, now swiftly speeding along, now with quick, short turns trying to waylay each other.

Marzuki leaned forward in his saddle and signaled me to follow him.

With the aid of another man, we almost succeeded in separating Ghazal and his mare, but the stallion turned and held off Marzuki's horse, roaring and pawing the ground before him.

The mare came on flying hoofs toward Ghazal, lightly touching his croup as she passed him. With a squeal he whirled about and followed her toward a rise in the ground where we lost sight of them. When they reappeared, the giddy little mare, lost in love with Ghazal, was following obediently at his heels. They halted as we rode near, and I listened to Ghazal's wild scream. The mare quivered when she heard the challenge, but she waited him, limbs braced, ears alert.

Ghazal rose, eyes shining, neck arched. Standing on his hind legs and squealing, with ears drawn back, he threw his whole weight against her.

She screamed and turned away in a flash. One foot struck Ghazal's chest, but he thundered along at her side, his neck stretched along her back, his teeth nipping her ribs. Without warning, both hoofs of his forefeet lashed across her croup, and brought her down. At once she was up again, but she was suddenly very quiet.

Only the shadow of man now stood between them as the trembling little mare yielded to Ghazal.

Marzuki waved off the approaching riders, as over the brow of the hill the two horses appeared, Ghazal jostling his mate, kicking her with playful jabs of his heels. Now it was easy to separate them. Marzuki and I took the grey mare between our horses, never losing touch of her in spite of her uneasiness.

In an effort to return to the side of his mare, Ghazal almost vaulted over Marzuki's horse. I cried to Ghazal; he pricked up his ears at the sound of my voice and came in full gallop toward me. I started my horse on a run in the opposite direction to draw him away from Marzuki and the grey mare, but he raced madly past me.

When I dismounted, Ghazal noticed it instantly and swerved about, dashing back to me with flying mane and tail. Panting noisily, he pawed the ground, his hoofs turning up the soil like iron spades. His hair was full of sweat, and there was blood on his coat where the mare had nipped him with her teeth.

He watched me curiously now with the gentle gaze of his large eyes, and his ears switched in lively play. The flame was still there, but subdued and calm.

Only after I scolded Ghazal, did I allow him to step closer. His nose carefully searched over me until he found his favorite spot, the pit under my left shoulder, where he snorted contentedly, inhaling my friendly scent—the sign of his surrender.

Jumper

NICHOLAS KALASHNIKOFF

Here we have one of the rare examples of a horse tale which shows things from the point of view of the horse himself. Anna Sewell, in her work Black Beauty, *was one of the first writers to make such an approach. A few authors, mainly among those writing for children, have followed her example. This little description of the very first feelings experienced by a newborn foal is credible and endearing.*

Jumper was born just before dawn.

The colt's first sensation, after coming into the world from his mother's warm and quiet womb, was that of knifelike pain cutting his body. Miserable but uncomprehending, he lay on the soft straw and shivered while something big and dark hovered over him, giving forth anxious sounds. He wanted to rise and press close to this creature in response, but he had not the strength. As the minutes passed and the blood congealed on his body the convulsive shuddering increased. He heard a distant noise of wolves howling, but was neither disturbed nor interested. He was conscious only of a need to still—to escape from—this dreadful shaking misery. Seeking protection, he lifted his mouth and whimpered. Then his head fell limply on the straw and he knew no more.

Some time later an abrupt noise wakened him. Indifferent, incapable of response, he gave no sign until he felt a pleasant sensation of something soft stroking his body. Strong arms lifted and carried him, and a delightful warmth enveloped him. He opened his eyes and was assailed by a bright light through which vague shadows moved. Some of the shadows approached and touched his head caressingly, making odd sounds the while. He was curious, but not frightened. The only important realities were the warmth, the sweet scent of straw and a hazy awareness that he was the object of solicitude.

Now he no longer kept his head lowered, but sought to discover more about this new world into which he had been plunged. His mouth opened of its own accord, and it was not a whimper this time, but an expression of confident satisfaction. In response the strange shadows crowded around making loud noises that meant nothing whatever, patting his head, his back, his legs. Though he could not understand, he nevertheless knew that there was no cause for fear. The hands, the voices invited trust, and he stretched his head this way and that, the better to acquaint himself with his surroundings. Had it not been for a vague irritation arising from a half-formed desire he would have been content. He wanted something. He did not know what. But swallowing the moisture that had collected in his throat he experienced a delightful sensation that in part satisfied his need.

When a large and hairy object bent over him, wrapped him in something soft and warm, leaving only his head free, then lifted him and carried him outdoors, he accepted this new adventure as a part of the greater miracle. A blast of cold air striking his head caused his eyes to smart, and momentarily he struggled, but strong arms held him close and a comforting voice spoke to him. He submitted and became calm. Instinctively he knew that the one who was carrying him could be trusted.

Suddenly he heard a loud and resonant neigh that seemed to confirm this knowledge. "He-ee-ee-ee-aa. . . ." It was a joyous outcry which he instantly recognized as a greeting. With no less joy, though very gently, he answered: "He-ee-ee-ee!"

As the colt's slight body came in contact with the great warm body of the mare, he turned his head and met her dark, liquid eyes. In the light of day they looked him over tenderly, anxiously. Then the friend who had brought him there stood him unsteadily upon his legs and, supporting him, pushed his muzzle against something soft and warm. Automatically he opened his mouth and grabbed, and a sweet liquid trickled down his throat, filling him with an in-

credible pleasure. This was the thing he had craved, this the fulfill-
ment of his desire.

Gulping down the milk, lost in physical enjoyment, he twisted
his little tail in delight and grabbed now one, now another magic
dug. With the milk he absorbed something more and there was born
in him an attachment for the mare. The caressing thrusts of her
nose and her soft neighing indicated her delight at his touch, and
now joyously she was feeding him. With his whole being he acknowledged her as part of himself—his mother.

When he had drunk his fill, strong arms lifted him again and
bore him away. He heard the mare neigh—sharply, anxiously—and
replied: "Hi-ee-ee-ee." The sound carried contentment and reas-

surance. He was not in the least afraid—neither of the daylight, nor of the white blanket of snow, nor of the varied noises and strange blurred objects in the yard across which they traveled. He gazed upon everything with uncomprehending but trusting eyes.

In a different but none the less positive sense the one who carried him, as much as his mother, belonged to him. In the man the colt sensed a friend, a protector, and he simply accepted it as a fact.

Back in the house, resting on a pallet of fragrant straw, he suddenly felt the overpowering weariness of utter contentment. Closing his eyes, and with his legs crooked under him, he dozed. Someone spoke unintelligible words above him, but he even lacked the curiosity to open his eyes.

Soon he fell into the healthy sleep of a well-fed infant.

Red Tobal

HERBERT RAVENEL SASS

Herbert Ravenel Sass is noted for his understanding and appreciation of nature. In this stirring story he presents us with some of the pitfalls which confronted the imported Spanish horses when they escaped or were turned loose by their exploring and conquering masters and were forced to live in a wilderness, depending only on their own resources. None of these animals had been so situated for many generations, yet some survived, as the vast number of wild horses throughout the western regions of the United States testifies. If Red Tobal did not actually live and have the adventures described, his prototype did. The author sets the reader down in a wilderness inhabited by wolves, panthers, bears, and Indians, and shows us clearly how a horse, finding himself in such circumstances, would have managed to survive.

Andres Bardo, cursing the weight of his musket, kept his eyes fixed upon Captain Solis. Captain Solis was riding the red stallion—he was the only mounted man in the company. That was why, Andres Bardo reflected darkly, this march through the heavy heat of the wilderness meant nothing to Solis; that was why he would not let the men rest. He was a hard man, this black-browed captain, a man of iron inside and out. Andres Bardo hated him and hated the red horse that he rode.

Andres Bardo was one of thirty Spanish soldiers sent out from Fort San Felipe, on the coast of what was later to become South Carolina, to chastise the Edisto Indians who had ambushed the

Ensign Moyano and twenty-two of his men. The detachment had been marching for three hours through an endless forest of gigantic pines. Interlacing green boughs sixty feet overhead, draped with pennons of gray moss, made a roof that shut out the sun so that the little army moved through a perpetual twilight; yet the sweat oozed from every pore of Bardo's body, his lips were dry and scaly, the barrel of his gun was as hot as though it had been held over flame. These discomforts, however, did not annoy him; he was no longer aware of them. He was aware only of his hatred of Captain Esteban Solis, erect and handsome on his great red horse, his black plume nodding disdainfully, his long straight sword swinging at his side.

Andres Bardo marched in front rank some ten paces behind Captain Solis. Now and again he smiled craftily. He was thinking of something that he had done that morning. To him had fallen the duty of saddling the Captain's horse, the stallion Cristobal—Tobal, as he was called. Bardo had performed this task; he had performed it in his own fashion. *Donde hay gana hay maña*—where there's a will there's a way; and Bardo, after saddling the horse, had cut the saddle girth two-thirds through in a place where a leather flap hid the cut so that Captain Solis would not see it. Moreover, he had chosen a bridle that he knew to be rotten.

Something had snapped years before in Andres Bardo's brain. It was a fantastic scheme of revenge. Yet, with one important exception, the thing happened as he planned it.

It happened with the suddenness of a thunder-clap from a blue sky. This was a safe country through which they were marching; for ten leagues around Fort San Felipe the dominion of Spain was secure. Captain Solis, knowing the country, knowing the enemies with whom he had to deal, knew that his men were as safe here as on the parade ground at the fort. He rode carelessly, thinking of a luscious girl in San Augustine, no scouts ahead, his men marching in columns of fours. It was the stallion Red Tobal that sounded the warning. Suddenly the horse jerked his head high and snorted, and Captain Solis woke from his amorous dream.

A single whoop rang out—a signal; then, instantly, a bedlam of whoops and yells, a hail of arrows raining in from every side. For a moment Andres Bardo stood staring stupidly; next moment he fell on his back as suddenly as though some invisible hand had given him a mighty push. He lay quite still, a long cane arrow in his throat.

Captain Solis wheeled the red stallion, his black eyes blazing, his long rapier bright above his black plume. A bone-pointed arrow struck his steel breastplate and glanced off. He shouted an order, pointing with his sword; the red stallion reared and leaped forward as spurs dug into his flanks. Andres Bardo, dead upon the ground, did not see the saddle girth part where he had cut it, did not see Captain Solis reel crazily and fall as the saddle slipped sideways under him.

He fell heavily on his shoulder, his brown, sinewy hand clutching the bridle rein, and he had scarcely struck the ground when a flint-headed arrow gashed the stallion's haunch. Red Tobal plunged forward, dragging Solis over the smooth, slippery pinestraw carpeting the soil. For twenty feet he dragged the man; then the head-strap of the bridle, which Andres Bardo had selected because it was rotten, broke.

With a powerful toss and twist of his head, Red Tobal jerked himself free. Captain Solis, staggering to his feet, saw the red horse, saddleless and bridleless, racing off amid the pines. The yells were louder, fiercer, the rain of arrows thickened, he heard wild cries in Spanish, the crash of muskets. From behind a great tree-trunk at his left a stone hatchet came whirling. It struck Captain Solis on the side of his head and he dropped in his tracks.

In this way, in the days of New Spain's power, before there was an English settlement in the New World, Tobal the red stallion that had come from Andalusia with Esteban Solis, his owner, became a masterless horse in a vast wilderness where horses were unknown. Andres Bardo had accomplished an important thing: unwittingly he had so contrived it that when Red Tobal was thrown upon his own resources in that tremendous wilderness, no saddle burdened his back, no bridle hampered his stride. At the very beginning, through Andres Bardo's plotting, the stallion was freed from impediments that might have been fatal to him amid the dangers that he had to face.

He had no liking for those dangers, no desire for the freedom that had come to him. Three days after the fight in the pine forest, he made his way back to the spot where Fort San Felipe had stood. He found no fort but only a blackened ruin from which in places thin smoke still curled. After ambushing Solis' detachment, the Indians, some fifteen hundred of them, had attacked the fort. The Spaniards, perceiving that they were face to face with a great Indian revolt, had withdrawn in the night, going down the river in their canoes to the deep water where their ship was anchored, leaving behind them the horses, cattle and pigs that they had brought from San Augustine. In a delirium of triumph, followed by an orgy of feasting, the victorious Edisto braves had slaughtered horses, cows and swine. One mare only, terrified by the tumult, had broken from the corral and escaped into the woods. She, too, had returned later, looking for companionship, and in the savannah near the ruins of the fort, Red Tobal found her.

They grazed for a while together, happy in each other's company. Then Red Tobal, as though he understood that for him and for her a new life had begun, turned his back on the ruins of Fort San Felipe and led her into the forest.

It was a new life indeed. They were strangers in a strange land. Far to the south, the Spaniards at San Augustine had horses. Perhaps in the remote Mississippi forests a few of the horses abandoned by De Soto on his ill-fated march to the Great River had survived. Still farther to the west, stray Spanish mares and studs had wandered up from Mexico to run wild on the buffalo ranges and give rise in later years to the mustang herds of the Plains. But in all the virgin wilderness of the South and East where, now that Fort San Felipe was gone, there was no settlement of white men—a wilderness that reached from the Spanish posts in Florida to the shores of the polar sea and from the Atlantic far beyond the peaks of the Appalachians —Red Tobal and his mare were the only ones of their kind.

He led her into the forest that had encircled Fort San Felipe and already there was something new in him, a thing intangible yet plainly evident, a change that was, perhaps, in essence a subtle realization of the wilderness. In the three days since he had become free and masterless he had experienced a foretaste of the life that he was to lead. Esteban Solis, a proud man, had valued him for his pride, his arrogance. Something of this was gone from Red Tobal now, or rather it was curiously altered and blended with something else.

He moved carefully, warily, all his senses alert. He was afraid, and yet there was courage in him to face the dangers that he feared. Both this fear and this courage were visible in his eyes, in the way in which he carried himself, the way in which he moved. He was as handsome as ever, but now it was another kind of beauty—the beauty of a wild creature, of an antlered stag in a forest hunted by fierce beasts of prey.

Of that pure Andalusian strain which preserved almost unchanged the characteristics of the Moorish steeds from which it sprang, Red Tobal was larger than most stallions of his kind; in all other respects, except, perhaps, the rich sorrel color of his coat, he was true Arab. His head, slightly arched from forehead to nose, was rather small, the nostrils were wide and sensitive, the eyes large and full of fire. He was slim-bodied and slender of limb, light of bone but powerfully muscled; his mane and tail, almost golden in color, were full and flowing; there was a lithe, sinewy gracefulness in every line and curve. The mare with him was a poor thing by comparison: an undersized animal, cream-colored and inclined to shagginess, yet showing more than a trace of Barbary blood. She walked meekly at his heels. There was no visible change in her, no new quality of alertness, no realization of the wilderness.

Red Tobal followed a narrow path through the forest, a winding trail trodden out by the deer. He pushed on rapidly, the shaggy mare just behind him. He did not like these low, dense woods close to the sea where impenetrable thickets and tangles of vine hedged him in on either side. The sultry May air brought many scents to him, some of which he recognized, while others were strange. He was traveling by chance up the wind so that his own scent was not wafted on ahead, and now and again he caught glimpses of deer in the path in front of him and of small furry animals with black-ringed bushy tails.

The forest teemed with life. Besides the deer and the raccoons, Tobal saw many opossums, a pair of gray foxes, innumerable rabbits and squirrels, a bearded white-fanged lynx, as large as a dog, that snarled at him as he approached, then vanished like a ghost.

The trees and thickets were alive with small bright-colored birds. Twice he saw flocks of wild turkeys; and once, where the deer path skirted a marshy opening in the woods, he startled into flight a great host of white and black wood ibises that had been sunning themselves there.

A new scent came to him presently, faint and puzzling, a scent that he did not know. He halted and sniffed the air, listening keenly, searching the shadowy path ahead. He saw no movement. The path had turned so that he no longer faced the wind, and the scent was strangely elusive—he could not tell whence it came. Soon he moved forward again, slowly, doubtfully, his head high, his muscles tense.

In front of him, perhaps six feet above his head, a live-oak limb, partly hidden by leaves and pendant moss, overhung the path, and from this limb a large spider web was swung, a silken wheel or disc, four feet in diameter, composed of shimmering, interlacing golden threads. Red Tobal knew these great golden webs well. He had seen them often when he carried Captain Solis through the woods around Fort San Felipe, and he had always hated the feeling of those clinging, sticky strands across his nose and face. Here, however, there was no way around. The thickets walled in the path; he must break through this web or else go back along the way he had come.

He walked slowly to within ten feet of the silken barrier across the path; then, plunging suddenly forward, he burst through the web and passed beyond the oak limb from which it swung. This sudden plunge saved him. In another fraction of a second, a panther, stretched on the oak limb above the path, its tawny body hidden by the leaves, would have dropped upon the stallion's back. As it was, the shaggy mare became the panther's target; but the mare, too, startled by Tobal's plunge, had leaped forward when he leaped, and the big forest cat, confused by these swift, unexpected movements of the two horses, launched its attack a fraction of an instant too late.

It dropped upon the mare, but, instead of landing squarely on her back, it struck her hindquarters and, when these gave way under its weight, it slipped off and for a moment lost its footing. She screamed as the panther struck her, and Tobal sprang forward, then wheeled in the path, while the mare dashed past him, her ripped haunches gushing blood. The panther, eyes mere flaming slits, white fangs bare, long tail weaving from side to side, crept forward slowly, its belly almost touching the ground.

The stallion seemed transfixed, fascinated. He stood motionless, head high, nostrils quivering, his eyes fastened upon that crouching, creeping form. Suddenly, with the swiftness of light, the panther leaped. Tobal reared high, striking with his forefeet. The beast was on him, wrapped round him like a huge snake, its fangs deep in his shoulder, its claws gashing his belly and legs.

Tobal screamed, his bare teeth reaching for the panther's body. The great cat's weight pulled him down. He tottered and fell heavily on his side, the panther underneath; somehow he got to his feet again and stood swaying, his chest and forequarters red with blood. The panther lay writhing, its ribs crushed by the stallion's bulk. For a moment Tobal gazed down at it, his eyes wild and staring; then he turned and dashed madly away along the path.

Thus Tobal learned early of the traps that the wilderness could set for him and of the great lion-like cat that was the master of the wilderness—the panther or puma that the Indians called the Cat of God. Thereafter, of all the scents of the forest, he respected this one most. At first he feared it with a fear that was utter panic, that sent him dashing off at full speed whenever the breeze bore that odor to his nostrils; and at first, too, the scent of a black bear filled him with terror, and he trembled whenever he heard the hunting cry of wolves. Both of these abounded in the vast park-like pine forest, interspersed with open savannahs of grass and maiden cane, to which he made his way after leaving the vicinity of Fort San Felipe and which became his home.

The bears, as a rule, hunted singly or in family groups. The wolves, smaller than the big timber wolves of the Northern woods and varying in color from brownish gray to yellowish-white, ranged everywhere in packs of a dozen or more, and there was scarcely an hour when he could not hear their hunting cry. He feared them at first almost as much as he feared the panther—perhaps their fierce voices woke in him some dim inherited memory of the more savage wolves of Spain. Yet, for weeks after his encounter with the panther, the wolves displayed no interest in Red Tobal and his mate. With numberless deer to prey upon, they would not turn aside in pursuit of new and untried game. Then, early one warm afternoon, in sunny open woodland where the tall pines stood far apart and a green carpet of short sweet grass covered the level forest floor, Red Tobal fought his first pitched battle with the wilderness.

He was grazing quietly with the shaggy mare when suddenly, down the wind, a wolf gave tongue. Immediately, as though this had been a signal, the clamor of a great pack filled the woods. Tobal, already in full flight, saw them coming under the column-like trees —saw, too, that the mare lagged far behind him, running stiffly, laboring at every stride.

His own hurts were healing well; hers were still raw and angry, for the panther's claws had cut deep into her haunches: and now, leaping suddenly away as the wolf cry smote upon her ears, she had reopened the deepest of her wounds. Blood oozed from it and pain almost paralyzed her left hind leg. Almost at once the wolves were all around her, running silently beside her, and the next moment two of them sprang at her throat.

She screamed, and at the sound a strange thing happened to Red Tobal—instantly there was something in him that was stronger even than his fear. He whirled and came racing back to her, and before they could pull her down he struck them, a snorting, squealing demon of flashing teeth and flying hoofs, scattering them like leaves. The smell of blood gave them courage. They rallied and closed in on him, fighting wickedly, leaping up at his throat, chopping at his flanks, trying to hamstring him as they hamstrung deer. He was the center of a mad whirling mêlée, while the mare, swaying weakly on her legs, looked on with wild terror-stricken eyes.

Almost in an instant Red Tobal was red with his own blood. His legs and haunches were ripped in half a dozen places, but he was unconscious of pain. Biting, kicking, plunging, he fought his way through and leaped clear; then, wheeling, he charged through the brown and gray mob of them and, rearing high in their midst, struck downward with his forehoofs, breaking a she-wolf's back.

They drew away from him then, eyeing the she-wolf avidly where she lay writhing in agony, and Tobal charged them again. They fell aside and let him pass, and the stallion whirled to find them in a struggling, ravening mass upon the she-wolf's body, tearing her limb from limb.

He was on them once more like a thunderbolt, trampling them down, pounding them under foot, his bare teeth and curled lips foul with hair and blood. For a minute, perhaps, they fought him, and a yellow wolf, fastening on his neck, clung there like a giant leech until Tobal, rearing high and whirling in a half circle, flung the beast from him. Then, all at once, they were gone—all except the dead mangled she-wolf and two others that dragged themselves painfully over the ground, their crippled legs trailing behind.

This was Red Tobal's first pitched battle with the wilderness, his first pitched battle with fear. Thereafter, fear was never again his master, and, though for a time he still experienced it often, he never gave way to it completely, never forgot everything else in an over-whelming surge of terror. The wolves thenceforward he treated with a fierce disdain, and they, finding him always ready for battle, left him severely alone. The black bears, which were almost as numerous as the wolves, were entitled to greater respect, but Tobal learned gradually that not one in five of them would come on if he held his ground. Thus, in time, the bears became mere incidents in his daily life, though he was careful, when a big one approached, to remove himself from its path before it had drawn too near. Among his four-footed foes, only the huge alligators of the rivers and lagoons and the long-bodied, velvet-footed panthers that moved without a sound along the forest trails held their place as enemies to be dreaded al-ways, antagonists with whom no liberties could be taken.

He avoided the alligators by keeping away from the waters where they lived. The panthers he saw seldom—they were far less numerous than the wolves and bears—but occasionally he scented them and little by little he acquired knowledge of their ways. He learned that, like the bears, they varied much in size, but he did not learn until long afterwards that they varied also in courage, that while some of them would attack him instantly, in general they were daunted by his bulk and preferred to prey upon their ac-customed victims, the deer. The respect in which he held the whole panther race, as a result of that first encounter, prevented him from making this discovery; as soon as he saw or scented one of the big hunting cats he sought safety in flight. He passed no more under leaning tree-trunks or overhanging limbs from which an enemy, hidden by the leaves, might drop upon his back. He avoided the edges of dense thickets; he kept out of jungly tracts of woods so thick that they could be traversed only by following the narrow paths made by the deer; he learned, while grazing in the broomgrass savannahs, to watch for a slow, sinuous weaving motion of the tall grass blades as though a huge serpent were winding through them.

A dramatic incident impressed this last lesson upon his memory. By that time, fortunately, the flesh wounds received in his battle with the wolves had practically healed, while the mare's injuries no longer hampered her activity. Tobal was grazing with the mare in a grass-grown savannah where many deer in groups of three or four were feeding. Presently, down wind from him, he saw four young does that had been grazing together lift their heads and go bounding away.

They ran perhaps fifty yards, then halted and stood at gaze, looking back towards the spot from which they had fled. Red Tobal, puzzled, searched the surface of the savannah but could see no enemy. He saw, however, near the place where the deer had been feeding, a slow progressive movement of the grass, a queer, rippling, winding motion of the tall, close-growing stems.

It drew nearer and Tobal watched it curiously. The whitetails had resumed their feeding; the light breeze blowing down the savannah prevented any hint of danger from reaching the red stallion's nostrils. Nevertheless, he whinnied a warning to the mare, and the two stood watching while that strange movement of the grass came slowly nearer and nearer.

At last, perhaps in a momentary lull of the breeze, Tobal caught a faint telltale scent. He snorted and wheeled in his tracks; and up from the grass, where the weaving movement had been, a great, yellow-brown, flame-eyed beast leaped high and came bounding on. For a minute it was a close and desperate chase, for the panther for short distances can run at race horse speed; but when once Red Tobal and the mare were fairly under way, the big cat dropped behind and quickly abandoned the pursuit.

There was one other scent that Tobal feared, one other enemy against whom he was constantly on guard. Esteban Solis, the sternest

Indian fighter among the captains of New Spain, had taught him to hate and fear the red men against whom Solis waged cruel and relentless war. Solis had never sympathized with the policy of the priests and friars who labored to convert the Indians to the faith. His policy, on the other hand, was always one of ruthless domination, and somehow his hatred of the Indians had communicated itself to the stallion that he rode on a hundred dangerous expeditions in the wilderness.

Thus, long before he became a masterless horse in a primeval forest where only red men dwelt, Tobal had learned that these red men were his enemies; and long before then he had learned to know them by scent as well as by sight, to recognize them far off as beings of a different order from the white men among whom he lived. It happened that the region to which he had led the shaggy mare after leaving the ruins of Fort San Felipe was far removed from any village of the Edisto, and thus months passed before he had scent or sight of a human enemy. But early one September morning, not long after his adventure with the panther in the broomgrass savannah, Tobal received a startling reminder of the existence of these two-legged foes.

He was lying with the mare on a bed of pinestraw close to an opening in the woods where the ground was low and moist and where many tall white herons were standing at rest in the bright sun. Presently Tobal saw four wild turkeys fly out of the woods and sail across the opening, close over the heads of the white birds standing there. Something had frightened the turkeys, Tobal knew, and he rose quickly, his head high, sniffing the breeze. The mare caught his alarm and got to her feet, and the two stood motionless, watching and listening.

For some minutes nothing happened; then, on the farther edge of the savannah, a white heron took wing, another and another, until the whole great flock of five hundred or more were in full flight. All at once, Tobal saw, across the savannah, a long line of Indian hunters, walking abreast at intervals of twenty paces, advancing out of the woods into the open space where the herons had been resting.

Tobal turned and trotted into the forest, the mare at his heels. But the keen eyes of more than one hunter had seen the two horses, and a shrill whoop rose from the advancing line. Tobal did not know that this whoop was a signal. He did not know that the Edisto often hunted deer in this fashion, one party of hunters marching through the woods in a far-flung rank perhaps a quarter of a mile from end to end and thus driving the game toward other hunters waiting in ambush. He trotted on, the mare just behind him; and because the Edisto, in arranging their deer drives, always took careful note of the direction of the wind so that the fleeing game would get no warning of danger in front, Tobal and the mare ran full into the ambuscade awaiting them.

Suddenly an arrow sang past him, missing him by a hair. At the sharp, remembered sound, he sprang forward as though a hornet had stung him, and another cane shaft stood quivering in a pine trunk at his left. He wheeled and raced off at right angles to his former course, the mare, as always, following in his track. Three more arrows sped by them as they ran, but none touched them, and presently they were clear of the ambuscade, and safe.

Tobal did not know that, for a brief momentous interval, as he raced off amid the far-spaced trees, a tall thick-set Indian standing behind a giant pine had covered him with bent bow but had not loosed the shaft. He passed in his headlong flight within twenty paces of this hunter, and at that distance the Indian could have driven the arrow halfway through the stallion's body. Red Tobal, even if he had seen the Indian, could not have understood the light in his small, black, eager eyes.

Two days later swift runners passed through all the villages of the Edisto. Cherokee hunters had encroached on the Edisto lands and had ambushed a messenger sent to warn them away. In the great round council house in the Edisto chief-town, the Old Be-loved Men and the chiefs sat for long hours around the sacred fire. They offered sacrifices and consulted the signs. The omens pointed to war.

Painted and feathered war parties took the trail and returned with Cherokee scalps; once and again the dreaded Cherokee war whoop sounded in the outlying Edisto towns. It was a busy time for Alusta, war captain of the Edisto—his first war as leader of his tribe. He had become war captain when his predecessor was killed by a Spanish bullet in the attack on Fort San Felipe; this quarrel would test his cunning and skill. The Cherokee were a powerful nation, but they lived at a great distance, among the inland foothills and the high blue peaks of the Appalachians. Alusta fought a wary campaign, luring the red mountaineers down to the swamps and canebrakes of his own low country and harassing them there.

Red Tobal knew nothing of all this. It did not occur to him as strange that during that autumn he caught only once or twice the scent of human enemies. The Edisto braves were fully occupied. They had no time for hunting the red stallion and the shaggy mare seen by a party of their hunters in the late days of summer while driving deer—a stallion which they recognized at once as the horse that the hated Spaniard Solis had been riding when he was killed. But again and again that autumn, while following the war trail or lying wakeful in some ambush under the stars, Alusta thought of that day when he had bent his bow against the red stallion and had not loosed the shaft.

He desired the red stallion. The instant he saw the horse he coveted him. Horses were strange to the red men. They had never seen a horse until the Spaniards came, and, their customs fixed through countless generations, it had never occurred to them that they too might utilize the horse—*"Echo-clucco,"* or the "great deer," as they called the animal—in warfare. Moreover, they believed and their wizards and conjurers encouraged this belief, that the Spaniards had some magical power over their horses enabling them to control these mighty beasts and that the red men could not learn the secret of this power. Hence, on the rare occasions when the Spanish horses fell into their hands, the Edisto killed and ate them and continued to fight and hunt on foot as their ancestors for thousands of years had fought and hunted.

Alusta, a deeper Indian than most, saw, vaguely at first, then more and more definitely, the error of this policy. He did not know what the Spaniards' secret was, but he believed that it might be learned. The Indian often tamed the common deer, and he believed that they might tame the "great deer" also if the effort were made. He had tried vainly, for he had no authority then, to stop the slaughter of the horses taken at Fort San Felipe. When suddenly, on that day of the deer drive, he discovered that Solis' stallion had survived, there leaped into Alusta's brain, as he stood with bent bow aimed against Red Tobal, a vision.

It was a splendid, and intoxicating vision. He saw himself owner and master of this red stallion, riding him, ruling him as the Spaniards ruled the horses that they rode. How he would do this, how he would capture and tame the stallion, he did not know; but the idea, flashing into his mind as Tobal raced past him that day, held his hand so that no arrow sped from his bow. The idea grew swiftly, developing and expanding in his cunning brain. He foresaw what glory would come to him if he alone among Indian warrior-chiefs rode the "great deer" as the Spaniards rode it. His fame would spread far; it would extend through all the neighboring nations. Perhaps a time would come when he would be chief not only of the Edisto but of all their kindred tribes: Combahee, Yamassee, Coosaw and Kiawah.

The Cherokee war intervened. Alusta had no time to give to the red stallion. At last, when the scalps taken by both sides were equal, peace talks were held and the quarrel ended. A plan that had shaped itself in Alusta's mind ripened into action. Day after day, ranging the forest alone, he studied Red Tobal's ways, using the utmost care that no hint of danger should reach the stallion's nostrils. Then, well content, confident that success was only a matter of time, he laid his ambush.

Red Tobal and the shaggy mare roamed far and wide. Autumn had passed and winter had come—the sunny, brilliant winter of the lowland South. The great flocks of herons and ibises had disappeared; in their place came companies of tall cranes, some white, some golden-buff, to stride with slow, stately steps along the moist edges of the shallow pineland ponds. The turkeys, their numbers swelled by the summer's increase, walked in flocks of a hundred or more through the level leaf-strewn woods. The deer, more numerous than ever, grazed in droves of forty or fifty in the cane savannahs; now and again small bands of elk came down from the hill country and the mountains to enjoy the richer browsing of the lowland glades. Once a vast army of wild pigeons swept over, their swift-flying legions darkened the sky. They passed on—from early morning until late afternoon there was no break in that incalculable feathered army—but down from the air road which they traveled came other hosts of wild fowl to swarm upon every river and marsh; squadrons of great white swans, clamorous regiments of geese, wild ducks of many kinds in untold multitudes.

A new vigor pulsed in the veins of Red Tobal and his mate. Day after day the air was still and crystal clear, the sky bright blue. Sometimes in the early mornings a thin film of ice coated the edges of the streams and the little pineland lakes, but only once came a flurry of snow. Tobal ranged far not because of any shortage of food; the grass in the savannahs was always green and all along the edges of the swamps were large beds of tender maiden cane. A spirit of restlessness throbbed in him, a spirit born perhaps of perfect physical fitness and an assured self-confidence.

This latter was the more important. It had been growing in him, developing slowly, and now it had flowered. In the mare also a change had taken place, but she had not changed as Tobal had changed. Her senses had grown sharper; she was better able now to read the signs of the forest, to interpret its scents and sounds. But she was still a tame thing gone wild against her will, a child of tame generations, with centuries of domestication behind her, thrown by a strange chance into a primeval wilderness.

The change that had come over Tobal was far deeper. It was not, in reality, a forced and unwilling response to new conditions, a new environment. Rather it was, increasingly, a joyful and eager stirring of latent impulses and desires long submerged, needing only the touchstone of opportunity to quicken them into life. Something deep in him had been awakening slowly and now was fully awake. He had become a part of the wild life of the wilderness; he was one now with the deer and the panther and the bear and all the wild creatures of the woods and swamps.

He was one with them, although he had no friendship for them, although some of them were his relentless and dangerous foes. He had learned to live life as they lived it, to face the dangers that they faced, to meet them on their own ground at their own game. He had not conquered the wilderness; no wild creature could do that. But he had learned its hard lessons, he had met the stern tests that it imposed. He was sure of himself now; and, in a somewhat altered form, his old pride, his old arrogance, returned. He no longer feared the wilderness, although he knew and recognized its dangers. It was his home, his refuge. It might destroy him in the end but he loved it and gloried in its freedom, and he was not afraid.

The thing that happened happened without warning. Tobal and the mare ranged far, but night after night they returned to the same place to sleep; and, coming and going to and from this safe refuge, walled in by thickets of cassena and partly surrounded by a shallow pond which no panther would cross, they used one of two deer paths. Four times, in passing along one of these paths, Tobal, always in the lead, brushed unknowingly against Alusta's snare. The fifth time, the trap closed on him.

He did not see it. A small holly, over which a smilax vine had clambered, stood here beneath the pines and thrust its evergreen branches across the deer path. The deer that used the path passed under this leafy barricade, but Tobal, much taller than the deer, always brushed through the holly foliage, deriving a certain pleasure from the gentle scratching of the twigs along his shoulders and back. One morning, as he pushed through this yielding barrier of dark-green leafage, something tightened across his chest and slipped along his throat.

He could not see it, but he took it to be a loop of smilax, and he pressed on through the holly branches and beyond them. The loop across his throat did not break as he expected; he put his weight against it, and it tightened instantly, clasping his throat and neck. In sudden alarm, he leaped forward and dashed along the path—a jerk threw him back upon his haunches so violently that he toppled and nearly fell. He stood still, trembling in every limb.

Alusta watched him from the concealment of a pine trunk fifty yards away. So far the Indian's task had been easy. His noose, of jackvine and hickory fibre made doubly strong and supple by a process well known to the Indian hunters, had been hidden skillfully amid the holly twigs above the path. The stallion had thrust head and neck clear through it as he pushed through the evergreen foliage. Once it had tightened on him it would hold forever, and the long buckskin rope to which it was attached, and which was in turn made fast to a stout sapling, was strong enough to hold a buffalo bull.

Alusta waited and watched. His black eyes glittered like the eyes of a coiled snake; the muscles of his powerful body, shining with bear's oil and naked except for a deer skin about his middle, were tight and hard. Two long eagle feathers in his hair, roached in a crest and reddened with puccoon root, trembled with the intensity of his eagerness. Yet craftiness taught him patience. There was no hurry; he wanted to see what the red stallion would do. He had, of course, selected his hiding place with due regard to the direction of the wind. The wild horse could not scent him. Something, he thought, might be learned, something that might help him in taming his captive, if he studied the stallion carefully before revealing his presence.

Red Tobal stood like a statue of bronze. The quivering of his
limbs had ceased. He was absolutely motionless, as still as though
the life had gone out of him. It had gone—the new, free life that
he had learned to love. His head was high, yet somehow he had
changed. The proud curve of his neck had vanished; there was a
strange laxness in his body like the laxness of utter fatigue; he
seemed smaller, thinner than before.

The shaggy mare, cropping the grass under the pines thirty yards
away lifted her head and looked at him uneasily. She was wondering, perhaps, why he lingered here where the grass was short and
sparse. She whinnied to him but Tobal did not answer her call. He
did not turn his head or move.

He understood what had happened. The noose about his neck,
the tug of the buckskin rope, had told him the whole story in the
winking of an eye. In a flash, at the touch of those familiar fetters,
Tobal knew that he was again the captive and the servant of man.
The buckskin rope had fallen slack; it lay loose upon the ground,
half hidden in the short grass. But Tobal knew that it was still there,
still holding him prisoner. Alusta had expected him to struggle
desperately. Instead, he stood wholly docile, utterly still—waiting.
Presently, he knew, the hand of a man would be laid upon his neck.

The Indian uttered a low grunt, a grunt of satisfaction mingled
with surprise. His thin lips moved in a faint smile. His task might be
simpler than he had supposed. The wild horse might not, after all,
be hard to conquer; his wildness seemed to have vanished already,
at the touch of the jackvine halter, the pull of the buckskin rope.

Suddenly a light broke upon Alusta, his crafty eyes gleamed
with a new brilliance. He had discovered the secret of the Spaniards,
the secret of their power over the horses that they rode. There was
no mystery, no magic—or if there was magic, he had learned where
it lay. It was the rope that quelled these mighty beasts, that conquered them and made slaves of them so that men could mount
upon their backs.

There before him was the proof—at the pull of the rope the red
stallion's spirit had broken. Pride swelled in Alusta, the vainglory
of the successful warrior. In a low voice he began to chant the
words of his song of triumph, the paean of victory that he sang
when he had slain an enemy.

The song worked on him like wine. He had done a great thing; he would do a greater one now. Singlehanded, he had taken the red stallion. Now, singlehanded, he would tame him, if he needed further taming, and perhaps that very day he would ride him home in triumph to the chief-town of the Edisto. He saw, as though it were visible before him, the amazement of the warriors and the women, the fame and the glory that would be his when he came riding out of the forest mounted on that great animal of the Spaniards that no Indian had ever ridden before.

Alusta moved out from his hiding place behind the pine. Beside his hip his quiver of spotted fawn skin held his arrows of hickory and cane. In his right hand he carried his locust bow; but as he walked forward he shifted the bow to his left hand, and, with the right, drew from his belt a bright, keen knife of fine Spanish steel that he had found when Fort San Felipe was taken. He would not need the knife, but he would have it ready. His lips still chanted, almost inaudibly, the words of his victory song, yet now he was cool and wily and watchful. His eyes, as he advanced slowly, were riveted upon the stallion.

The shaggy mare snorted at sight of him and galloped off amid the pines. Alusta noted again what he had already observed—that she was heavy with young. Red Tobal turned his head and gazed at the approaching Indian. The stallion made no effort to break away or run. His nostrils quivered, his muscles tightened, a light—a light that Alusta could not see and would not have understood—gleamed momentarily in his eyes. For the first time Tobal knew that the man whose captive he had become was not a Spaniard but a red man, one of that race that he had always hated and feared.

Alusta walked up to the stallion. He placed his right hand, the hand that held the knife, on Tobal's neck. Tobal flinched, his head drooped as though the weight of the Indian's hand pressed it down. Alusta stood motionless, his hand on Tobal's mane.

The Indian's eyes glittered with triumph, but he was frowning— he was, for an instant, puzzled as to his next move. The stallion seemed docile, completely submissive. Yet it was too soon to mount him. It would be well to test once more the power that kept him in subjection. Alusta dropped his bow upon the ground and, with the hand that had held it, grasped the buckskin rope attached to the jackvine noose around Tobal's neck. He tightened slowly on the rope, watching the stallion narrowly.

Suddenly Alusta sprang backward. He had felt Tobal stiffen as the rope tightened, had seen the flare of madness in the stallion's eyes. But in the very instant that the warning of danger came to him, the danger itself burst upon him. He leaped for safety, but he could not leap beyond the radius of the rope, and at once the stallion was upon him, a mad-eyed, snorting, screaming fury, lips curled, teeth gleaming in open jaws.

Those teeth raked the Indian's naked shoulder, slashed deep into his flesh. Twice with all the strength of his right arm, Alusta struck with his knife, and at the second stroke the keen blade sank into something hard and tough, something that held it fast. Tobal reared high, and as the buckskin rope drew taut with a jerk, the jackvine noose around his neck parted where Alusta's knife had all but severed it. Tobal's descending forehoofs struck the Indian squarely on the chest. They hurled him backward and downward in a crumpled mass. . . .

Red Tobal sprang forward, wheeled and stood at gaze. Blood welled from his shoulder where the knife had gashed it, but he seemed unaware of the wound. His eyes were brilliant, they blazed as though red fire were in them; his nostrils quivered and dilated, his neck was proudly arched. In every line and curve of his body there was a lithe, wild gracefulness, an exultant beauty that was strength and swiftness and freedom. For a moment he stood gazing at the trampled body of the Indian. Then, with a snort, he whirled and galloped into the forest.

In out-of-the-way places on the Atlantic coast, from the pine-lands, and islands of South Carolina to Virginia's Eastern Shore, there exists today a race of horses concerning which many stories are told.

Some of these horses are wild, others are half wild, still others are wholly tame. Hard living and inbreeding have stunted their bodies but not their brains. They roam, generally in small bands, about the marshes and the sandy islands of the coast or in the pine woods and savannahs near the great lowland swamps. In spite of a characteristic slenderness of limb and, more rarely, a certain shapeliness of head and neck recalling the Andalusian of Arab blood, they are poor things to look at. Unless, that is, one looks at them through the eyes of romance. Then legend gilds them and gives them dignity.

On Hatteras Banks, where they are known as banker ponies, it is said that they are the descendants of Barbary horses brought over by Sir Walter Raleigh's colonists. At Chinconteague in Virginia there is a story of a Spanish ship wrecked off the capes in the early days and of Spanish horses swimming ashore through the surf. In the South Carolina plantation country there persists an ancient and curious legend linking the marsh tackies, as they are called in that region, with the horses lost by De Soto nearly four centuries ago on his march to the Mississippi.

I never believed this tale. It was more likely, I thought, that these hardy little horses of the lonely pinelands and the coast islands trace back to the forts which the Spaniards built on the Carolina coast and which were later abandoned to the Indians. I knew one of these ponies, a little lop-eared sorrel who lived and still lives on Edisto Island, not many miles as the crow flies from the site of old Fort San Felipe, and one afternoon he and I talked together after the fashion of horses and men. He told me (chiefly with his eyes, which were dreamy and vaguely melancholy) about Red Tobal, his great ancestor.

Tzagan

CLEMENT WOOD

To my mind this is one of the finest stories of its kind, and it has the additional merit of being laid in a country which rarely forms the background for horse stories. Tzagan, his character, his problems, his adventures live and breathe. Furthermore, the story is entirely about horses, with no human being to claim attention.

Midway of the mountains that bound on the northwest the demon-land of Mongolia rises the stiff peak Jagisstai. On an icy August morning a troop of wild dun horses cantered briskly along the undulating road that led from its crest to the river valley below. This was the last herd of the tarpans, the wild horses of Tatary, ancient children of the untamed steppe, who have never known bit or bridle.

At their head loped Tzagan, the white stallion, undisputed lord of the herd. He was the only white tarpan within the long memory of wild horses; the rest were dun-colored, or at most mouse-colored, with dark mane and tail and legs. Tzagan's mane and tail were shining jet, his legs a suave black; but his soft white coat was a thing new to them. Soon after he was foaled he had been recognized as a prodigy, and shielded tenderly. He had grown agile and strong, a hand taller than most and heavier in build.

Old Taiga, the Forest One, the head stallion for long cold years, grew old as the white colt matured; at last his cunning dozed. The day came when Tzagan rubbed an inquisitive white muzzle against the graying one, then drew back, to neigh out challenge for combat.

72

A few bitter rushes and the age-withered head horse moved aside; young Tzagan swaggered to the van of the line and gave the signal for the advance. The tarpans at once looked to the White One to lead them; and a shrewd leader he had made.

Down the rocky road from Jagisstai, with its thick crust of snow, the horses hastened. The frozen whiteness crunched under their tread; at times the icy balls that formed on their hoofs broke loose, and rolled away over the brittle surface with a sound like crackling twigs. Around the shoulders of the ridge, in and out of the descending ravines, the trail zigzagged. Squirrels chattered from the squat green cedars, bullfinches flew with flaming breasts over their heads, white partridges whistled by. They passed scanty herds of bighorn and antelope, busily digging through the snow to the nutritious grasses below. To the side of the road writhed great balls of snakes; an occasional hare thumped casually away; a brown bear below giant boles of larches stared stupidly at their snow-cloudy passage.

As they reached a ravine that fed one of the headwaters of the river, Tzagan stopped abruptly, large head raised, nostrils twitching. His ears grew tense. They caught a far, faint whinny of distress, almost of despair. Across the ravine his keen eyes made it out at last —a cloud of black in a grassed clearing, a winged cloud, stridently squawking. Again the pitiful whinny.

A sharp neigh from the leader and the horses swerved into a steeper path that led into the very heart of the ravine. Across fallen larches they leaped and floundered, then over a burned area beneath leafless skeletons of trees. They forded an open stream, began a stiff climb. There was no sight or sound from the grassed clearing above, but they knew what they would find there.

Long before they had neared the place other eyes discovered it. On the top bald crag of Jagisstai, all morning, had sat a living thing, hunched and huddled toward the brooding east, facing away from the shrieking devil-winds that whirled over the Siberian steppes. His far eyes could pick out the lazy sources of streams that writhed through all enchantments to the drowsy swell of the Pacific.

Had he looked north he could have seen the headwaters of the river that crept under frozen horror to the frozen Arctic. An easy day's journey to the west and he would have found a stream that made its way through the locked Caspian and more populous seas, beyond the very Pillars of Hercules. A day's travel to the south and he would have encountered water that would know the Indian Ocean, and wash at the end the final polar floes. He sat brooding above the vast highland whence all the waters of earth are fed.

Good for them that no hunted Mongols, no avenging Tatars, came upon that lone living thing huddled high upon Jagisstai. They would have fallen to their faces in the snow in holy terror. "Demon of Jagisstai!" they would have cried. "Spare us, spare us! We will build you an *obo* of branches—we will build you a tower of rocks. Spare us!" And Zaberega, the living thing, the great hunched mountain-eagle, would have turned his eyes again to the swimming horizon, and at last vaulted upward to cleave heaven.

In frigid isolation, this icy morning, he held his peak. His hooked eyes, which could see beyond what men call sight, had observed the cantering passage of the wild horses down his valley road. Now they fixed upon the stir far down the rich head-plain of the river. The great throat lifted unconsciously, the eyes blinked rapidly. What should be moving in his domain?

It had been a long time since trespassers had disputed his suzerainty. In younger days he had had to fight back full-grown hawks from the fringes of the Gobi Desert; ponderous erns, the sea-eagles from the edge of the northern ocean. He had now no rivals. And yet this stir.

As if flung by springs of steel he catapulted into the air. His wings beat upward in a long slant, then sloped in an easy spiral down toward the grassed height. As he neared the ground, they dug more savagely into the stinging air. He knew now what he had to face— that blatantly cawing cloud of black bodies. His hurled passage warmed the air as he made the last low swoop and burned his tornado way into the noisy swivet of jet wings and red beaks.

Just before he struck, a few of them saw him—a wandering Indian pie, his black beak stained crimson; a great gray shrike, larger and more murderous; an evil old chough, claws gripping the poor horse's torn flank. There was red blood too on the chough's vivid red beak—she had hardly time to open it for a sharp scream of warning, when the eagle was upon her. One slash with powerful talons— the dead bird hurtled through the air. Right and left they rose in flying panic, all the hateful flock of pies and crows, ancient foes of the eagle folk. Zaberega, the winged demon, slanted and slashed left and right, with startling activity taking bird after bird in its flight.

The last one shrieked out of vision. Tired, deeply pleased, the eagle swung slowly back and lit on the ground a score of feet from the drooping horse.

It was a tarpan mare, he saw at once—a mare with a reddish-dun coat. Her bleeding back, where the dreadful birds had troubled her, was one vast spreading sore. Zaberega knew how these cowardly killers, that hunted only in winged clouds, fastened themselves to any horse or bull whose back showed the slightest wound, and scratched and pecked at it until it was an incurable thing; how they kept at their hateful killing until at last they gorged themselves upon the splendid creature.

He preened his ruffled feathers and muttered deep in his throat.

The mare was too drooping to raise her head and see her rescuer. She stood, patiently awaiting horrid death.

Zaberega turned to make a meal of the black bodies scattered over the ground. Ah! A wounded shrike, dragging itself below the grasses. One powerful pounce—one more foe gone. Here were glossy choughs, like feathered balls of jet with ruby beaks and feet; here were ungainly crows, glittering magpies. His curved beak tore cruelly into the warm meal.

He raised his head in sharp surprise; something drip-dripped from the beak upon a stone. Out of a dense cedar covert topping the rise broke the white head of Tzagan, the head stallion, his black mane streaming behind him. Another—a third—a dozen of the tarpans all at once appeared out of the fringing forest. Their feet clicked together; they poised uncertainly.

After a moment's scrutiny Zaberega continued his feeding.

Timidly, Tzagan led the way closer. His black feet were printed deftly together, his black tail swished against his snowy coat. He neighed a salutation to the great demon-bird.

Grasping a dead chough in each claw, the eagle lifted from the grass, and flew back to the wind-bedeviled height at Jagisstai.

Tzagan's head drooped slightly. Delicately, whinnying a soft greeting, he neared the wounded one.

His sensitive eyes widened as he recognized the mare, a softer note sounded from his throat. This was Ulan, the Red One—once his favorite. She had been driven from them less than two months ago.

At the familiar whinny the mare lifted her tired head. She answered as well as she could—a feeble, discouraged response. The other horses thronged around her, exchanging their greetings. With horror they observed the evil thing on her back—the wide, bleeding wound.

A sudden unease shook Tzagan: he remembered his duty.

Head lifted, black mane stringing out on the chill wind, he trumpeted the call for the onward journey.

It was the time of the last summer migration—you could have told that by the thinned hair of the horses. In winter their coats were thick and soft, almost like a bear's; but as the warmer months came this fell away, until their underbodies were almost hairless, and only a sparse covering remained on back and flanks. It was now midway of the thinned season.

Again Tzagan neighed the advance.

They trotted after him, hoofs clicking on the rounded rocks.

Ulan, the red mare, started feebly to follow. She saw the herd drifting past her; she strained to keep up. The blood woke afresh on her back; her limbs would not respond to the commands of her will.

Out of the distant forest the menacing caw of shrike and chough sounded; the heavy black birds began to near the place again.

She struggled forward; a pitiful whinny died in her weakness.

Tzagan stopped, sensing the breach in the herd. He parted the others, cantering between them until he reached her side again.

As Ulan lifted her tired head to greet him, the first of the choughs flew greedily up; it lit on her unprotected flank. Her teeth showed in sickly fashion; the head sagged again. Dispiritedly her tail shook, a menace no longer.

Tzagan was different. Eyes blazing, the white head snapped at the first bird. An untasty mouthful of black feathers was his reward.

The chough flew mockingly out of reach, cawing derisive hatred.

More and more of the birds circled around Tzagan's head.

The other horses surrounded the mare again. They sought to nudge her on with them; feebly she responded. As she moved, her escort of death continued. The whole troop of horses slowed to her painful gait; several of the angered dun heads curved above her sick flanks, keeping the pies and crows at a safe aloofness. They came constantly from every direction, swirling above in a dense flock, jeering just out of reach of the snapping teeth.

At length there was grumbling among the foremost horses.

Tzagan sensed it as soon as it began. They must go forward with all speed to the northern grazing-place, the mutters told him; they had delayed too long already. He knew that his part was to direct this powerful will of his followers, or that they would choose another stallion to lead. A leader must lead, not his own way, but the way of the herd.

Again he tried to hasten Ulan's progress. The Red One drooped more and more.

The grumbling among the horses grew more open.

He could face them, and stay with the wounded mare. Let them go away without him—abandon his leadership.

No. His place was at the head of the herd.

A sharp neigh—Tzagan cantered lightly ahead. Gladly the van tarpans leaped after the flashing White One. One by one the others abandoned the hurt straggler. The birds flapped closer and closer. The last horse passed her.

Cawing discordantly, the birds came to rest upon the bleeding back. The mare's head bowed to the ground. The living death was again upon her.

The troop arrived at last at the final pass that opened to the long slope to the lower end of Lake Kosogol. Tzagan knew this demon country well—this land of sliding sand-demons. There were constant fallen larch-trees, that must be circled cautiously; underneath these, even below clear stretches of the turf, were miry swamps—still, hidden pools of putrefying water, where a horse might sink and never rise again. The swamp snakes rustled beside them; a lone red fox swayed on his haunches and barked mockingly.

The road turned upward. There were no more quagmires, but instead a path along the top of a precipice, paved with cobbles and small stones that rolled deceptively from under their feet, and threatened to throw them over the great split in the hills. At times the very road melted away beneath them, in great ugly slides of stone and sand; it was all they could do to leap to scrambling safety, when one of these unexpectedly opened under their very way.

A small army of goldfinches whistled past the cautious steps of the tarpans. A white ermine snaked close to the ground across their path. In the willows below they could see a drove of wild camels munching phlegmatically. A flock of cranes cut between them and the sun.

Unnoticing, the horses continued this last rise.

Ah! The fringing valley at the head of the Kosogol in full sight! Now for a wild gallop down the ultimate slope to the rich grazing below.

But Tzagan stopped uncertainly. His feet lifted and dropped in perplexity. Here—before him—the old way, but altered. A vast cup-like depression sliced across the path—a wide new slide. Above the road were sharp gray rocks, steep and hard to climb; these curved in a great horseshoe to the firm path more than a hundred yards ahead. Sagging below this was the queer sink of sand and stone, with gray rocks again at its lower left end, and the precipice beyond that. Trees sprawled in ungainly fashion upon it; several lay on their sides, torn, impotent roots whitening in the air. It was all strange, all new.

Behind him crowded the others, eager to get down to the lush grass below. The foremost horses nudged him speculatively.

Circle around the top?

But they might be injured in the wild, rocky scramble.

Go back a few miles, and cross above?

The nudges grew more definite. He made up his mind to try it.

One tentative hoof went forward, then another. It seemed firm enough.

Cautiously he began to make his way across it.

The sliding demon heaved abruptly beneath him. His front legs slipped in to the hock, then to the knee; he felt the ground yield below his back feet. He tried to leap aside; the viscid sand held. He was moving, at increasing speed, toward the top of the abyss.

He became acutely aware of the other horses. A young stallion was a length below, at his right; behind his left flank was a third one, the Wood Mouse, a clever, timid tarpan, named also from his color. Tzagan tried to leap forward, and gained a doubtful yard. At the same moment, he sensed the Wood Mouse's backward spring to safety. A second afterward Tzagan heard the despairing sound as the stallion below, in a vain effort to leap out of the sand, stumbled over upon his side. A quick glimpse out of the corner of his eye showed the thrashing legs, the anguished head, as the quickening masses of sand and rock began to cover him with hissing clatter.

Tzagan thrust all power into his legs and sprang. Almost out of the depths. His front hoof struck a stone; he leaped again—and into deeper sand, sliding ever more rapidly. Again, again he tried.

He was tiring now; it took all of his energy to remain upright. Far behind he caught the troubled whinnies of the rest of the troop. There were choked sounds below him.

He had veered around now, and faced down-hill. In full view was the body of the lowest stallion, desperately floundering beneath its crushing load of sliding death. The distance between them increased rapidly.

Tzagan's feet were poised together below him as well as could be. The treacherous sand was well above his knees. If he could only remain upright until the bottom was reached, and then leap free.

This hope fled swiftly. He saw the last despairing heave as the lowest horse was rolled over the edge of the precipice. He heard the dreadful clamor of the rocky mass pouring in a cataract over the sheer edge of the great clove—the sound of tree-boughs crackling and breaking as the stallion's body ricocheted to death among them.

Queerly enough, his part of the slide was more sluggish than that to the right. Ahead, he could see where the stream turned before him, avoiding the obstruction of gray rocks. If he could reach them—!

Cautiously he began to work himself farther to the left in order to be swung as close to the stones as possible. They were a kind of rock wall, that made the slide veer away to the right and narrowed its lower end. In his eagerness he nearly lost his footing. A great rock bounded across his shoulder; he shivered in pain. Desperately he steadied himself upon his feet; the inevitable tug of the sand dragged him again to the right.

Here—right at him—hardly four feet away—the gray rocks. One desperate drive with his legs, all his power pushing into the yielding mass. He felt himself lifting out of it. One wild second spring—he hurled himself sideways against the gray crags. A leg tripped on the nearest rock. He fell, rolling over twice. Against an uptilted slab of stone he came to rest. Just beyond this gaped the final drop of a thousand feet.

Weakly he pulled himself up, legs trembling from exertion and excitement. Over the edge his glazed eyes peered. The stallion below was out of sight. The sand-slide poured by, dropping deafeningly into the void. Far below, the screaming caw of chough and pie.

So near to death—and now so far from it!

Skirting the left end of the slide, he set out painfully up the rocky wall that had meant such amazing salvation. As he stepped his shoulder stung. There was a damp feeling, a drip on the rocks when he paused to rest. He sniffed at it—it was the red water that comes when the skin is broken. Shaking his head clear, he neighed once toward the top of the hill, and continued on his way.

At the far end of the wide curve at the top, he came upon the others. In their eyes was fear, that might easily turn into panic as they watched his approach. This could not be Tzagan, who had disappeared in the rumbling death!

He whinnied reassuringly.

Their white muzzles smelled of him; their warm tongues licked the wounded shoulder.

Back with his own again!

He resumed the lead, and took up the march down to the grazing-ground beside the lake.

Out of the woods he heard the harsh chatter of rook and chough. At first he did not heed it; evidently they had found some new victim. Over the backs of the horses they flew and slanted until they had reached the head of the line.

Suddenly he felt a sharp pain on his shoulder. One of the birds dashed against him, ripping with red beak at the red wound.

Viciously Tzagan snapped back.

The chough veered away.

From the other side a second one slashed at him.

Thoroughly infuriated, he champed back. The other horses aided in this.

More slowly than the first stages of their journey, they came down to the grassy ground at the head of the lake.

The horses lowered their muzzles for the ample grazing.

But Tzagan, the White One, found it impossible to crop the sweet, soft food. The ominous birds circled slashingly around his head, ever more and more of them. His full energy was needed to deal with them.

Then began dreadful days and nights for Tzagan.

Again and again, that first afternoon, he sought to lower his head, to nibble at the delicate grass. Each time half a dozen of the winged murderers seized the moment to stab into the living flesh. They were always at him. Evening found him unfed, wearied, pain-racked.

It was a little better after the sun had gone. At least he could doze.

Toward morning he dispiritedly cropped at the nearer grass, which the herd had already gone over. Dawn came all too quickly, and with it again the flying menace.

That day and that night—the next day, the next night—endless days, endless nights—passed in the same horrid fashion. The wound was worse now and spreading—that he knew. At night he ate as best he could, but his strength was no longer up to that of the rest of the herd.

He was still regarded as leader. But long ago he had dropped back toward the rear, weakly proud that he could keep pace with the poorest of the cantering hoofs. The other horses did what they could to aid him; but they must eat sometimes, and the devil-birds never rested.

Day by day it grew harder to keep up. The day came when he was last in the line. Far ahead the Wood Mouse was leading. There had been no battle with the formal change of leadership; Tzagan was too ill to dispute his sick abdication.

The cloud of winged death never left him, from the thin gray bud of dawn to the blankness of night. Even in day-bright moonlight a few overgreedy birds stayed to plague him. Only in the scant black hours was he his own at last; and he was too tired and drowsy to eat much at this time.

The day came when the last mare in the line loped away, and Tzagan could not follow. The birds descended in a jubilant cloud upon him, tearing at his very life.

He backed against some trees, snapping with all his vigor at the menacing claws. The low boughs were partial protection; without this they would leech to his very back. With sick despair he heard the thud of the last hoofs dying away in the distance.

Alone—abandoned.

His thought was all of Ulan, the red mare. By now, long ago dead, on the grassed clearing below Jagisstai, the peak of the demon. Pictures of her dreadful plight bewilderingly passed over him, strangely blurred and altered. He seemed to be the red mare, torn to death.

A faint wave of denial swept over him. At least he could still slash with his tail and snap with his teeth.

His blows grew feebler and feebler.

It was only a matter of how long he could hold out. There would come a time when he could not.

Day after hideous day he stood, backed against the screen of trees, fighting back the hovering death that gave him no moment's rest. The evil hordes were always upon him; their evil odors pained his sensitive nostrils. Harder and harder the effort to snap back; it had been many days since he had eaten a full meal. And food was life.

He crept out in the black of night and cropped what herbage he could. One morning dawn came before he knew it; he was still far from the trees. The hordes of slaughter gathered unexpectedly. A killing half day he snapped back, keeping them away as best he could. His legs trembled from the pain of the vast hurt, extending now across his shoulders and almost to his tail.

Noon came, and tiring afternoon. His head rose slower each time; ever more feebly he fought away the tearing death.

Suddenly his body stiffened with strange hope. He sensed a stir of deliverance.

Out of the menacing air it came—the whir of great beating wings, the cyclone breath of passage, as the demon-bird, Zaberega, swept down among the cowardly killers. The great pinions fanned his back as they swept over him. He felt spasmodic clutchings as the birds, too late, sought to rise. Right and left Tzagan saw bodies fall amid cawing screams of terror. The eagle slew a score before the last of the enemies had made a panicky escape.

For the first time in weeks Tzagan knew life that was not torn by the talons of death.

The trees. He must reach them before the killers returned. He started his trembling journey; Zaberega, as if understanding that his presence was relief, drifted along beside, pouncing upon the foolhardy shrike or chough that ventured out again.

The trees were hardly a hundred yards away now. One satisfied, menacing scream, and Tzagan heard the great wings thrash the air as the demon-bird soared off to his lone peak.

At once he grasped what this might mean. Glazed eyes fastened to the distant trees; he sought to master and hasten his weak steps.

The rooks and pies cawed their summons. Closer, closer, came the sound.

Desperately he pushed forward. Worn knees suddenly betrayed him; he staggered sideways, and fell heavily, his chin striking a projecting stone. The tired body rested a moment on the old earth. It was so easy to give up, to die. Now as well as later. He was tired, tired.

A piercing pain in his shoulder—the winged fiends again! Inflamed eyes hardened to terrible determination. He pulled up to his feet and set off at a feeble canter for the last hope of life.

The rooks and pies dashed against his face, ripped his back, clung to him like evil river-leeches. This time he did not fight them away; all energy must be saved for the final yards. Before him the trees. And, more than that—he blinked his eyes painfully to make sure that they were not deceiving him—more than that, a cave, a hallowed opening below a great rock—a slight cave, hardly his height. It might mean shelter. With every ounce of reserve in his body, he held his legs to the torturing canter. Death tore at his life. He stood this, determined to make the shelter, or die.

He made it.

Here—just before him, the scooped-out place, barely higher than his neck. With despairing briskness he slued his body around and began to back in. The birds, realizing that their prey was trying to escape, screeched and shrieked. The low top of the caveway struck the birds clinging above his tail, and rasped them off. Sharp, burning pains shot through him at their last wild clawings. Farther and farther in he pushed; he could feel the living body of one bird caught between his sore back and the cave's top. He arched his body; the bird, breath squeezed out, slid past his flanks to the ground. Vengeful hoofs ground it into the soil.

He was entirely within it now but for his head. There was no more room. The birds whizzed back viciously, seeking to tear his face. Summoning what little strength was left, he snapped at their approaching threat and kept them off. There was at least no wound on his face that they could claw.

It was late afternoon. Until after dark the magpies and crows massed in front of the cave entrance, waiting for him to come out. There was one especial chough, an old fellow, larger than the rest, gleaming jet body contrasting bravely with scarlet beak and scarlet feet, that planted himself on the ground right before Tzagan's face. The baleful bird eyes, below a feather torn rakishly awry, watched for some sign of weakening. If he could wait, the old chough seemed to say, so could they.

At last the sun drowsed below the hills. The chill vacancy of night strode eerily over the basin. One by one the birds flapped away.

He was all alone.

His legs gave; he sagged forward to his knees. His head collapsed to the half-frozen ground. His eyes closed.

After a half-hour's rest he managed to rise again upon his shivering legs. Step by step he staggered out of the cave. Every instant he expected the birds to hurl their punishing beaks upon him. No; black night was his protection. By some dim supersense he knew that the moon would rise after a few hours. He must make the most of this short space; the terrors might return in the false dawn of moonlight.

Just beyond the cave's mouth commenced the grass. Hungrily his weary lips crunched the succulent stems. At length he had his fill. Not far to the left, he remembered, there was a stream. Quietly he trudged over and drank. He did not go farther; if there was to be life for him, it lay in that cave; he must always be within reach of it.

At last the moon washed the sky gray. Guzzling another drink, he cropped his way back to the hollow scooped below the big rock, senses alert for the onrush of the birds.

They did not come.

For a few hours he dozed; then he ate again, before the gray promise of dawn brought back the jeering enemies.

Day after day passed the same way. A few of the birds tired of the long wait; evidently the rest had found a slaughtered prey near by. The next day most of them were back again. Always just below his nose squatted the old black chough, one feather still rakishly awry, gleaming scarlet beak waiting for scarlet food.

One morning Tzagan was slow in returning to the cave. The birds came at him before he reached it, tearing him. As he backed wildly in, the big chough, with the feather aslant, flew in ahead and sought to claw him from behind. With firm assurance the horse closed up the opening with his body. Methodically he kicked backward, once—twice—thrice. Ah! On the third kick he felt his hoof strike something yielding, squirming. One horrid scream of anguish. His hoofs danced the body of the would-be murderer into the rocks. White throat lifted, black mane tossing as it had not for days, he neighed victory—victory! Here was one enemy who would not plague him again.

After that the birds were more careful. There was more than one morning, when he was tardy in his return, that several tore the wounds open again. Never as bad as at first, however. Day by day he grew stronger, more able to travel; day by day the birds grew more doubtful as to this meal that had once seemed within their very beaks.

More than six weeks passed. The winter chill came into the air. There would come a day when the tarpan troop would return up the grassy bank of the lake and seek again the southern fields beyond Jagisstai. Meanwhile, below the healing wound the winter hairs, thick and soft, like the covering of a bear, were pushing their way. The hour came when he knew there was no more open wound—only healing scabs. The hour came when the last of these dropped away, and he was whole again.

But still the crows and choughs waited; still Tzagan was unwilling or afraid to come out, so used had he become to this imprisonment from the threat of clawed day.

It was a morning in late October when the horse's nose wrinkled at an unexpected odor upon the wind out of the brooding east. His ears pricked up, his senses sharpened acutely.

In scattering alarm the black birds rose. Some flew away, others settled a short distance away, in cawing uncertainty.

Down the wind came the sound of faint neighings. Tzagan,

strangely excited, pranced up and down in the narrow caveway.

Across the grassy plain he saw them at last—the tarpan herd, the wild horses, with the Wood Mouse dancing along in the lead.

He took two or three uncertain steps forward. He was out in the sunshine of day for the first time in two months. Speculatively the crows observed him: one or two flung themselves upon his twitching flanks and sought to bury their beaks in the thick, matted hair. His teeth clicked vigorously at them; they cawed out of sight into the far woodlands.

The horses loped ever closer.

Alone, before the cave, the white tarpan stood.

There was a sudden whinnying from the front ranks. A hundred feet from him they came to a stop; intent doubt was on their faces. A sudden noise and they would have wheeled and galloped off in veritable panic. A White tarpan! There had never been but one; and he was dead long ago, pestered to his death by the punshing birds.

He neighed an old greeting.

There was an answering neigh, half joyful, half unbelieving.

Delicately he stepped out. The sun shone on his bright black mane and tail, on his shining black legs; it spangled on the tangled mat of thick white hair covering the rest of his body. He came to a stop ten feet away from the Wood Mouse.

Threateningly the darker stallion raised his head; a red glaze came across his eyes. He approached the stranger, menace in his bearing.

Tzagan did not move. The other turned, and neighed the command for all to fall in and resume the journey.

Out of the sky came the far whir of great wings. Black against its brazen deeps, they could see the high blur of Zaberega, the demon-bird, returning to his aerie on the crest of Jagisstai. The sight of the familiar eagle brought back to the Wood Mouse remembrance of those days when he was only a follower and the White One the leader. The great wings passed out of sight. The dark stallion eyed the other in some perplexity.

Cruelly Tzagan held his eye until the usurper looked down at the ground. Then, lifting his throat, until the wind sprayed out his mane like a black pennon of victory, the White One trumpeted the call to advance. A bit sullenly, the Wood Mouse ranged himself behind the old leader, so strangely returned to them. A sudden clatter—the clicking hoofs struck the pebbles of the way again—a swirl of dust.

Up the long road the herd of wild horses cantered, with Tzagan, the White One, back with his own again.

The Ghost Horse

CHIEF BUFFALO CHILD LONG LANCE

I picked this story for two reasons. It has the merit of presenting a true analysis of horses' intelligence and psychology; it also gives us an insight into the character and qualities of the American (in this case Canadian) Indian. Chief Buffalo Child Long Lance, a well-known character in Canada, is a member of the famous Blackfoot tribe. His careful description of the Indian methods of catching and breaking the wild horse of the range, teaches us a great deal about the patience, skill, intelligence, and kindness which these people employed. One is reminded of Xenophon and his advice on how to break and train the young horse through firm kindness rather than fear. Many, many horse stories by writers less well versed attribute all sorts of characteristics to the horse which he does not have; others infer that he is a creature of extremely low mentality. Chief Buffalo Child knows the animal thoroughly and has painted in simple, picturesque language a scene which has all but disappeared.

With the first touch of spring we broke camp and headed southwest across the big bend of the upper Columbia toward the plateau between the Rockies and the Cascades. It was on this lofty plateau that the world's largest herd of wild horses had roamed during the last hundred and fifty years. Several hundred head of them are still there, where every summer efforts are being made to exterminate them by the provincial government of British Columbia. It was these horses that we were after, to replace the herd which the storm had driven away from our camp.

We struck the herd at the season of the year when it was weakest: early spring, after the horses had got their first good feed of green grass and their speed had been slowed by dysentery. Since these wild creatures can run to death any horse raised in captivity, it is a doubly hard job to try to ensnare them on foot. But, like wolves, wild horses are very curious animals; they will follow a person for miles out of mere curiosity. And, when chased, they will invariably turn back on their trail to see what it is all about, what their pursuers look like, what they are up to.

The big timber wolves would do the same; when we were traveling in the north country, they would trot along behind us all day. When we would stop, they would stop, and stand motionless and look at us with one foot raised. And when we would start again they would continue to follow. If we made a noise at them, they would jump back and hide behind the nearest bush. From then on, they would keep out of sight, but whenever we looked back we would see them peeping at us from behind the farthest bush.

They used to scare us children, but our fathers told us not to be scared; the wolves would not hurt us; they were just curious about us—although, they said, if the wolves followed us all day, they might try to snatch off our dogs when we camped that night. So they told us boys who were traveling in the rear to keep trying to "shoo" them away before we should make camp for the night. Wolves like dog meat better than any other, though male wolves will never harm a female dog.

But with the wild horses it was different. They always traveled ahead of us, but they had a way of turning back on their own trails and coming upon us from the side or rear, to keep watch on us. It was this never-satisfied curiosity of the wild horse that enabled our braves to capture them on foot.

The method of our warriors was to locate a herd and then follow it unconcernedly for hours, and maybe for days, before making any attempt to round it up. This was to get the horses used to us and to show them that we would not harm them.

We had been trailing fresh manure for five days before we finally located our first herd away up on the expansive Couteau

Plateau of central British Columbia. There they were: a herd of
about five hundred animals grazing away over on the side of a
craggy little mountain on top of the plateau. Their quick, alert
movements, more like those of a deer than those of a horse, showed
that they were high-strung beings that would dash off into space
like a flock of wild birds on the slightest cause for excitement.
There was one big, steel-dust stallion who grazed away from the
rest and made frequent trips along the edge of the herd. It was
obvious to our braves that this iron-colored fellow with the silver
mane was the stallion who ruled the herd, and our warriors directed all of their attention to him, knowing that the movements of
the entire herd depended on what he did.

When we had approached to within about five hundred yards of
the herd, our braves began to make little noises, so that the horses
could see us in the distance and would not be taken by surprise
and frightened into a stampede at seeing us suddenly at closer
range.

"Hoh! Hoh!" our braves grunted softly. The steel-dust stallion
uttered a low whinny, and all the herd raised their heads high into
the air and, standing perfectly still as though charmed, looked intently over at us with their big, nervous nostrils wide open. They
stood that way for moments, without moving a muscle, looking hard
at us. Then, as we came too near, the burly stallion tried to put
fear into us by dashing straight at us with a deep, rasping roar.

Others followed him, and on they came like a yelling war party,
their heads swinging wildly, their racing legs wide apart, and their
long tails lashing the ground like faggots of steel wire. But before
they reached us, the speeding animals stiffened their legs and came
to a sudden halt in a cloud of dust. While they were close they took
one more good look at us, and then they turned and scampered
away with the rest of the herd, which had already begun to retreat
over the brow of the mountain.

But the big, steel-dust stallion stood his ground alone for a
moment and openly defied us. He dug his front feet into the dirt
far out in front of him, wagged his head furiously, and then stopped
long enough to look and see what effect his mad antics were having
upon us. Around and around he jumped gracefully into the air,
swapping ends like a dog chasing its tail. Then again he raised his

head as high as his superb stature would carry him, and with his long silver tail lying over his back, he blazed fire at us through the whites of his turbulent, flint-colored eyes. Having displayed to us his courage, his defiance, and his remarkable leadership, he now turned and pranced off, with heels flying so high and so lightly that one could almost imagine he was treading air.

Our braves laughed and said: "Ah, *ponokamita*, vain elkdog, you are a brave warrior. But trot along and have patience. We shall yet ride you against the Crows."

For five days we chased this huge herd of horses, traveling along leisurely behind them, knowing that they would not wander afar, that they would watch us like wolves as long as we were in the vicinity.

By the fifth day they had become so used to us that they merely moved along slowly when we approached them, nibbling grass as they walked. All during this time our braves had been taming them by their subtle method. At first they just grunted at them. But now they were dancing and shouting at them. This was to let the horses know that although man could make a lot of noise and act fiercely, he would not harm them, that no injury could come to them through closer contact with man.

Nothing scares a horse quicker than a quiet thing that moves toward him and makes no noise. He will jump and break his neck at a noisy movement of a rodent in the grass or a falling twig, while a roaring buffalo or a steaming train will pass him unnoticed. That is because he has the same kind of courage that a man has: real courage, the courage to face any odds that he can see and hear and cope with, but a superstitious fear of anything ghostlike. The mountain-lion, and most other animals of prey, have a courage of a different kind. A slight unexplained noise will bring them to a low, crouching, waiting position, while a loud noise will send them scurrying for cover. They have more discretion and less valor than man or the horse.

On the tenth night of our chase our warriors made their final preparations to capture the herd. They had maneuvered the horses into the vicinity of a huge half-natural, half-artificial corral which they had built of logs against the two sides of a rock-bound gulch. From the entrance of this corral they had built two long fences,

forming a runway which gradually widened as it left the gate of
the corral. This funnel-shaped entrance fanned out onto the plateau
for more than half a mile, and it was covered over with evergreens
to disguise its artificiality. It was a replica of the old buffalo corral
which we used to build to round up the buffaloes when they were
plentiful on the plains.

The mouth at the outer end of this runway was about one
hundred yards wide. From this point on, the runway was further
extended and opened up by placing big tree tops, stones and logs
along the ground for several hundred yards. This was to direct the
herd slowly into the mouth of the fenced part of the runway, where,
once wedged inside, they could neither get out nor turn around and
retrace their steps. They would be trapped; and the only thing
left for them to do would be to keep on going toward the corral gate.

Subdued excitement reigned in our hidden camp on this tenth
night of our chase, for it was the big night, the night that we were
going to "blow in" the great, stubborn herd of wild horses. No
one went to bed that night. Shortly before nightfall more than half
of our braves, comprising all of our fastest traveling scouts and
young men, quietly slipped out of our camp and disappeared. According to prearranged directions, they fanned out toward the place
where the herd had disappeared that afternoon. All during the
early night we heard wolves calling to one another; artic owls,
night hawks, and panthers crying out mournfully in the mystic
darkness of the rugged plateau. They were the signals of our men,
informing one another of their movements.

Then, about midnight, everything became deathly quiet. We
knew that they had located the herd and surrounded it, and that
they were now lying on their bellies, awaiting the first streaks of
dawn and the signal to start the drive. One of our subchiefs, Chief
Mountain Elk, now went through our camp, quietly giving instructions for all hands to line themselves along the great runway to
"beat in" the herd. Every woman, old person and child in the camp
was called up to take part in this particular phase of the drive.
We children and the women crept over to the runway and sprawled
ourselves along the outside of the fence, while the men went beyond
the fenced part of the runway and concealed themselves behind the
brush and logs—where it was a little more dangerous.

Thus we crouched on the ground and shivered quietly for an hour or more before we heard a distant "Ho-h! . . . Ho-h!" It was the muffled driving cry of our warriors, the cry which for ten days they had been uttering to the horses to let them know that no harm could come to them from this sound. Thus, the horses did not stampede, as they would have done had they not recognized this noise in the darkness.

We youngsters lay breathless in expectancy. We had all picked out our favorite mounts in this beautiful herd of wild animals, and to us as we lay there it was like the white boy lying in bed waiting for Santa Claus. Our fathers had all promised us that we could have the ponies that we had picked, and we could hardly wait to get our hands on them. My favorite was a beautiful calico pony, a roan, white and red pinto—three different colors all splashed on his shoulders and flanks like a crazy-quilt of exquisite design. He had a red star on his forehead between his eyes, and I had already named him *Naytukskie Kukatos,* which in Blackfoot means One Star.

Presently we heard the distinct rumble of horses' hoofs—a dull booming which shook the ground on which we lay. Then, "Yip-yip-yip, he-heeh-h-h," came the night call of the wolf from many different directions. It was our braves signaling to one another to keep the herd on the right path. From out of this medley of odd sounds we could hear the mares going *"Wheeh-hagh-hagh-hagh"*—calling their little long-legged sons to their sides that they might not become lost in the darkness and confusion.

Our boyish hearts began to beat fast when we heard the first loud "Yah! Yah! Yah!" We knew that the herd had now entered the brush portion of the runway and that our warriors were jumping up from their hiding-places and showing themselves with fierce noises, in order to stampede the horses and send them racing headlong into our trap.

Immediately there was a loud thunder of pattering hoofs— horses crying and yelling everywhere, like convulsive human beings in monster confusion. Above this din of bellowing throats and hammering feet we heard one loud, full, deep-chested roar which we all recognized, and it gave us boys a slight thrill of fear. It sounded like a cross between the roar of a lion and the bellow of

an infuriated bull. It was the massive steel-dust stallion, furious king
of the herd. In our imagination we could see his long silver tail
thrown over his back, his legs lashing wide apart, and stark murder
glistening from the whites of those terrible eyes. We wondered what
he would do to us if he should call our bluff and crash through
that fence into our midst.

But, now, here he came, leading his raging herd, and we had
no further time to contemplate danger. Our job was to do as the
others had done all along the line: to lie still and wait until the
lead stallion had passed us, and then to jump to the top of the fence
and yell and wave with all the ferocity that we could command.
This was to keep the maddened herd from crashing the fence or
trying to turn around, and to hasten their speed into our trap.

"Therump, therump, therump." On came the storming herd.
As we youngsters peeped through the brush-covered fence, we
could see their sleek backs bobbing up and down in the star-lit darkness like great billows of raging water. The turbulent steel-dust
stallion was leading them with front feet wide apart and his forehead sweeping the ground like a pendulum. His death-dealing heels
were swinging alternatingly to the right and left with each leap of
his mighty frame.

Once he stopped and tried to breast the oncoming herd, but
these erstwhile slaves of his whims struck and knocked him forward with terrific force. He rose from his knees, and like something
that had gone insane, he shot his nostrils into the air and uttered a
fearful bellow of defiance at any and everything. He seemed to
curse the very stars themselves. Never before had he tasted defeat,
utter helplessness. The loyal herd that had watched his very ears
for their commands was now running wildy over him.

I believe that, if at that moment there had been a solid iron
wall in front of that stallion, he would have dashed his brains out
against it. I remember looking backward into the darkness for a
convenient place to hop, if he should suddenly choose to rush headlong into the noise that was driving him wild with helpless rage.
But, even as I looked back, I heard a whistling noise, and my eyes
were jerked back to the runway just in time to see the steel-dust king
stretching himself past us like a huge greyhound. With each incredible leap he panted a breath that shrieked like a whistle.

No one will ever know what was in his brain, why he had so suddenly broken himself away from his herd. But on he went, leaving the other horses behind like a deer leaving a bunch of coyotes. A few seconds later the rest of the herd came booming past us. As we went over the fence, shouting and gesticulating, we looked into a blinding fog of sweat and breath, which fairly stung our nostrils with its pungency.

I thought that the herd would never stop passing us. I had never seen so many horses before, it seemed. We stuck to our posts until it was nearly daylight, and still they came straggling along; now mostly colts limping and whinnying for their mothers.

When we climbed down the fence and went down to the corral at daylight, the first thing we saw was four of our warriors lying on pallets, bleeding and unconscious. They were four of the best horsemen in our tribe: Circling Ghost, High Hunting Eagle, Wild Man and Wolf Ribs. When our mothers asked what was the matter, someone pointed to the corral and said: *"Ponokomita—akai-mah-kah-pay!"* ("That very bad horse!")

We looked and saw a dozen men trying to put leather on that wild steel-dust stallion, who, with his heavy, moon-colored mane bristling belligerently over his bluish head and shoulders, looked now more like a lion than a horse. He was splotched here and there with his own blood, and his teeth were bared like a wolf's. Four men had tried to get down into the corral and throw rawhide around his neck. While the other wild horses had scurried away to the nethermost corners of the corral, this ferocious beast of a horse had plunged headlong into them and all but killed them before they could be dragged away.

He had proved to be one of the rarest specimens of horse known to man—a killer—a creature that kicked and bit and tore and crushed his victims until they were dead. One might live a hundred years among horses without ever seeing one of these hideous freaks of the horse world, so seldom are they produced. He had already killed two of his own herd, young stallions, right there in our corral. Little did we wonder, now, that he was the leader.

Our braves were taking no more chances with him. They were high up on top of the seven-foot corral fence, throwing their rawhide lariats in vain attempts to neck the murderous monstrosity.

But this devil disguised as a horse had the reasoning of a human being. He would stand and watch the rawhide come twirling through the air, and then just as it was about to swirl over his head, he would duck his shaggy neck and remain standing on the spot with his front feet spread apart, in devilish defiance of man and matter. None of our oldest men had ever seen anything like him.

It was finally decided to corner him with the firebrands and throw a partition between him and the rest of the herd, so that our braves could get busy cutting out the best of the animals, before turning the rest loose. This was done, and by nightfall we had captured and hobbled two hundred of the best bottoms anywhere in the Northwest.

The next day our braves began the arduous task of breaking the wild horses to the halter. They used the Indian method, which is very simple and methodical. While four men held on to a stout rawhide rope which was noosed around the animal's neck, another man would approach the horse's head gradually, "talking horse" to him and making many queer motions and sounds as he went nearer.

"Horse talk" is a low grunt which seems to charm a horse and make him stand perfectly still for a moment or so at a time. It sounds like "Hoh-hoh," uttered deep down in one's chest. The horse will stop his rough antics and strain motionless on the rope for a few seconds; while he is doing this and looking straight at the approaching figure, the man will wave a blanket at him and hiss at him—"*Shuh! Shuh!*" It takes about fifteen minutes of this to make the horse realize that the man is harmless, that no motion which he makes, no sound that he utters, will harm him in any way.

It is a strange fact that a wild horse, of either the ranch or the open ranges, will not react to quiet kindliness at first. He must first be treated gruffly—but not harshly—and then when he is on a touching acquaintance with man, kindness is the quickest way to win his affections.

When the man has reached the head of the horse, his hardest job is to give him the first touch of man's hand, of which the horse seems to have a deathly fear. He maneuvers for several minutes before he gets a finger on the struggling nose, and rubs it and allows the horse to get his smell or scent. When this has been done, the brave loops a long, narrow string of rawhide around the horse's nose and then carries it up behind his ears and brings it down on the other side and slips it under the other side of the nose loop, making something like a loose-knotted halter, which will tighten up on the slightest pull from the horse.

This string is no stronger than a shoe-lace, yet, once the warrior has put it on the horse's head, he tells the other men to let go the strong rawhide thong, and from then on he alone handles the horse with the small piece of string held lightly in one hand. The secret of this is that whenever the horse makes pull on the string, it grips certain nerves around the nose and back of the ears, and this either stuns him or hurts him so badly that he doesn't try to pull again.

With the horse held thus, the warrior now stands in front of him and strokes the front of his face and hisses at him at close range. It is the same noise that a person makes to drive away chickens— *"shuh, shuh"*—and perhaps the last sound an untrained person would venture to use in taming a wild, ferocious horse; yet it is the quickest way of gaining a horse's confidence and teaching him not to be afraid.

When the warrior has run his fingers over every inch of the horse's head and neck, he now starts to approach his shoulders and flanks with his fingers. The horse will start to jump about again at this, but a couple of sharp jerks on the string stop him, and as he stands trembling with fear, the warrior slowly runs his hand over his left side. When this is finished he stands back and takes a blanket and strikes all of the portions of his body that he has touched and shouts *"Shuh!"* with each short stroke of the blanket.

When he has repeated these two operations on the other side of the horse, he now starts to do his legs. Each leg, beginning with his left front leg, must be gone over by his hand, with not an inch of its surface escaping his touch. This is the most ticklish part of the work, for the feet are the horse's most deadly weapons. But two more jerks on the string quiet the horse's resentment, and within another fifteen minutes every square inch of the horse's body has been touched and rubbed, even down to his tail and the ticklish portions of his belly and between his legs.

Now the job of breaking the horse is all but finished. There is just one thing to do, and that is to accustom the horse to a man hopping on his back and riding him. This is done very simply, and within about five minutes.

The warrior takes the blanket and strikes the horse's back a number of blows. Then he lays the blanket on his back very gently. The horse will at first buck it off, but another jerk on the string, and he is quieted. The warrior picks the blanket up and lays it across his back again. The horse jumps out from under it perhaps twice before he will stand still. When he has been brought to this point, the man throws the blanket down and walks slowly to the side of the horse and presses down lightly. He keeps pressing a little harder and harder, until finally he places his elbows across his back and draws his body an inch off the ground, putting his full weight on the back of the animal. A horse might jump a little at the first experience of this weight, but he will stand still the next time it is tried.

After the warrior has hung on his back by his elbows for several periods of about thirty seconds each, he will now very gradually pull himself up, up, up until he is ready to throw his right foot over to the other side. It is a strange fact that few horses broken in this manner ever try to buck. He will stand perfectly still, and the man will sit there and stroke him for a moment and then gently urge him to go, and the horse will awkwardly trot off in a mild, aimless amble, first this way and that—so bewildered and uncertain in his gait that one would think it was the first time he had ever tried to walk on his own feet.

The reason a horse can be broken in the above manner is that he is a remarkably intelligent being with rationality. A chicken has no reason; therefore it goes through its life running away from "shuhs" that will never harm it. This keeps it from getting many extra crumbs that it could leisurely eat if it only had the reason to learn from experience as the horse does.

Four months later we were again back on our beloved plains in upper Montana. Our horses were the envy of every tribe who saw us that summer. They all wanted to know where we got them. Our chief told the story of this wild-horse hunt so many times that it has since become legend among the Indians of these prairies.

But at the end of the story our venerable leader would always look downcast, and in sadly measured words he would tell of the steel-dust stallion with the flowing moon-colored mane and tail, which he had picked out for himself. He would spend many minutes describing this superb horse; yet he would never finish the story, unless someone should ask him what became of the spectacular animal.

Then he would slowly tell how our braves had worked all day trying to rope this beast, and how that night they had decided to leave him in the little fenced-off part of the corral, thinking that two or three days contact with them might take some of the devil out of him. But the next morning when they visited the corral he had vanished. The horse had literally climbed over more than seven feet of corral fence, which separated him from the main corral, and there, with room for a running start, he had attacked the heavy log fence and rammed his body clear through it. Nothing was left to tell the tale but a few patches of blood and hair and a wrecked fence.

That should have ended the story of the steel-dust beast, but it did not. On our way out of the camp on the wild-horse plateau we had come across the bodies of seven wild stallions and a mare, which this fiend of the pleateu had mutilated in his wake. He had turned killer through and through, even unto the destruction of his own kind. Our old people said that he had been crazed by the fact that he had lost control of his herd in that terrible dash down the runway. This blow to his prowess and pride of leadership had been too much for him; it had turned him into a destructive demon, a roaming maniac of the wilds.

This horse became famous throughout the Northwest as a lone traveler of the night. He went down on to the plains of Montana and Alberta, and in the darkest hours of the night he would turn up at the most unexpected points in the wilderness of the prairies. Never a sound from him; he had lost his mighty bellow. He haunted the plains by night, and was never seen by day. His sinister purpose in life was to destroy every horse he came across.

This silent, lone traveler of the night was often seen silhouetted against the moon on a butte, with his head erect, his tail thrown over his back like a statue, his long, moon-colored mane and tail flowing like silver beneath the light of the stars. Owing to his peculiar nocturnal habits and to the fact that his remarkable tail and mane gave off in the moonlight something like a phosphorescent glow, he became known throughout the Northwest as the *Shunka-tonka-Wakan* —the Ghost Horse. The steel-blue color of his body melted so completely into the inky blueness of the night that his tail and mane stood out in the moonlight like shimmering threads of lighted silver, giving him a halo which had a truly ghostly aspect.

That Colt Pericles

HENRY H. KNIBBS

*There have been many stories, some good, more bad, about
the horse of the west and how he must finally succumb to the
rope of man. There will be many more. "That Colt Pericles"
is typical of the best of these stories and was therefore in-
cluded. There will be those who feel that it has been used too
often, but there will also be those to whom it is new.*

For more than two years he ran the Arizona uplands with as wild
a bunch of broom tails as ever pawed snow to get winter feed.
His mother, a strawberry roan with a wide eye and a black stripe
down her back, taught him how to keep alive, chiefly by instructing
him what not to do. At first young Pericles thought that his feet
were simply to stand on, and his nose merely a guide to a warm
meal. But not very long after he was born he discovered that his
nose was his best friend, and that his heels would be next best when
he could kick hard enough; also that he had a voice.

One day, straying beyond sight of his mother, he suddenly
discovered that he was alone. On the edge of the timber encircling
the mesa a long gray shadow caught his eyes. He didn't know what
it was, but tribal instinct told him it was an enemy. He quivered
with fright. The gray shadow squatted and grew shorter. Pericles'
shrill cry for help was quick with terror. Over a low, rounded ridge
appeared the head of his mother. Her ears flat, she came swiftly.
As Pericles started toward her, the gray shadow rose in the air.

Pericles heard a thud behind him. The mare whirled and kicked, the mountain lion dodging and leaping at her. Once he leaped clear over her, missing her neck by a few inches.

The colt Pericles stood in one spot and kicked at nothing, like an old-fashioned pump handle gone crazy. Out of the timber surged another shadow, flashing silver in the sunlight—the big gray stallion that Pericles had been warned to keep away from. Eyes furious, teeth bared and head twisted sideways, the stallion charged into the fight. Rearing, he struck with his forefeet. The gray shadow rolled over and over, screamed, and was up and bounding down the meadow, the stallion following like a thunderbolt.

Young Pericles wobbled up to his mother. He was frightened and expected sympathy. But she merely nosed him all over and, finding he was uninjured, paid no more attention to him. To make it worse, the gray stallion was coming back. Foam-breasted, magnificent, he plunged to a stop and whistled. Pericles got behind his mother, remembering that she had once told him the stallion didn't like colts. Pericles felt that his mother should have been grateful. The stallion had undoubtedly saved them from a terrible fate. But when he offered to touch noses with her, she promptly kicked him in the ribs. However, he didn't seem specially offended. He simply shook his head and walked off in a stately manner. Pericles was puzzled. But that wasn't all of it. When Pericles pressed against his mother's shoulder for the comfort of her nearness, she gave him a nip on the rump that told him to trot along back to the spot where he had left her. Didn't he see what might have happened if it hadn't been for his father?

When two years old, Pericles considered himself not only grown up but a mighty fine specimen. Already he had whipped two young stallions of his age and had managed to keep out of reach of the big gray who led the band. Long since, his mother had ceased to act at all maternal. One stretch of country in particular interested him—the lowlands on the north side of the high mesas where he had been born. For some reason the wild horses had always shunned this country, although the grass stood thick and green, and the climate was much warmer than that of the high country. But Pericles was inquisitive.

Toward the end of June, on a bright morning with a tang of

melting snow still in the air, young Pericles stood on a ridge looking down upon the rolling green reaches below. He was alone. Neck arched like a drawn bow, ears sharply forward and his nostrils wide as he drank the breeze, the young roan stallion seemed a part of the bronze-hued rock on which he stood. In his dark eye was mirrored the figure of a tiny horse, grazing placidly along that queer line of little posts his mother had told him to keep away from. Quivering with suppressed excitement, his young life hot in him, he trumpeted a shrill call. The horse down below raised its head, then went calmly to grazing again. Pericles whistled, snorted, reared and pawed the air in sheer exuberance. But the tiny figure below paid no further attention.

The water-soaked earth spraying from his hoofs, young Pericles took a long slant down the slope, and fetched up opposite the stranger on the other side of the range fence. He was grayish around the eyes and nuzzle, this old horse, and had some big white spots on his back. His knees were swollen and stiff. And that queer scar

on his shoulder? Pericles looked at the scar curiously, with a sharp tingle. Not of fear, he told himself. But that scar meant something he not only did not understand but for which he felt a blood distrust. The old cow horse watched him with benevolent amusement.

Pericles' nostrils worked. Who was he? What was he? And what was he doing on the other side of those funny posts? The old horse turned his head and gazed down the drift fence. Another horse came plodding along in a leisurely fashion. Pericles stared. It was a horse, yet it looked queer—had something on its back. Pericles' eyes grew big.

So that was a man! It stepped off its mount to inspect a sag in the drift fence then, and young Pericles was amazed. Something was wrong with it. It walked on its hind legs. And it wasn't half as big as a horse!

A look came into the old cow pony's eyes which seemed to say, "Keep wild as long as you can, young fellow. Stick to the high mesas. And if you happen to see a cow-puncher riding your country, high-tail it for the pinnacles. You're too young and handsome to take any chances. There isn't a cowboy on the Moonstone that wouldn't give a month's wages to get a rope on you."

Even then Pericles was loath to take the hint and go. The idea that the strange animal walking around like a horse on its hind legs could catch him seemed humorous. But presently when a drift of wind brought the smell of man, the young roan thrilled with the old primordial fear. He struck up the slope on a run. Halfway to the ridge, he turned and looked down. The old cow horse was grazing placidly. But the man was standing staring up at the wild stallion. "What a mount!" said the man.

Trumpeting shrill defiance, young Pericles curled his tail and struck on up the slope, chunks of water-soaked earth rocketing from his hoofs.

The man was Peter Annersley, owner of the great Moonstone ranch, a solid, comfortable-looking man, neither young nor old. Peter had never outgrown his fondness for a good saddle horse. He was riding a splendid mount. And he had several other top horses in his personal string. But never had he seen so handsome a piece of horseflesh as the wild roan stallion.

"I'd admire to get my twine on that broom tail," he said as young Pericles disappeared over a ridge.

But the roan didn't hear that. His only idea was to get back into the high country and find his wild kindred again. From now on he would keep that fence between himself and horses that worked for a living.

In the uplands the leaves of the quaking asp were changing color. Mornings were nippy with the tang of fall. Pericles grazed, grew bigger and stronger, and began to take on a heavier coat. One day, overtaken by one of those inexplicable terrors that suddenly beset horses, the band started on a wild run through the timber and swept down to the lower country. Pericles again saw the old cow horse, Piecrust. The band quieted down and began to graze south of the drift fence. Pericles lagged behind, signifying his willingness to visit.

The horse that worked for a living drifted up to his own side of the fence. Pericles arched a proud neck. He hadn't been caught yet! The old cow horse looked wise. Bleak Saunders—foreman of the Moonstone—and Buck Connor had ridden over his way recently. After the fall round-up, Bleak said, he was going to establish a relay clear across the high country to the desert, keep the bunch away from water till he tired 'em out; then trap 'em in Blue Canyon. There was a young roan stallion running with the wild horses that the Old Man wanted. The old cow pony knew only too well that when Peter Annersley set out to get something, he usually got it. Pericles felt that he was being warned of some danger. He was grateful for this friendliness. He touched noses with Piecrust, wished that he ran with the wild horses of the high mesas. At times Pericles was lonesome.

The mares and colts had strung out and were climbing the hill, the big gray stallion nipping the laggards. Swinging wide of the band, young Pericles took his own trail up the slope. Halfway he turned and nickered a farewell to the old cow horse. Piecrust answered in a tremulous, hoarse whinny. The old cow horse watched him enviously. Pericles was the stoutest pony he had seen for many a day. But that wouldn't help him much if Peter Annersley sent Bleak Saunders after him.

Streaming across the tops of the pines, the morning sunlight flooded the mountain meadow, which shimmered like a lake of pale gold. In the middle of the meadow was an emerald hollow where a tiny stream ran, spreading to a shallow pool edged with wild iris—a spot known to the Moonstone cowboys as "the place where the ponies come to drink." Young Pericles never understood why the old gray stallion would not allow the band to graze that meadow for any length of time.

Twice this morning the old stallion had started toward the timber on the edge of the meadow, and twice he had sheered back, snorting as if he had smelled a rattlesnake. The mares and colts paid little attention, nipping the dry grass as they drifted slowly across the open.

Pericles hung toward the rear of the band, carrying on a mild flirtation with a young mare. That the old stallion permitted this was evidence of his intense preoccupation.

The old gray stallion had good reason to be nervous. Without warning, two horsemen appeared on the southern edge of the clearing. The band crowded together. The gray stallion whistled, shot across the meadow and plunged into the timber along its northern edge. Heads and tails up, the colts bobbing awkwardly beside them, the mares followed.

"There he is!" cried one of the horsemen as they spurred out into the meadow. "That red roan with the blaze face and one white foot."

Instead of following the band, Pericles swung south through the timber. A half mile farther south he stopped and looked back. There were no riders in sight. But the wind told him they were following. Again he headed south, going at a steady lope. Striking through a belt of timber, he swung out into another meadow. He could hear no sound of pursuit, but again the wind told him he was followed. It was not the band the horsemen followed. They were after him!

West of this meadow the timber ran up to the barren ridges of Barlow Peak. For an hour Pericles traveled toward the peak, slowing from a lope to a trot, and finally, as the wind brought him no scent of his pursuers, to a walk. But the nerves in his spine, his neck, his shoulders—every nerve in his body—told him they were still following him. As he climbed higher his wind grew short. Pausing on an open ridge, his flanks heaving, he looked back. Far below, the two horsemen were crossing the second meadow, riding easily. Young Pericles would have enjoyed the hot excitement of a chase. But this slow, dogged tracking worried him.

In an hour he reached timber line. Scant grass, fed by the melting snows of summer, showed among the rocks and boulders. A hundred yards ahead stood a square something made of tree trunks. Pericles was puzzled. Never having seen a building, he could not know it was the summer lookout of the fire patrol. Whatever it was, it was wrong. He went cautiously, nosing the wind. As he passed the ranger station he smelled horses, commingled with an alien smell that sent him bounding on up among the rocks and pinnacles.

From in back of the station two horsemen swung out. Young Pericles had crossed the peak and, the loose shale and broken rock slithering beneath his feet, was going down the steep western slope on the run. Far below, the timber swallowed up the figure of Pericles. Wade and Bill Varney took up his tracks. At the foot of the mountain the stallion had turned south down Barlow Valley. Two more riders were out after him; but unaware that still farther south each known water hole was watched by Moonstone bands, young Pericles kept on down the valley. The sweat was drying on him and he was beginning to get thirsty.

Two hours later he came in sight of open country again. Occasionally he stopped to view the back track, his eyes white-rimmed, his nostrils wide. A few miles below was water. Excitement had made him sweat fully as much as exercise. With no pursuers he could have made twice the distance without feeling thirsty. Pericles approached the water hole warily. Being chased was one thing, but having men bob up in front of you was quite another matter. Within a hundred yards of the water hole he stopped. His mane bristled. His forefeet drummed the hard earth. Near the water hole stood two horses. Their riders were sitting on the ground, playing seven-up.

Tonto Charley and Shorty White dropped their cards and rose. "Reckon there's our meat," said Shorty.

"When we get it," said Tonto. "That son of a gun's playing a lone hand."

The young roan whirled and started back up the valley, Shorty and Tonto Charley after him. Presently the wind brought him more bad news. Men were also riding down the valley. He plunged up the western slope and struck across the ridge. He now wished that he had stayed with the band. Not until nightfall did he get a chance to rest. And then he sought a high, barren ridge, dozing only occasionally. Never once that night was he off his feet. With the first ray of dawn he was on his way south again. He walked, and grazed a nip at a time. His coat was stiff with dried sweat, and dust had caked on his back and sides where he had rolled.

It was red-earth country, dotted with pinons and junipers. There was little grass and the ground was spotted with outcroppings of red rock. Horse tracks there were none. Toward noon thirst bothered him so much that he crossed the low ridge into Barlow Valley again. On the flat far below, strung out and going at a slow trot, were the wild horses, the old gray stallion in the lead.

Young Pericles whinnied. Out from the water hole came two horsemen. Instantly the gray stallion swung away from the water hole and struck up Barlow Valley, the mares following. This time the horsemen's ropes were up and circling. Young Pericles dashed down the slope and among the mares and colts. He was with his own again. The two horsemen drew nearer. Halfway up the valley they crowded the band so close that it split, one bunch taking to the timber of the eastern slope; the old gray's bunch, Pericles among them, taking to the western. All that day the old stallion led the remnant of his band, craftily circling each relay camp. And all that night the band drifted from meadow to timberland, restlessly searching for water.

The morning of the third day, with the mares pinch-flanked and weary and the colts all but used up, the band followed the old gray stallion back toward their own country. Past Turkey Springs, rimmed with lush green in the heart of the timberlands, sped the jaded horses. Bill Varney, Wade, Bleak and Buck Connor followed at a judicious pace, so as not to stampede and scatter them. Across a stretch of slick rim rock, Varney, a reckless, hard rider, roweled his tired horse. A piece of loose tufa turned under the horse's forefeet. The leg-weary animal pitched forward, struck on its head and, turning completely over, crashed down on Varney. Varney lay on his face, his head twisted far to one side.

"Varney's quit," said Buck.

"Stay with him, Wade," said Bleak.

Bleak and Buck Connor rode on after the horses. And they rode fast. Thundering along the rim rock, the mares and colts followed the gray stallion. As the band approached the narrow cliff trail leading down into Blue Canyon, the gray stallion swerved. The band shot past him, stringing down the steep trail on the run. Young Pericles would have followed, but the old gray stallion reared and struck at him. Pericles swung his head and seized the old stallion's neck. Squealing, the old stallion whirled and broke loose. He kicked as he whirled. A hoof crashed on Pericles' jaw. Mad with the fury of battle, Pericles rushed at his foe.

But the old gray saw that which young Pericles in his rage did not see—Bleak Saunders, his loop wide and singing, coming at a short lope. Dodging Pericles' mad rush, the old gray took off down the canyon trail after the mares. Too late, Pericles swung round. He reared to strike down Bleak's horse, his hoofs raw gold as he hammered the sky. Bleak's loop circled. A vicious, whining whisper, and the young horse felt an invisible snakelike something bind his forelegs, burn and bite, and he went down. As Pericles' hind feet flashed in a wild struggle to rise, Buck Connor swung a short loop and heeled him. Blind mad, Pericles kicked and struggled, battering his head on the rim rock. Again and again his enemies stretched him, but each time he managed to fight up to his feet, battling so close to the canyon rim that both men were put to it to keep from being dragged over.

Pericles heard the dull plodding of hoofs on the rim rock as Tonto Charley rode up. The cowboy said nothing; simply sat his horse gazing at the fallen stallion. Slowly the Tonto man took down his rope. He whistled. Pericles' head came up. Again that vicious, whining whisper, and young Pericles felt something grip and bite into his neck. As Tonto took his dally, Pericles, half blind and raging, struggled to his feet. He never knew just what happened, only that the sky grew black, and he fell, and all feeling went out of him.

Bleak and his men gazed down upon their captive. "He's a wonder!" said Tonto Charley.

"A fightin' fool," murmured Buck.

"What I mean"—Tonto's experienced eye traveled over the magnificent young stallion from muzzle to hoofs—"he's the best-made hoss I ever laid my twine on."

"And he's cost the Old Man plenty."

"You mean Varney?"

No one answered. The weathered faces of the Moonstone punchers grew grave. Bill Varney had gone out—not in the hot excitement of a chase, but crossing a smooth little stretch of rock at a lope. But their eyes never left the young stallion stretched on the gray rim rock. That was the job in hand.

Pericles became conscious of the sound of voices. He didn't know, at first, where he was. The voices were low and mild. He did not understand. Had he not battled with them? Would he not have killed them had he been able? Now they had him down and unable to move. Why didn't they go ahead and kill him?

"We'll just haze him over to the old log corral," he heard the lean foreman say.

Sullen and savage by turns, young Pericles fought every foot of the way. It was a bitter thing to him that his own kind were so keen to help their riders conquer him. When, after a sullen spell, Pericles launched into a savage break for freedom, Buck's wise old pony, Rowdy, would set back on the rope and stop him. If Pericles persisted in fighting, Bleak's mount would whirl and start off at right angles, jerk Pericles off his feet and, facing him, squat almost on his haunches to keep the rope taut.

At the edge of a broad meadow stood the old log corral with its scarred and weathered snubbing post. Near the corral was the chuck wagon. A team of paint ponies, gaunt-flanked and their bellies plastered with mud, stood hitched to a buckboard. Bed rolls lay on the ground around a heap of ashes. All this flashed across Pericles' vision. But rage had dulled his curiosity. He felt only that these strange things were his enemies.

Boomer, the cook, left the wagon and let the corral bars down. The smell of water came to Pericles. Mad with thirst, he made a final, desperate struggle to get free. But again the ropes flickered out and he was thrown. The round, log-sided inclosure awakened a new fear. It was a trap. He lunged to his feet and tried to break back. Behind him three riders yelled and beat their chaps with their quirts. The rope on his neck drew down. Frenzied, he dashed into the corral, stopped and gazed wildly about. There was Bleak on his pony, Walking John. With ears back, Pericles charged. Walking John side-stepped cleverly, the rope was flipped off Pericles' neck, and Walking John and his rider shot out through the gateway, leaving him there. Pericles made for the opening. He crashed against heavy bars that somehow a few seconds ago were not there. All lust for fighting was consumed in the burning desire to get back into the open again.

Gaunt, weary and weak from hunger and fatigue, he hadn't the strength to put up much of a fight when, in the morning, he was again roped and hazed out of the corral. Already he had begun to fear a rope. From morning till noon he went sullenly. When the outfit reached the Moonstone fence and he was turned loose in the horse pasture, he thought he was free again. Twice he charged straight into the heavy barbed wire. His breast lacerated and bleeding, he gave up trying to break through the fence, and took to following it, searching for a way out. Finally he began to graze a few minutes at a time, moving along the fence, always looking for a way back to the high country.

That afternoon he met the old cow horse, who didn't seem at all surprised to see him. Pericles snorted. They had caught him, but they wouldn't keep him. Some day he would get away! As they grazed together, Pericles wondered what they would do to him. The old cow horse gazed at the wire cuts on Pericles' breast. The young stallion had been fighting the fence. Well, any wild horse would do that, any horse worth his feed would—at first. But it never did any good to fight a fence or a rope or a man.

The old cow horse knew what it was like. Pericles didn't question that. But he didn't believe that any little two-legged animal could best him. Before Piecrust went over to a cedar to take a little nap, Pericles learned that there were certain things worth

remembering. Don't strike with your forefeet. Don't bite. And
above all things, don't go against a spade bit. The old horse lolled
his tongue. Across it ran a deep scar. Pericles' eyes widened. The
very thought of having his tongue cut or lacerated chilled him.

The old cow horse dozed in the shade of the cedar, one hind
leg hunched and his head low. A sudden homesickness beset young
Pericles. He yearned for his kindred, for the freedom of the high
mesas, fenceless, rugged and wild. It amazed him that the old cow
horse had shown no special dislike for men, nor for the work he had
been obliged to do.

Grazing near the south fence of the horse pasture that afternoon, Pericles became aware of movement far up on the edge of
the timber. No bigger at that distance than mice, six or seven
horses had come out of the timber and were traveling slowly toward the west. They were his kindred. Charging up to the fence,
he lifted his head and trumpeted. But the wild horses kept on, moving in single file along one of their own narrow trails. Pericles
started running west along the inside of the fence. Somewhere he
would find a way out and rejoin the band. He came upon the gateway through which he had entered. He battered the heavy gate
with his forefeet; fought it as if it had been a living thing.

All that day he ranged the horse pasture looking for a way
out. Why had the Moonstone riders captured him? The old cow
horse had said something about his being a handsome young fellow.
Handsome? Perhaps. But lonely. Again and again he came back
to the drift fence and gazed up at the far, timbered hills, yearning
for his kind.

Early the following day, along with five or six cow ponies,
Pericles was hazed into the home corral. When the dust had settled
the other horses were gone.

He moved about restlessly. He could smell horses and men.
And his ear was sharpened toward every sound. Peter Annersley,
his wife and the hands were joking and laughing, but underneath
their talk ran a current of seriousness. Between the bars he saw
Tonto Charley shake out a rope and re-coil it. The rope! That
was something he couldn't fight. It would shoot out and take hold
before you could strike it or dodge it. Facing the entrance, Pericles

stood stiff-legged, watching. He didn't know what was going to happen, but he knew it was something concerning himself. He could feel it in the air. Worst of all, he was alone. With the other horses he would have felt less fear. He was afraid, not of the men but of the rope and the unknown.

Wade crawled through the bars and shook out a loop. Pericles snorted and circled. Tonto Charley rode into the corral, and Buck on his mount, Rowdy. Wade made a backhand cast. The loop spread. He dodged as the young stallion made for him. The loop jumped from the ground and drew tight around Pericles' forelegs. He reared and fought. Something whistled close to his head. Too late, he dodged. Tonto Charley had him roped round the neck.

Behind him Buck was swinging a short noose. Pericles lashed out with his heels. "Got him!" cried Buck.

Rearing, Pericles tried to strike with his forefeet. He was blind mad with fear and rage. His legs were jerked from under him and he landed on his side. Still he fought to get free. Slowly his head was drawn short up to the snubbing post. The noose round his neck slackened a little. He lay still, his flanks heaving. He felt the cinch slip under him, felt the saddle clamp down.

Something was slipped over his head—another kind of rope that didn't choke him—but the feel of the hackamore round his nose drove him frantic. Buck was standing astride him. The rope on Pericles' neck grew slack. He lunged up. As he felt the clinging weight on his back all his pent-up fury was let loose. Buck was in the saddle, his spurs in Pericles' shoulders. Pericles went into the air like a catamount. There was no shouting, no comment. This was no ordinary bronc taking his first lesson in manners. This was a stick of dynamite spinning in a cyclone.

Twice Pericles jolted his rider loose and almost threw him. A spur shot across his ribs like a string of hornets. He went up, his back bent like a bow. When he hit the ground the cinch snapped. Again he went up. Flying ends of the broken cinch and Buck, the saddle gripped between his knees, flew skyward. Clearing the top of the corral, man and saddle lit in a heap outside, and directly under the noses of Mrs. Annersley's team of paint ponies.

Snorting, the team broke away from Shorty, who was standing

on the seat looking into the corral, and high-tailed it for home.

"Never mind the team." Ma Annersley's voice was placid. "We need a new buckboard anyway. . . . Are you hurt, Buck?"

He sat on his wrecked saddle, looking about in a dazed manner. "No, ma'am," he said. "But I'd sure like to know which way is north."

Pericles circled the corral, the hackamore still on his head. So that was what was meant by riding him? Well, he had got rid of that rider! But here was Tonto Charley again, a coil of rope in his hand. Pericles dashed across the corral and battered at the heavy timbers. He couldn't dodge the rope, but he could run away from it.

Bleak Saunders rode in on Walking John. Pericles stopped, whistled and laid back his ears. He had three men to watch now—three men and three ropes. Tonto moved forward. Pericles reared and started away. From somewhere that all-but-invisible rope shot out and he felt the loop tighten on his forelegs. Again he was snubbed up to the post and saddled. Before Bleak could get his foot in the right stirrup, Pericles was on his feet and in the air. But the foreman kicked his foot home as Pericles came down.

Furious, Pericles pitched and pin-wheeled, but he could not get rid of that clinging weight that gave to every jolt with a swing and a recovery that were maddening. The cinch biting into him, the rowels scoring him, he did a hump and a twist in the air that became known later as his specialty—the double corkscrew. Bleak was an old-time, straight-up rider. This double corkscrew was a new one to him. He went out of the saddle and he went high. As he turned over in the air, Pericles lashed out with his heels. Bleak hit the ground, rolled to one side and tried to rise. His right leg was broken between the knee and ankle. Shorty ran in and dragged Bleak to safety, while Tonto and Wade fought Pericles down.

Ma Annersley made Bleak as comfortable as she could while Vinegaroon went for the buckboard. Peter Annersley, who had been watching the riding, began to buckle on his own chaps.

"Peter Annersley, what are you doing?" cried Ma Annersley.

"Buckling my chaps."

"You keep off that horse!"

"Yes, ma'am." Peter went on adjusting his chaps.

"You're old enough to know better."

"Yes, ma'am. But I kind of like that little horse."

"Peter!"

But Peter had crawled through the bars.

Snubbed close to the post, Pericles stood watching out of a white-rimmed eye. Another one! A big man, solid without being overheavy. And calm and easy-going as sunshine. Pericles remembered. It was the man he had seen the first day he had met the old cow pony and wondered about the scar. Now he wondered no longer. That scar was a brand. They put it on all the horses that worked for a living.

The young roan stallion felt a hand on his neck. "Why, you ain't bad!" The voice was deep and friendly. "You're just a mite scared. So am I. But don't let on to the boys." Peter stroked Pericles' shoulder. Pericles sidled and kicked, but the big man wasn't there.

"Now, I wouldn't do that," said Peter. " 'Cause why? Why, I'm goin' to ride you, little horse. Depends on you whether we get along comfortable or not."

Pericles felt differently toward this man. Not that he wouldn't pitch and unload him if he could. But toward Peter Annersley, Pericles held no definite enmity—only the natural fear of a wild creature captured and bound. Peter was not a better rider than either Bleak Saunders or Buck. Yet man for man and horse for horse, he could outride them.

"The Old Man puts something on 'em," the superstitious Vinegaroon used to say.

No spell, no magic accounted for Peter Annersley's success with broncos. However, he did put something on them. Peter weighed close to a hundred and eighty—heavier than either Buck or Bleak Saunders by some twenty or thirty pounds. Heavier, but not a whit less active. Though Peter was called the Old Man, he was younger than Bleak, and considerably more painstaking in educating a bronco. Instead of using the short hackamore rope, Peter tied his own rope to the jaws of the hackamore, took the coil in his hand and slipped into the saddle like a hand slipping into an old glove.

Pericles knew that he now had something different to contend with—a rider who, although knowing that he would, did not urge him to pitch. Pericles arched his back, bunched his feet as he came down. Peter took the jolt with bent knees, and told Pericles to try

again. Never once did he use the spur. Try as Pericles would, he
could not shake the solid weight from his back. Jumping forward,
he began to pitch from side to side.

"Drop the bar!" cried Peter.

Pericles made for the opening. With the loose coil Peter whipped
the stallion's flanks from side to side. Rocketing into the open in
long, plunging pitches, Pericles lit out across the pasture on the run.
Mrs. Annersley and the boys watched the young stallion bore into
the distance like the speeding end of an express train. Horse and
rider grew smaller and smaller. Ma Annersley smiled. Vinegaroon
pulled up to the corral with the runaway team and an apparently
undamaged buckboard. Bleak was loaded in and Ma Annersley
climbed to the seat. "Tell pa I've got a name for that colt, when he
gets back."

Far down the pasture Pericles and his rider were having an
understanding. Pericles was sweating from ears to hoofs, and he was
breathing hard. The saddle was empty. He hadn't pitched Peter
Annersley, however. Peter, afoot, the sweat dripping from his face,
had the coil of the rope in his hand. About fifteen feet of the rope
was taut between Peter and Pericles' head. Peter began to work up
the rope toward the stallion. Pericles quivered. Peter set back. The
hackamore pinched down. Pericles reared as it shut off his wind.
When he came down he could breathe. It didn't take him long to
realize that if he came to the rope he could go on breathing.

Peter grinned. "Remember, young fellow, I'm just as scared as
you are—but don't you let on to the boys!"

Again he began to work up the rope. This time Pericles allowed
him to get within a few feet before he reared. When Pericles came
down, Peter was still there, his body hot, but his brain cool. Pericles'
body and brain were both hot. Peter was giving the stallion a chance
to cool his brain. Then he could be reasoned with.

The roan stallion couldn't understand it. The man at the other
end of the rope didn't seem to want to fight, and he wouldn't let go.
The constant repetition wore on the young stallion, numbed his will.
Only occasionally the man spoke, and then in a low, easy tone without startling or maddening him. Pericles never knew exactly when
he gave in to that solid figure, that quiet, easy tone. Finally Peter's
hand was on Pericles' hot neck. Pericles quivered, but stood still. If

he had known what he wanted to do, he might have tried to break away. But his will to do anything was submerged in the will of the man.

Telling Pericles he was a good little horse, Peter reached slowly for the stirrup and eased himself into the saddle. Pericles started off at a sullen trot. He went in a big circle. At the pull of the hackamore he made the second round in a smaller space. At last he was moving in so narrow a circle that Peter stopped him. A touch of the spurs and Pericles jumped forward. This time he was headed toward the home corral.

Buck and Tonto and Shorty shaded their eyes against the morning sun. The young stallion was coming back at a lope, Peter sitting him easily, the hackamore rope slack. On either side of Pericles, Tonto and Shorty hazed him quietly into the corral. Peter snubbed him, worked the saddle off and turned him loose. Again Pericles found himself alone. He snuffed at the bars and, walking over to some loose earth, lay down and rolled.

"Did ma get Bleak over to the house all right?" Peter asked.

"Yep. And say, chief, she said to tell you she's got a name for that colt."

"Uh-huh?"

"Ma said his name was Pericles."

Peter scratched his head. "Did ma say that?"

"She done did!"

Peter put on his hat aslant. "Pericles, eh?" He tried it out to himself: "That colt Pericles. Huh! Ma's been reading in that dictionary again. I knew she'd get even with me some way."

Free of the saddle and hackamore, away from the sound of voices, Pericles began to recover himself. The man called Peter had made him do things, then he had gone away. Would he come back and make him do things again? Pericles gazed out toward the southern country, the distant, high mesas edged with timber. He couldn't go back there—not yet. He put all his distraction, all his loneliness, into a shrill neigh of protest.

Shorty, riding beside Peter Annersley on their way to the house, turned and looked back. "By gosh! Sounds like he ain't through yet. Now, I thought when he lay down and rolled—"

Though Pericles had been ridden to a standstill once, there

wasn't a hand on the Moonstone who was foolish enough to imagine the young stallion wouldn't pitch again. Both Tonto Charley and Buck were willing to make the experiment. But the Old Man declared he thought his saddle fitted Pericles just a mite better than Buck's, and that as Bleak's leg had just been set, it might be as well to let Nature take its course.

"What did he mean—Nature takin' its course?" said Buck.

Bleak, propped up in his bunk reading his old stand-by, *Robinson Crusoe,* frowned. "I reckon he was referrin' to dismountin' with your saddle between your knees. It's kind of a new style round these parts."

"Like busted legs, eh?"

"You kin go plumb to hell. But wait just a minute afore you start. The Old Man's tooken a fancy to that ——" Bleak paused. "Is ma around anywhere?"

Buck shook his head.

"And such bein' the case," continued Bleak, "he don't want to have to fly over the top of the corral every time he gits off that —— Where is ma, anyhow?"

"Over in the kitchen. The name of that hoss is Pericles."

"Thanks. He's a one-man hoss, and allowin' you bronc stompers all the glory you might git if you was able to stick on him, the Old Man is the one. No use bowin' your neck and pawin', Pete's got us all beat when it comes to ridin' lunatics."

"Or dismountin'," added Buck, gazing pointedly at Bleak's unbending leg.

Each morning for a straight week Peter Annersley had ridden Pericles, and ridden him hard. Then, to the surprise of the hands, he turned the young stallion loose. The boys argued that the Old Man would have it all to do over again. But Peter Annersley didn't think so. Pericles had begun to go sour. The young stallion had learned saddle, cinch, spurs, bit and hackamore. He was even beginning to understand a few words—his name for one. "Here, you!" or "That'll do, now!" or "Quit your nonsense!" all meant about the same thing, only in a different degree. He soon found out that when, like a proper cow horse, he gave to the pull of the hackamore, nothing else happened. If he fought, something always happened.

It wasn't so much the reprimand or the rowels as having to do it all over again.

Intuition told him that Peter Annersley was giving him a square deal. Yet the pride of the wild was still in his blood. Once more away from corral, saddle and Peter's voice, Pericles ranged the south pasture, his tail arched, his neck like the bend of a breaking wave, the reach of his stride as free as when he ran with his kindred of the high mesas.

Straight for the fence he thundered. He slid to a stop and snorted, his breast almost against the wire. Whirling, he rocketed out into the pasture again, kicking as he ran. This was the life! . . . What? A bunch of cow ponies grazing over there? Whoosh! Pericles bored down the pasture. The cow ponies raised their heads. He veered off as he came near them, expecting them to run with him. But they went to grazing again. He swung back and, kicking right and left, scattered them like wind-blown leaves. On he went, the wind singing past his sharpened ears. Somewhere, sometime, he would find a way out. Then the high mesas again—miles and miles of unfenced country, clear down to the Tonto Basin.

The old gray cow pony stood near the water hole, apparently deep in thought. Pericles dashed up. Piecrust stretched a stiff hind leg. Curiosity was in his eye. Now that the young stallion had been ridden, how did he like it?

Pericles didn't. But, it surprised him to reflect, the Old Man was different. One felt that he expected you to behave. With the others, Pericles felt that they expected him to throw a whing-ding. And maybe he didn't. The old horse nodded. He would always be a one-man horse, that magnificent roan. And he was lucky. The other rawhides would keep off him, now that the Old Man had taken a fancy to him. The veteran sighed and rubbed his nose on his foreleg. "I was the Old Man's top horse once," he mused. "I was lucky too."

When Piecrust had become so old and stiff and short-sighted he couldn't do his work, one of the hands said it was about time to shoot him. That riled the Old Man. He said Piecrust had earned the right to take it easy the rest of his life. Pensioned, they called it.

Piecrust had been lucky—and lonesome until he and the young

stallion became friends. But it's hard to keep a friend when you grow old. Something always happens.

"I suppose," thought the old cow horse mournfully, "that some day he'll find a break in the fence and high-tail it for the mesas again."

Pericles dropped his head to graze, but the far-away look in his eye said plainly: "That's exactly what I intend to do!"

When spring came and the snow-softened earth let some of the fence posts sag until in two or three sections the wire was down, Pericles found the chance he had been looking for. Peter Annersley, riding him along the drift fence, saw the down wire and dismounted.

Pericles, who had been taught to stand to rein, waited until Peter's back was turned. Now was his chance! With reins dragging sideways, he dashed through and started for the high country. He heard Peter call to him. But no! Up there were his kindred, grazing the open reaches and running—running. Pericles stepped on one of the reins. The spade bit cut his mouth. He stopped. All the weeks of his training bore in on him. And now the Old Man was coming toward him, coming slowly, talking quietly, telling him to stop his nonsense.

Quivering, Pericles faced him. Step by step Peter approached. One more step and Pericles would turn and run. The Old Man saw it in his eyes. He stopped.

"Perry," he said, "don't be a fool. You ain't wild any more. You only think you're wild." Peter chuckled just as though he didn't care much whether Pericles stayed or not.

It all hung on Peter now. If he had made one wrong move, raised his hand or changed the tone of his voice, Pericles would have left on the instant. But the owner of the Moonstone simply came forward as if he expected the roan stallion to stand, raised his hand so slowly that Pericles hardly knew it, took up the reins and, reaching for the stirrup, mounted leisurely.

"Let's go back and look at that fence once more," he said as Pericles moved forward like a creature in a dream.

They returned to the damaged fence. Pericles was still quivering inside. Not another hand on the Moonstone would have chanced it. But as casually as if his mount were an old trained cow pony, Peter stepped off him and again let the reins fall. Pericles rolled his eye toward the high country. He fidgeted, breathing deep of the warm spring air. But he did not move from where Peter had left him.

For a half hour the Old Man worked at propping up the fallen posts. With a stone for a hammer, he restapled the wire. Then he came back to the waiting Pericles and took up the reins. "That was the best thing you ever did, little horse," he said as he mounted and rode on down the fence.

Pericles wondered.

Joys of the Hunt

County Down

MURIEL BOWEN

*I have chosen the following pages from Miss Muriel Bowen's
interesting history of* Irish Hunting *for several reasons. It
gives in detail the history of the oldest Hunt of the British
Isles and therefore of the world—the County Down of Northern Ireland. That this is not a fox hunt but a stag hunt is another reason for my choice. I have hunted carted stag in
Southern Ireland, and found it a marvelous sport. It is fast,
exciting, and on the whole I think safer than fox-hunting, as
the stag tends to keep out in open country where the going is
good and everyone, including the stag, enjoys himself. For unlike the procedure in France, where a noble animal is butchered after affording an afternoon's pleasure, in Ireland the stag
that has usually been bred for his career and is accustomed to
comfortable affluence, is released, followed as long as the hunt
can keep up, and then, when he tires, he has only to take to
the water. Hounds surround him, the huntsman comes up, the
stag is returned to the "box" or van and goes home to rest up
for the next run. Or, as described in this article, he escapes
entirely and becomes an "outlyer" for several seasons.*

*Furthermore, Miss Bowen brings out one of the nicest fea-
tures of Irish hunting, the democracy of the field. Only in
amateur orchestras does one find so many people of different
financial, national and cultural backgrounds meeting together
to enjoy an activity solely for pleasure with no thought of
financial benefit. The rivalry is friendly and the performance
of each participant is the only thing that counts.*

*The description of the Taylor family, all of whose mem-
bers have become Hunt Servants, and one of whom, at the age
of seventy-four, took up the horn again to replace a son killed
in an accident, shows again how important the chase is considered and how it has affected the careers of so many people.*

125

In Ulster, matters of business or of sport are always thoroughly well looked after, and no exception can be made to the stag hounds, which are admirably brought out by George Taylor and the Joint Masters, Lieutenant-Colonel J. G. Cunningham and Mr. Archie Willis. Though Ulstermen have hunted hares for generations, and latterly turned their attention to fox hunting, the carted stag has always taken precedence in the Province.

The greater proportion of the field come from Belfast and this sport is admirably suited to them. Like most devotees of stag hunting, they like to get the day's business well in hand before they indulge in recreation.

The first to ride to hounds in Northern Ireland is believed to be Squire Nicholas Price of Saintfield. Born in 1754, he started hunting the country round his home from 1775 onwards. . . .

. . . The Hunt uniform, which dates from 1811 would seem to be the only remaining link with the very early days. At that time two uniforms were proposed, one by Mathew Forde, M.P., of Seaforde, and the other by John Reilly. This pair were requested to "appear at dinner in the dress they respectively proposed in order that their comparative merits may be taken into consideration and resolved on."

Both appeared and Mr. Reilly won the day. His dress, which has been worn ever since at meets of the Hunt, consists of a black coat lined with scarlet silk, black velvet collar, gilt buttons, and a white Marseilles waistcoat.

It was considered a crime for members to arrange meetings, or still worse to entertain members during the fortnight of the Hunt meeting. In 1841 the High Sheriff, Robert Perceval-Maxwell, was fined one guinea for convening a county meeting during the meeting of the Hunt, and in 1844 D.S. Ker was fined two guineas for entertaining members during its session. To fall oneself was bad; to tempt others to fall brought double punishment.

Of the same nature as the fines was the system of imposing casts of wine, and though this saved members' pockets, it was no benefit to the Hunt funds. Casts were introduced in 1829 and lasted until 1883. Oxford undergraduates have experienced this practice in the sconces which are imposed on those who break the rules of Hall. The offender instead of being fined was compelled to pay a round of drinks to the assembled members. This levy proved so acceptable that often fourteen or fifteen casts were imposed on a single night. On one occasion twenty-seven were imposed.

The Hunt has never lived merely for its own enjoyment. From time to time large contributions have been made to deserving funds and the Hunt has always had an open purse for national and provincial needs. This practice started in 1798, when "the sum of one hundred sporting pounds" was given to the relief of widows and orphans of those who died when Admiral Lord Duncan's forces defeated the Dutch Fleet.

The bill of fare for dinners in the early days makes amusing reading. Dinner cost "one English shilling," which makes one wonder what there was to eat. But by all accounts the Hunt was done well. Oysters were provided and paid for usually in consignments of two thousand. The best came from Carlingford and cost 6/6 a hundred. Occasionally there was dissatisfaction and fines varying from 10/ to two pounds two shillings were inflicted on the caterer for dinners badly dressed, or more especially for beef being hard or underdone.

Membership of the club goes far outside the limits of the county, but one hundred and fifty-two proposed for membership have been rejected. A story told of the Hunt meeting of 1840 speaks volumes for the loyalty of members. Duty kept two members away, one in his London office and the other in Bath; neither forgot or wished others to forget the importance of the week. So they appeared each day, one in Bond St. and the other outside the Pump Room in the uniform of the Hunt, and strange to say, each met one other similarly attired.

The scene changes to Canada in 1872, but the story is strikingly similar. Lord Dufferin (later the first Marquess of Dufferin and Ava), then Governor General, was a member of the Hunt; so were his two A.D.C.s, and they all appeared each night in Hunt uniform.

In early days amongst the most important people connected with the Hunt were the runners. They would run thirty miles a day on a message before horses became cheap and motor cars common. They would set out in the dark of a Winter's evening to inform a new member of his election. Two of the runners, Tom Welch and Barney Case, a barefooted Downpatrick chimney sweep, were quite famous.

In 1825, Tom Welch was backed to beat the mail coach from Belfast to Dublin which he did, appearing each stage in advance of it. Finally he greeted its arrival at the General Post Office in O'Connell Street, waving his hat in the air and dancing in triumph on the street.

As early as 1773 keepers of game were employed by the Down Hunt for the preservation of hares. Penalties in relation to hares were very strict and Hunt membership was by those who kept a greyhound within four miles of a hunting country. The record for the longest membership of the Hunt is easily held by the Squire of Saintfield, Nicholas Price, already mentioned, who was a member for seventy-four years. Elected in 1773, he remained in the Hunt until his death at the age of ninety-three, in 1846.

In the late fifties and early sixties of the last century, there were still a number of packs of hounds in Northern Ireland. Foremost amongst these were the Newry Harriers, Killultagh Harriers, and the Old Rock and Chichester Harriers. The two leading private packs were those of Mrs. Caroline Ker, who had hounds at Montalto and hunt them herself and of Captain Ker, D.L., who kept a pack of pure bred harriers at Portaferry which were hunted by David Ker.

The County Down Staghounds were really a development of Captain Ker's Harriers which had occasionally hunted fallow deer. In 1881 they became known as the County Down Staghounds and turned their attention solely to red deer. It was in that year also that Captain Ker brought his hounds to an invitation meet of the Down Hunt and we read of the Hunt giving thirty pounds towards the maintenance of staghounds.

Captain Ker (1881–87) was a big jolly man, with a big voice, and he hunted well into the eighties. His hunting establishment was in every way a splendid one and commented on with much favour throughout these islands. He had a bull's eye dinner story which is quoted to this day. It was the Captain's ready answer to those who said they could not hunt because it was too expensive.

When stationed with the Dragoons in Yorkshire a chimney sweep turned up regularly at meets. The sweep was a nailer to go and rode a horse which pulled his brushes round during the remainder of the week. Because of his jolly manner and being ever ready to lend a helping hand to a member of the field in difficulties, he was deservedly popular. Everybody regretted when the sweep arrived at a meet one day on a bicycle, his horse having dropped dead while pulling the brushes. In the mess that night it was decided to start a collection to buy the sweep another horse, and Captain Ker was given the job of asking him what a new hunter would cost.

"Ah," said the sweep, "if you give me one pound I can get a good 'un, but if you give me /30—I'll get an outer!"

Next Mastership is that of Mr. A. H. Gordon, D.L. (1887–92), who gave much valuable service to the hunt and remained Deputy Master during the term of office of his successor, the Marquess of Downshire (1893–94).

Prior to coming to County Down, where he had two estates, Hillsborough Castle and Murlough House, Lord Downshire had Mastered the Berks and Bucks Harriers. This period was followed by Mr. Gordon again taking control for two seasons, and his successor was Mr. Frank Barbour (1896–1903), afterwards a very famous Master of the Westmeath and the donor of the celebrated Barbour Cup. He owned many a good horse, among them the great 'chaser, Easter Hero. Tommy Taylor, father of the present huntsman, was whipper-in and kennel huntsman, having been grounded in the essentials of hunt service by his uncle, then huntsman to the Killtulagh Harriers.

A noted member of the day was the Honorary Treasurer, Mr. Charles Blakiston-Houston, who exhibited many good jumpers at the Dublin Horse Show, notably Knockabout, who used to approach each jump in the most unorthodox manner, then whip round at the last minute and jump over it. Mrs. Blakiston-Houston was a daughter of Burton Persse of Galway Blazers fame.

Other Masters during the early years of the century were Mr. R. W. Lindsay, Mr. David Ker, D.L., and Mr. S. B. Combe. Mr. Lindsay was very devoted to coaching and maintained a coach-and-four both in London and Belfast. Mr. Combe was a director of his family's engineering firm and had many successes point-to-pointing, usually riding other people's horses. He was killed in action in the early part of World War I.

Hounds were out three days a week and by all accounts sport often reached great heights. On St. Stephen's Day, 1908, hounds met at Hillsborough and enjoyed a twelve mile point. The 1909–10

season was one of the severest ever in Northern Ireland with very
cold weather and much snow throughout the season. Though sixteen
days were missed because of bad weather hounds were out on fifty-
eight days. On April 5th, 1910, a stag enlarged at Sentry Box ran to
Ballywill, a twelve mile point and twenty as hounds ran. On the
15th of the same month followers enjoyed a run from Ballyerine to
Ednigo, a distance of twelve miles over a fine line of country in one
hour and forty minutes. It was during this season that a stag was
taken in the sea at Newcastle.

  . . . The county has numbered many notable characters among
the hunting fraternity. There was Johnny McRoberts who kept about
forty horses in his stable and helped a great many young riders between wars. To the Hunt he was of untold service and he has been
described to me as "the living best to square up trouble with the
farmers." Then there was John Read, father of Drew Read the
noted show jumper, a real dare devil to cross a country, who once
took on the river Bann when in flood and nearly got drowned. Gussie
Martin was another regular in his day, complete with morning coat
and an ash plant pivoted on his knee.

  Greatest character among the stags hunted by the County Down
was "McRoberts" named after Johnny McRoberts. Bred at the deer
park at Montalta, McRoberts had an auspicious career, being
hunted for eleven seasons. From 1924 to 1933 he remained at large
and in March, 1933, he was taken in Lough Henny after a three-
hours' hunt. During that month five stags, which had all been at
large for long periods, were taken on four consecutive days. Mc-
Roberts gave two or three good hunts each season and died in the
deer park at the age of fifteen. One of his hoofs is preserved at
Glencairn, the home of Lieutenant-Colonel J. G. Cunningham, the
Joint Master.

  Special trains, commonly called hunt specials, operated up to
1928 on the County Down Railway. For a good meet it was not
unusual to see up to forty horses unloaded at Ballinahinch. Transport of a horse from Belfast cost as little as 10/6d.

  Many a good horse has made his first public appearance with
the County Down Staghounds, notably Bohermore, winner of the
Prince of Wales Plate at Punchestown and the Irish Grand National,
and originally bought for sixteen guineas. Several famous show

jumpers have followed the staghounds, including Meta, brought out by Mr. Sam Baille, V.S. This mare won all the big jumping events in Dublin and Belfast shows and used to go down on one knee when a distinguished personage presented the rosette to her rider. Jumping and hunting at the same time was the chestnut, Perfection, winner of the High Poles championship at the Dublin Show in 1938, ridden by his owner Mr. Waring Willis.

Hunting in County Down one finds an obstacle called a "Flax Hole" which is not found elsewhere in Ireland. It is dug at the side of a fence and is about twelve feet wide. Large stones are used to hold in the flax and these are placed at the outer edge of the hole and add to the hazards.

Since 1946 hounds have been hunted by George Taylor, who comes of a remarkable family of hunt servants. His father, already mentioned, retired from the hunt service in 1950 at the age of seventy-five. For his last season he was huntsman of the East Antrim Harriers, taking the place of his son Robert who had been killed in a car accident. His six sons were all entered to hunt service with the Killtulagh.

George, the present huntsman, was for years with the Ormond. Tommy is huntsman to the North Devon Harriers, Jack for years with the Kildare is now hunting the East Antrim, Sam was killed on active service during World War II, having temporarily vacated hunt service, and Ernie is the present huntsman of his father's old pack, the Killtulagh. Lucky indeed is the country which can produce families like the Taylors, who have given such long and distinguished service to hunting.

For the past few seasons black and tan blood has been introduced with great success from the Drumfriesshire, Sir John Buchanan Jardine's hounds. The first draft, by French stag hounds was introduced in 1950. Of recent meets, that at Sentry Box in February, 1951, is deserving of mention. Hounds had an eight mile point, fifteen as they ran, and the time was one hour and fifty minutes. Both pace and jumps were a rasper all the way.

A Quiet Bye with Mr. Jorrocks

ROBERT SMITH SURTEES

Here is Mr. Jorrocks at his best. An ardent huntsman as long as hounds are in covert, not so keen when they get running in the open, and completely downed by the sight of a fence, the lovable old tea salesman, newly made master of the fox-hounds of Handley Cross, has a day's unexpected hunting with his untried pack and huntsman James Pigg. The language and perhaps the style of writing have changed since Surtees wrote his famous masterpiece, but the language and style of hunting have not, and anyone who has hunted in England will feel at home when he reads this.

. . . Then before Mr. Jorrocks got half through his City letters and made his pencil observations thereupon—who to do business with, whose respectability to inquire into, who to dun, who to decline dealing with, the gossiping *Handley Cross Paul Pry* with its list of arrivals, fashionable millinery, dental surgery advertisements, etc., having passed the ordeal of the kitchen, made its appearance with the following important announcement:

THE HANDLEY CROSS (MR. JORROCKS') FOX-HOUNDS
Will meet on Wednesday at the Round of Beef and Carrots, Appledove Road, and on Saturday at the Mountain Daisy, near Hookey's Hutch, each day at ten o'clock.
N.B.—These hounds will hunt Mondays and Fridays with an occasional bye on Wednesdays in future.

"Why, you're advertising, I see!" exclaimed Charley, on reading the above.

"I am," replied Mr. Jorrocks, with a grin, "comin' it strong, aren't I?"

"Very," replied Stobbs, "three days a week—will want a good many horses for that."

"Oh, I shan't be much troubled on Wednesdays," rejoined Mr. Jorrocks; "shall jest make that long or short 'cordin' as it suits."

"But you'll go out, I s'pose," observed Stobbs.

"In course," replied Jorrocks. "In course—only I shall go out at my own hour, may be height, may be sivin, may be as soon as we can see. Not many o' these waterin'-place birds that'll get hup for an 'unt, only, ye see, as I wants their money, I must give them walue received—or summat like it but there's nothing like the mornin' for making foxes cry '*Capevi!*' " added he, with a grin of delight.

"Nothing," assented Stobbs.

"We'll 'ave some rare chiveys!" exclaimed Mr. Jorrocks, his eyes glistening as he spoke.

"Hope so," replied Stobbs, adding, "let's give them a trot out today."

"Today," mused our master—"today," repeated he, thrusting his hands deep in his pockets, and then taking a dry shave of his chin—"couldn't well go out today. Tomorrow, if you like—got a lot o' letters to write and things to do—not quite right nouther—feel as if I'd eat a hat or a pair of worsted stockings."

"Tomorrow will be too near your regular day," observed Stobbs.

"Ah, true, so it would," assented Mr. Jorrocks, thinking he must attend to appearances first, at all events.

"Better give them a round today," continued Stobbs, returning to his point.

"Not prepared," mused Jorrocks—"not prepared, Pigg hasn't got himself 'fettled oop' yet, as he calls it."

"Oh, yes, he has," replied Stobbs—"saw him trying on his tops as I came downstairs, and his red coat and waistcoat were lying on the kitchen table."

"Indeed," replied Mr. Jorrocks—"wonder 'ow he looks in 'em. Only a hugly beggar out on 'em."

"He's a varmint-looking chap," observed Stobbs.

"Yes, he is," assented Mr. Jorrocks; " 'ope he's keen."

"How's Ben off that way?" asked Stobbs.

"Oh, Bin's a fine bouy," observed Jorrocks, "and I makes no doubt 'ill train on. Rome wasn't built in a day, Constantinople nouther."

"Certainly not," assented Stobbs, thinking if Ben made a sportsman he was very much mistaken.

After a vigorous attack upon the muffins, kidneys, fried ham, marmalade, and other good things adorning Mr. Jorrocks' breakfast table, our Yorkshire friend again tried to draw the great M.F.H. for a day.

"Couldn't we give the 'ounds a trot out by way of exercise, think ye?" asked he.

"Don't know," grunted Jorrocks from the bottom of his coffee-cup. "Wot good would that do?"

"Make 'em handy," replied Stobbs.

" 'Andy enough," replied our master, bolting a large piece of muffin. " 'Andy as ladies' maids. Can do everything 'cept pay their own pikes."

Despite this confident assertion, Stobbs still stuck to him. First he proposed that Pigg and he should take the hounds out together. This Jorrocks wouldn't stand. "Be sure to get into mischief." Then Stobbs thought it would do Jorrocks a vast deal of good to have a bump on one of his great rough horses. Our master couldn't quite gainsay this, though he did look out of the window, observing that the sun had risen very red, that he thought it would rain, and he shouldn't like to get wet.

"Oh, it 'ill not rain," replied Stobbs—"not till night at least," added he confidently.

"Don't know that," grunted Mr. Jorrocks; "Gabey seems to be of a different 'pinion," he added, as the noble old peacock now emerged from under a sun-bright Portugal laurel, and stretching his neck, and flapping his wings, uttered a wild, piercing scream.

"Dash my vig, but that looks like it!" exclaimed Mr. Jorrocks; adding, as he caught his right foot with a shake of his head, "Gabriel Junks is seldom wrong, and my corns are on his side."

Still Stobbs persevered, and, by dint of agitation, at length succeeded in getting Jorrocks not only to go out, but to have a draw in Newtimber Forest; Stobbs observing, and Jorrocks assenting, that there would be very little more trouble in running the hounds through the cover than in trotting them along the road. And, with some misgivings, Jorrocks let Stobbs go to make the arrangements, while he applied himself vigorously to his letters.

* * *

Pigg was all eager for the fray, and readily came into Stobbs' suggestion, that they should go out, and just take their chance of finding a fox, and of his going to ground or not as luck and his courage served.

"Ar'll gan to'ard Duncan's and get his grey for wor Ben," said Pigg, "gin ye'll set the lad on to seddle the rest," adding, "the Squi-er ar's warned 'ill ride Arterxerxes."

Off then Pigg went to Duncan Nevin's and returned with a woe-begone-looking horse in halter, before Stobbs had made any progress in his department. Ben was not to be found. Neither at Mrs. Candy the tart-woman's, nor at Mrs. Biffin's apple-stall, nor at Strap the saddler's nor at any of his usual haunts, was anything to be heard of the boy.

The fact was he had been unable to resist a ride at the back of

a return chaise passing along Juniper Street, and, being caught by his apron in the spikes, had been carried nearly to Copse Field before he got himself disentangled.

The oracle Gabriel having continued his monitions, Mr. Jorrocks thought to make the absence of the boy an excuse for not going, but now having both Stobbs and Pigg ranged against him, he was soon driven from the attempt. Pigg said, "Squi-er Stobbs wad de quite as weal as Ben," and Jorrocks, little loth at heart, perhaps, at length hoisted himself on to Arterxerxes with a sway that would have sent a light-carcassed horse over, letting the now smartly clad Pigg ride the redoubtable Xerxes. So with Stobbs in front, Jorrocks with the hounds, and Pigg behind, they set off at a gentle trot, telling the inquirers that they were only going to exercise, a delusion that Mr. Jorrocks' hat seemed to favour.

Bump, bump—jog, jog—on they went; Mr. Jorrocks now chiding, now coaxing, now dropping an observation fore or aft, now looking at the sky, and now at his watch.

"Des say we shall find pretty soon," observed Mr. Jorrocks; "for they tells me the cover has not been disturbed this long time; and there's lots of lyin'—nice, and dry, and warm—foxes like damp beds as little as Christians. Uncommon pretty betch, that Barbara—like Bravery as two peas—by Billin'sgate out o' Benedict, I think. 'Opes we may get blood; it'll do them a deal o' good, and make them steady for the Beef and Carrots. Wen we gets the 'ounds all on the square, we'll 'ave the great Mr. Pomponious Hego to come and give us a good boiling. Nothin' like soap."

"Hooi! you chap with the turnip-cart!" now roared out master to a cartman coming up; "vot do you mean by stickin' your great ugly wehicle afore my 'ounds!—Mr. Jorrocks' 'ounds, in fact! I'll skin you alive!" added he, looking at the man, who stood staring with astonishment. And again they went, bump, bump, jog, jog, at that pleasant post-boy pace, that has roused the bile of so many sportsmen, and set so many riders fighting their horses.

At length they reached the cover-side—a long wood stretching up the sides of a gently sloping hill, and widening towards the summit. On the crown there stood a clump of Scotch firs and hollies, forming a landmark for many miles round. Turning from the high-

road into a grass field on the right, the party pulled up to recon-
noitre the ground, and make their final arrangements.

"Now," said Mr. Jorrocks, standing erect in his stirrups, and
pointing with his whip, which had the effect of making half the pack
break towards the cover— "Now," said he, as soon as he had got
them turned, "this is a good big wood—two 'undred acres or more
—and they tells me the foxes generally lie on the risin' ground,
towards the clump. The vind's north-vest; so if we puts him at this
point, we shall draw up it, and p'raps get close to the warmint at
startin', which is a grand thing; but, howsomever, let's be doin'.
Draw your girths, Pigg, or your 'oss'll slip through his saddle. Now
observe, there are three rides—one on each side, on hup the middle,
all leadin' to the clump; and there are cross ones in all directions;
so no man need be 'fraid o' losin' himself. Now let's put in. Pigg,
open the wicket."

"It's locked," observed Pigg, running the hammer of his whip
into the rails, throwing himself off his horse, and pulling a great
clasp-knife out of his pocket as he spoke. "Sink, but it aye gars mar
knife laugh to see a lock put upon leather," added he, as he drew the
huge blade across the stiff band that secured the gate. Open flew the
wicket—in went the pack with a dash, a crash, and a little music
from the riotous ones, which gradually yielded to the "Have a cares!"
and *"Gently,* Wenus," "Gently, Lousey" (Louisa), with the cracks
of the whips of Mr. Jorrocks and his huntsman.

"Now, Pigg, my frind, let's have a touch o' North Country
science," observed Mr. Jorrocks, bringing his horse alongside of his
huntsman's. "I'd like *well* to kill a fox to-day; I'd praise you wery
much if we did."

"Aye, aye," said Pigg. "Hoic in, Lousey! Solid puddin's better
nor empty praise. Have at him there, Statesman, old boy—ye look
like a finder. Deil bon me, but ar thought ar winded him at the
crossin' there," added Pigg, pulling his horse short back to a cross-
ride he had just passed. "Hoic in there, Priestess, ould gal," said he,
to an old black and white bitch, feathering round some gorse among
the underwood; waving his hand as he spoke. "That's Gospel, ar
warrant ye," continued he, watching her movements.

"What will't tak' for t'ard nag?" inquired Pigg, of a besom-

maker, who now came down the ride with a wretched white
Rosinante, laden with stolen brushwood— "Have at him, there
Challenger!" speaking to a hound.

"Twenty shillin'," replied the man.

"Give ye eight!" was the answer— "Yooi, push him up!" to the
hound.

"Tak' twelve," rejoined the tinker. "Good horse—can get up of
hisself, top puller and all. . . ."

"Aye, but we dinna want him to poole; we want him to eat,"
replied Pigg. *"Had still!"* exclaimed he; *"ar has him!*—TALLI-HO,"
roared Pigg, cramming his spurs into his horse, and dashing past
Jorrocks like a shot. Out went both horns—twang—twang—twang
sounded Pigg's; wow! wow! wow! went Jorrocks' in deeper and more
substantial notes, and in a very short time, the body of the pack
were laid on the scent, and opened the concert with an overpowering burst of melody.

"Oh, beautiful! beautiful!" exclaimed Mr. Jorrocks, in raptures,
as each hound put his nose to the ground, and acknowledged the
correctness of the scent. "Oh, beautiful, indeed!" added he, thumping the end of his horn upon his thigh, as though he were cutting
large gun-waddings out of his breeches. " 'Ow true to the line! best
'ounds in England, by far—never were such a pack! Shall have a
rare chivy—all alone by ourselves; and when I gets home I'll write
an account to *Bell's Life* and *The Field,* which nobody can contra-
dict. Hark forrard! hark forrard! hark forrard! away!" continued he,
ramming the spurs into Arterxerxes' sides, to induce him to change
his lumbering trot into a canter, which having accomplished, Mr.
Jorrocks settled himself into a regular home seat in his saddle, and
pounded up a grass ride through the centre of the wood in a perfect
frenzy of delight, as the hounds worked their way a little to his right
with a full and melodious cry.

"Hould hard, ye sackless ould sinner!" now cried Pigg, crossing
the main ride at a canter, and nearly knocking Jorrocks off his horse,
as he charged him in his stride. *"Had* (hold) *bye, ar say!"* he roared
in his master's ear; "or ar'll be dingin' on ye down—fox crossed reet
in onder husse's tail, and thou sits glowerin' there and never see'd
him."

Out went both horns again—twang!—twang!—twang!—; wow! wow! wow!

"Hark together! hark! get forrard, hounds, get forrard!" cried Mr. Jorrocks, cracking his ponderous whip at some lingerers that loitered on the ride, questioning the correctness of their comrades' cry. *"Get forrard,* I say!" repeated he, with redoubled energy. "Confound your unbelievin' souls!" added he, as they went to cry. "Now they are on him again! Oh, beautiful, beautiful!" exclaimed Mr. Jorrocks, in ecstacies. "I'll lay you five pounds to a fiddler's farthin' they kill him. Mischief in their cry!—a rare scent—can wind him myself." So saying, he gathered up his reins again, thrust his feet home in the stirrups, crammed the spurs into his horse, and rolled back on the ride he had just come up. "Hark!" now cried our master, pulling up short and holding his hand in the air, as though he had a hundred and fifty horsemen at his tail to check in their career. "Hark!" again he exclaimed; "whoay, 'oss, whoay!" trying to get Arterxerxes to stand still and let him listen. "Now, fool, vot are you champing the bit for?—whoay, I say! he's turned short again! Hoick back! Hoick back! they've overrun the scent," continued he, listening, as the chorus gradually died out; "or," added he, "he *may* have got to ground."

"Tailli-ho!" now screamed Jorrocks, as a magnificent fellow in a spotless suit of ruddy fur crossed the ride before him at a quiet, stealing, listening sort of pace, and gave a whisk of his well-tagged brush on entering the copse-wood across. *"Hoop! hoop! hoop! hoop!"* roared Mr. Jorrocks, putting his finger in his ear, and holloaing as loud as ever he could shout; and just as he got his horn fumbled past the guard, Dexterous, Affable and Mercury dashed across the ride, lashing their sterns and bristling for blood, and Pigg appeared a little below, cantering along with the rest of the pack at his horse's heels. *"Here Pigg! there, Pigg!"* roared Mr. Jorrocks; "just by the old hoak-stump. *Gently* now! ah, ware 'eel—that's not the vay of him; he's hover to the left, I tells ye. That's him! Mercury has him! Hoick to Mercury, hoick! *get away, get away, get away, 'ounds!* hoick together! Oh, Pigg wot a wopper he is!" observed Mr. Jorrocks, as Pigg joined him in the ride. "The biggest fox whatever was seen—if we do but kill him—my vig! I'll eat his tongue for

supper. Have it grilled, *'cum grano salis'*, with a *leetle* bit Cayenne pepper, as Pomponius Hego would say."

"Aye," replied Pigg, grinning with delight, his cap-peak in the air and the tobacco juice streaming down his mouth like a Chinese mandarin. "Ar'll be the *death of a shillin'* mysel'!" Saying which he hustled his horse and turned to his hounds.

Away they go again full cry across the cover to the utmost limits and then back again to the far side. Now the fox takes a full swing round, but won't quit—now he cuts across—now Mr. Jorrocks views him, and swears he'll have his brains as well as his tongue for supper. Pigg has him next, and again comes Mr. Jorrocks' turn. "Dash my vig, but he's a tough 'un!" observed Mr. Jorrocks to James Pigg, as they met again on the rising ground at the top of the ride, where Mr. Jorrocks had been fifteen times and Pigg seventeen, both their horses streaming with perspiration, and the blue and yellow worsted fronts of the bridles embossed with foam.

"Dash my vig, but it's a million and a half of petties," continued Mr. Jorrocks, looking at his watch, and seeing that it wanted but twenty minutes to four, "that we adwertised, for there's a wast o' go left in him yet, and he'll take the shine out of some of our 'ounds before he is done with them—send them draggling 'ome with their sterns down—make 'em cry *'Capevi,'* I'm thinking."

"Niver fear!" exclaimed Pigg—"niver fear!—whativer ye de, keep Tamboreen a-rowlin'—yonder he gans! ar wish it may'nt be a fresh 'un. Arn't draggled a bit."

"Oh, I 'opes not!" exclaimed Mr. Jorrocks, the picture of despair. "Would eat him, brush and all sooner than that. Oh, dear! oh dear! a fresh fox would be cruel—'ounds deserve him—worked him well."

"Now they begin to *chass!*" exclaimed Pigg, listening to the ripening chorus. "Aye, there's a grand scent!— Ar'll be the death of a shillin' if we de but kill him. How way, ould man, how way," continued Pigg, cheeringly jerking his arm to induce his master to follow. "Whatever ye de, keep Tamboreen a-rowlin'!" continued Pigg, spurring and jagging his horse into a canter.

On man and master go—now they meet Charley, and all three are together. Again they part company for different rides, each according to his fancy. There is an evident improvement in the scent, but whether from a fresh fox, or the hounds having got nearer the hunted one, is a matter of doubt. Mr. Jorrocks is elated and excited beyond expression. The hounds are evidently working the fox, but the fear of a fresh one rather mars his enjoyment. The hounds turn short, and Pigg and Charles again join Mr. Jorrocks.

"Ah! man alive, but they are a-dustin' his jacket!" exclaimed Pigg, pulling up to listen;—"iv-ry hund's at him"; saying which he pulled out a large steel box and stuffed his mouth full of tobacco.

A sudden pause ensues—all is still as death—not a note—not even a whimper!

"*Who-hoop!*" exclaims Mr. Jorrocks in ecstacies—"*Who-hoop!* I say—heard the leadin' 'ound crack his back! Old Cruiser for a guinea!"

"*Yonder they gan!*" cried Pigg, pointing to a hog-backed hill on the left, over which three couple of hounds were straining to gain the body of the pack—saying which he clapt spurs to his horse and dashed off at full gallop, followed by Charles.

"Oh dear! oh dear!" exclaimed Mr. Jorrocks, the picture of despair—"wot shall I do? wot shall I do?—gone away at this hour —strange country—nobody to pull the 'edges down for me or catch my 'oss if I gets spilt, and there's that Pigg ridin' as if there was not never no such man as his master. Pretty kettle of fish!" continued Mr. Jorrocks, trotting on in the line they had taken. A bridle-gate let him out of cover, and from the first hill our master sees his hounds going like pigeons over the large grazing-grounds of Beddington Bottoms, with Pigg and Stobbs a little in the rear, riding as hard as ever their horses can lay legs to the ground.

" 'Ow that Scotch beggar rides!" exclaimed Mr. Jorrocks, eyeing Pigg going straight as an arrow, which exclamation brought him to his first fence at the bottom of the hill, over which both horsemen had passed without disturbing a twig.

" 'OLD UP, 'oss!" roared Mr. Jorrocks, seizing the reins and whip with one hand and the cantle of the saddle with the other, as Arterxerxes floundered sideways through a low fence with a little

runner on the far side. " 'OLD UP!" repeated he, as they got scrambled through, looking back and saying, "Terrible nasty place—
wonders I ever got over. Should ha' been drund to a certainty if I'd
got in. Wouldn't ride at it again for nothin' under knighthood—Sir
John Jorrocks, Knight!" continued he, shortening his hold of his
horse. "And my ladyship Jorrocks!" added he. "She'd be bad to 'old
—shouldn't wonder if she'd be for goin' to Halmack's. Dash my
buttons, but I wish I was off this beastly fallow," continued he;
"wonderful thing to me that the farmers can't see there'd be less
trouble i' growin' grass than in makin' these nasty rutty fields.
'Eavens be praised, there's a gate—and a lane too," saying which
he was speedily in the latter, and gathering his horse together he set
off at a brisk trot in the direction he last saw the hounds going.

Terribly deep it was, and great Arterxerxes made a noise like
the drawing of corks as he blobbed along through the stiff, holding
clay.

Thus Mr. Jorrocks proceeded for a mile or more, until he came
upon a red-cloaked gypsy wench stealing sticks from a rotten fence
on the left.

" 'Ave you seen 'ounds, ould gal?" inquired he, pulling up short.

"Bless your beautiful countenance, my cock angel!" exclaimed
the woman, in astonishment at the sight of a man in a scarlet coat
with a face to match; "bless your beautiful countenance, you're the
very babe I've been looking for all this blessed day—cross my palm
with a bit o' siller, and I'll tell you *sich* a fortin!"

"CUSS YOUR FORTIN!" roared Mr. Jorrocks, sticking spurs
into his horse and grinning with rage at the idea of having pulled
up to listen to such nonsense.

"I hope you'll brick your neck, ye nasty ugly ould thief!" rejoined the gypsy, altering her tone.

" 'Opes I *sharn't*," muttered Mr. Jorrocks, trotting on to get
out of hearing. Away he went, blob, blob, blobbing through the deep
holding clay as before.

Presently he pulled up again with a "Pray, my good man, 'ave
you seen my 'ounds—Mr. Jorrocks' 'ounds, in fact?" of a labourer
scouring a fence-gutter. "Don't you 'ear me, man?" bellowed he,
as the countryman stood staring with his hand on his spade.

"I be dull of hearin', sir," at length drawled the man, advancing
very slowly towards our master with his hand up to his ear.

"Oh, dear! oh, dear!" exclaimed Mr. Jorrocks, starting off again, "was there ever sich a misfortinate indiwidual as John Jorrocks?— 'Ark! vot's that? Pigg's 'orn! Oh, dear, only a cow! Come hup, 'oss, I say, you hugly beast!—there surely never was sich a worthless beast lapped in leather as you," giving Arterxerxes a good double thonging as he spoke. "Oh, dear! oh, dear!" continued he, "I wish I was well back at the Cross, with my 'ounds safe i' kennel.—Vot a go this is!—Dinner at five—baked haddocks, prime piece of fore chine, Portingal honions, and fried plum-pudding; and now, by these darkenin' clouds it must be near four, and here I be's, miles and miles away—'ounds still runnin', and adwertised for the Beef and Carrots on Wednesday—never will be fit to go, nor to the Daisy nouther."

"Pray, my good man," inquired he of a drab-coated, big-basketed farmer, on a bay cart-horse, whom he suddenly encoun-tered at the turn of the road, " 'ave you seen anything of my 'ounds? Mr. Jorrocks' 'ounds, in fact?"

"Yes, sir," replied the farmer, all alive; "they were running past Langford plantations with the fox dead beat close afore them."

" 'Ow long since, my frind?" inquired Mr. Jorrocks, brightening.

"Oh, why just as long as it's taken me to come here—mebbe ten minutes or a quarter of an hour, not longer, certainly. If you put on you may be in at the death yet."

Away went spurs, elbows, and legs, elbows and legs, Arterxerxes was again impelled into a canter, and our worthy master pounded along, all eyes, ears, and fears. Night drew on, the darkening clouds began to lower, bringing with them fog and a drizzling rain.

"Bad go this," said Mr. Jorrocks, rubbing his hand down his coat-sleeve, and raising his face to ascertain the precise amount of the fall. "Bad go, indeed. Got my Sunday 'at on, too. Hooi, bouys! did you see th' 'ounds?" inquired he of a troop of satchel-slung youths, plodding their ways homeward from school.

"Y-e-a-s," at length drawled out one, after a good stare at the inquirer.

" 'Ow long since? come, *quick,* bouy!"

"May be twenty minutes; just as we com'd past Hookem Snivey church, we see'd fox, and hounds were close ahint—he was *varra* tired."

"Twenty minutes," repeated Mr. Jorrocks, aloud to himself;

"twenty minutes—may be a werry long way off by this; foxes travel fast. Vich way were they a-goin'?"

"Straight for Staunton Snivey," drawled the boy.

"My vig!" exclaimed Mr. Jorrocks, "vot a run; if we don't kill werry soon, it'll be pitch-dark, and then there'll be a pretty kittle o' fish—th' 'ounds will kill all the ship (sheep) in the country—shall have a bill as long as my arm to pay."

Fear lent fresh impetus to our worthy friend, and tightening his hold on Arterxerxes' head, who now began tripping and stumbling, and floundering along in a most slovenly manner, Mr. Jorrocks trotted on, and reaching Hookem Snivey, saw by the foot-people standing on the churchyard wall that the hounds were "forrard"; he turned down a lane to the left of the village stocks, in the direction the people were looking, and catching Staunton Snivey in the distance, set off for it as hard as ever he could tear. A pretty clattering he made down the stony road.

Night now drew on apace, and heavy darkening clouds proclaimed a fast-approaching storm. At Staunton Snivey he learned that the hounds had just passed the turnpike on to the Downs, with the fox "dead beat *close* afore them"; and still unwilling to give in, though every moment increased his difficulties, he groped open a bridle-gate, and entered upon the wide-extending Plain. The wind had now risen, and swept with uncommon keenness over the unprotected open. The drizzling rain too became changed into larger, heavier drops, and thrusting his hat upon his brow, Mr. Jorrocks buttoned his coat up to the throat, and wrapping its laps over his thighs, tucked them in between his legs and the saddle. Dismal and disheartening were his thoughts, and many his misgivings for his rashness. "Oh, dear! oh, dear!" muttered he, "wot a most momentous crisis—lost! lost! lost!—completely lost! Dinner lost! 'ounds lost! self lost!—all lost together! Oh, vot evil genius ever tempted me from the lovely retirement o' Great Coram Street? Oh! why did I neglect the frindly warnin' o' Gabriel Junks? Change, change—storm, storm—was in his every scream, an' yet I would go. Cuss the rain, it's gettin' down my werry back, I do declare"; saying which he turned the blue collar of his coat up to his ears, and both laps flew out with a desperate gust of wind. " 'Ord rot it," said he, "it's not never no use perseverin', may as well give in at once and 'ark back to Snivey; my Berlins are wet through, and I shall be drenched in another second. "Who-ay, 'oss! who-ay; stand still, you hugly beast, and let me listen." The duck-headed brute at length obeyed.

"It *is* the 'orn," exclaimed Mr. Jorrocks, after sitting listening for some time, with his hand to his ear; "it *is* the 'orn, Pigg's not far off! There it goes again, but the 'owling wind carries so many ways, there's no saying whereabouts he is. I'll blow, and see if I can 'ail him," Mr. Jorrocks then drew out his horn, and puffed and blew most lustily, but the raging tempest scattered the notes before they were well out of his mouth, and having exhausted his breath, he again paused, horn in hand, to listen. Between each blast of the raging hurricane, the faint notes of the horn were heard, some coming more fully as the gale blew more favourably, and a fuller one falling on his ear, during a period of partial lull, Mr. Jorrocks determined on advancing and endeavouring to rejoin his lost huntsman. "Come hup, I say, you hugly beast!" exclaimed he, getting Arterxerxes short by the head, and digging the spurs freely into his sides. The lumbering brute acknowledged the compliment with a sort of half-hitch of a kick. "Great henterpriseless brute—do believe you'd rayther 'ave a feed o' corn than the finest run wot ever was seen," observed Mr. Jorrocks, cropping him. Night had now closed in, and even the sort of light of darkness that remains so long to the traveller who journeys onward with the closing day, deserted him, and earth and sky assumed the same sombre hue:

"The dragon wing of night o'erspread the earth." Scarce a star was visible in the firmament, and the few scattered lights that appeared here and there about the country, seemed like snatches of hope lit up for the moment to allure and perplex the wanderer.

"If ever mortal man catches me in such a quandary as this again," exclaimed Mr. Jorrocks, "I 'opes—*oh, dear!* who's there? *Speak, I say!—vot are you?*—Come hup, 'oss, I say!" roared he, ramming the spurs into Arterxerxes, who suddenly shied off with a loud snort. "Now for a murder!" ejaculated Jorrocks, still cramming in the spurs.

"E-yah! E-yah! E-yah!" went a donkey, greatly to the relief of Mr. Jorrocks' mind, who had clenched his huge hammer-headed whip by the middle, so as to give an assailant the full benefit of its weight. Out then went his horn again, and the donkey brayed a full accompaniment.

"Oh, the deuce be with the hanimal!" cried Jorrocks, grinning with vexation, "never saw a donkey yet that knew when to 'old his tongue. Oh, my vig, vot a vind! almost blows the 'orn itself; shall be blown to hatoms, I do believe. And the rain too! I really thinks I'm wet to the werry waistband o' my breeches. I'll lay a guinea 'at to a half-crown gossamer I haven't a dry thread upon me in 'alf a minute. Got a five-pund note i' my pocket that will be hutterly ruined. Sarves me right, for bein' such a hass as take these 'ounds—vy wasn't I content with the glorious old Surrey and an occasional turn with the Cut-'em-downs? Well; I thinks this night will be the last of John Jorrocks. Best master of 'ounds wot ever was seen. 'Orrible termination to a hactive life; starved on a common—eat by wolves, or shepherds' dogs, which is much of a muchness as far as comfort's concerned. Why, even yon donkey would be 'shamed of such an end. There goes the vind with my 'at—lucky it's tied on," he added, trying to catch it as it dangled at his back, "or I should never have seen it no more. I'd give fifty punds to be back at 'Andley Cross— know no more where I am than if I was among the Bohea mountains —oh dear, 'ow it pours! I'd give two 'undred punds to be back at 'Andley Cross—yonder's a light, I do declare—*two* on 'em—come hup, 'oss, I say. The hanimal seems to have no sense! I'll lead you, you nasty hugly brute, for I do believe you'll brick my neck, or my back, or both, arter all"; so saying, Mr. Jorrocks clambered down, and getting on to the sheltered side of the animal proceeded to plunge and roll, and stagger and stumbled across the common, with the water churning in his great boots, in the direction of the distant lights.

After a good hour's roll about the open Downs, amid a most pelting, pitiless storm, our much-respected master at length neared the longed-for lights, which he had kept steadily in view, and found they proceeded from lamps at lodges on either side of handsome gates, betokening the entrance to a large demesne. Mounting his horse, he rode quickly through the gates, and trusting to the sound of Arterxerxes' hoofs to keeping the road, he jogged on in search of the mansion.

The Crest of Athelling Hill

G O R D O N   G R A N D

*Nearly every rider who has hunted looks back on one particu-
lar event which stands out in his mind as the best run of his or
her life. All these will feel themselves kindred spirits with the
hero of this moving tale.*

I stretched my muddy hunting boots to the library fire and leaned
back in Colonel Weatherford's massive leather chair set upon enjoying one of those tingling late-afternoon hours that come only to
those who have spent the day afield. The Colonel rang for tea, pulled
his chair close to the fire and we sat together in mellow yet un-
communicative companionship.

It had been a gray, sombering afternoon out on those big hills
of ours. For hour upon hour a snarling, unrelenting wind had hurried leaden clouds across a leaden sky; a day for foxes to lie close;
a day when the very thought of one's own reflection sobered one.
Nature had seemed to be battling against all forms of life as though
life were no concern of hers and every living thing sensed it and
sought the companionship of its kind.

I finally found myself speculating as to whether sportsmen who
spent much time afield were not prone to belittle the need of social
and family ties and place over-reliance on the friendliness of nature.
Perhaps bachelors who have crossed the halfway mark occasionally
feel this way on dreary late afternoons. I wondered whether Colonel
Weatherford had ever been assailed by such thoughts and looked
over at him. To my surprise he was sitting bolt upright in his chair

and gazing intently at a newly arrived English magazine. There was
an expression on his rugged face I had never thought to see there.
The usual mask of reserve had vanished and in its stead there was a
note of sadness and longing. Resting the magazine on his lap he
gazed into the fire a moment or two and then, as though reading my
thoughts, said, "Pendleton, I don't suppose any of us are quite
sufficient unto ourselves and certainly a snarling fox-hunting day
like this suggests that nature is not always a kindly, sympathetic
playfellow. Loneliness is a common heritage." He picked up the
magazine again, looked long and intently at whatever had so engrossed him and continued, "My thoughts have been very far away
during the last few minutes, for I have just relived the most memorable day of my life. It was a day to hounds." He settled back in his
chair, again rested the magazine on his knees and went on:

Forty years ago, in the days when old George Trevelyn was
Master, I was hunting down in Pennsylvania. One Saturday morning
towards the end of October we met a fixture known as the Dutch
Minister's schoolhouse and were about to move on to our first covert
when a girl whom no one seemed to know arrived at the Meet. She
asked for Trevelyn, and seemed distressed at finding he was not hunting. We were rather agog about her for she was turned out as only
one woman in a million can turn themselves out for the field, and
was mounted on a small, clean-bred brown mare of exquisite quality
with her mane painstakingly braided. In those days very few women
rode blood horses.

Hounds found almost immediately, fairly crashed out of covert
and went away. I was riding a thoroughbred horse called Gay
Minstrel by St. Gatien, the best conveyance across a big country I
have ever owned or ridden; the sort you confidently ask to do things
you would not attempt on the average horse. I was young and as
hard as nails, and so settled down to ride and enjoy the sport to the
full. In the turmoil of getting well away I entirely forgot our unknown visitor.

It was soon evident that we had unkenneled a good fox and had
found him well for he ran a surprisingly straight and purposeful line.

The Dutch Minister's schoolhouse lay close to our northern
boundary and we planned to draw and hunt towards home. The fox

planned otherwise. At the end of twenty minutes, in view of the pace and the straightness of our line, we had slipped quite out of our country and were feeling our way through the vastness of the State of Pennsylvania. Riding a straight line became more and more difficult yet there was no abatement in the speed hounds were running. The field melted away not so much from pace, for they were exceptionally mounted, but the fences were terrific, and in trying to avoid unjumpable places we were forever getting into farmyards or orchard lots from which there seemed no forward way out. Whenever during this scramble I looked back, the girl on the little brown mare was right in my "pocket" and I had navigated some rasping big fences.

I finally galloped down into a stretch of bottom land that I had never seen before. In front of me I saw a line of willows and then beyond them a dark stream far too wide to jump and on the far side, three feet from the bank, rose a five-board fence. It must be jumped, or jumped at from the bottom of the unknown stream. I pulled up. Behind me I heard the others turn away and disappear. But hounds were running.

I brought my horse down to a walk, took hold of his head, stepped him into the stream and started him for the fence. He refused. I turned him around. Hounds were streaming on. The music was faint now. I must be with them. I would ride at that fence for a fall. I heard the stamp of a horse's hoof. There stood the girl on the brown mare. "Go back," I called. She started for the fence. "Hold hard," I bellowed. As she passed me she smiled.

That little mare went down to the branch with her head loose, her ears forward, and her great dark eyes on what was in front of her. She landed in the water, took one stride and jumped for it.

(The Colonel took a breath. Then he leaned forward and tapped me on the knee.) In fifty years I have seen many horses hit many fences but never anything comparable with that. I'm not exaggerating when I say that from directly back of them where I stood the mare's legs appeared to be straight out to the off side, giving the impression of a horse lying on its side in the air. There was nothing between the girl and the ground and I expected to see her pinned to the earth. I kicked my feet out of the stirrups preparatory to running to her assistance, but by some mysterious means the mare worked her near front foot around and connected it with the ground. She then pitched forward on her head with such a force that the reins were jerked out of the girl's hands, but the blood of Eclipse fought on. The mare made a desperate scramble; gained her feet, pitched forward a second time, recovered, and was up and sailing on. I saw the girl gather her reins, stop the mare, pat her, and look back at me. I went at the fence with what little heart I had left, leaving the task to Gay Minstrel. As he landed in the stream with a great, bold stride, the water sprayed over us and I loved the horse for his high courage. He gathered himself and jumped, but as he took off I felt his hind feet slip and knew the unseen bottom had been treacherous to him. He cleared the fence in front but hit it a smashing blow behind and landed sprawling. A terrific lunge forward brought him up on his feet only again to pitch him on his head, but he was indomitable and refused to fall. When we finally recovered ourselves I had been astride every part of him from his ears to the root of his tail.

Upon rejoining my lone companion the smile I had been noticing was gone. She had an odd little way of quizzically puckering up her forehead suggestive of concern, and she now looked searchingly at me. "You should not have done it," I said. "But you led on," she answered. It was the first time I had heard her voice. As we galloped on in quest of hounds she was, indeed, one for a man to conjure about, for from the beautifully ironed silk hat to the barbous Mother Hubbard riding skirt of that era, the picture was perfect; I was at an impressionable age.

That fox ran two hours and thirty-five minutes and we had it alone. Never have I worked as I did that day to stay with hounds, and no horse I ever owned could have lived with Gay Minstrel that afternoon and gone the route; yet the little French mare pressed him to the very end. I have never seen a woman's hunter comparable with her.

There is a great difference between an old hunting country and one that has never been ridden over. If an unjumpable brook didn't stop us it would be a swamp. If we circumvented the swamp there would be a monstrous fence with a drop on to a country road or something equally trying. We had in-and-outs over farm lanes that were never intended to be jumped. If hounds checked we still had to keep galloping on to get to them. There was little chance to breathe our horses.

During all that memorable journey I never heard the mare lay a toe to a thing except the big fence. As we rattled along over fence after fence, I would look back to see them come over, and every fence further complicated my feelings. It is seldom one ever sees a horse and rider so perfectly attuned to each other.

We at last climbed a high upland country to which my memory often reverts. It was a scantily populated area of vast enclosures with pleasant, old-fashioned post-and-rail fences, and we galloped together mile after mile over well-nigh perfect turf, meeting little covert and no plow.

Towards the end a fresh wind sprang up and blew the scent about. This came as a godsend to our tired horses, for on the high, windswept knolls hounds would be brought to their noses to work out the line.

For some miles a heavily wooded ridge had been looming up ahead of us, for which our fox was evidently making. I knew that if hounds once entered so vast a tract of woods we would never get them out, and felt that I should try and stop them. They were not my hounds, even though I had been thinking and acting otherwise for the last two hours.

Of a sudden hounds burst into a new and clamorous cry. Gay Minstrel's head and ears came up, and I felt a tautness under the saddle. Then my arm was clutched. "Look! Look!" the girl said. I looked, and ahead of us hounds were running their sinking fox from view.

We killed under the leafless branches of a dead oak tree standing as a beacon for all the country round; an ancient hoary giant which had probably guided our fox on his last valiant run for the covert.

After removing the mask and brush I turned to my companion to make the presentation. She was standing with her back to hounds, and her silk hat dangling from its cord. The mare stood by with the reins over the pommel.

When I came with the trophies she turned away and said, "Please don't. Why must our glorious adventure have such an ending?" and walked on down the slope with the mare following her. She was squeezing a small, crumpled handkerchief in her hand.

Turning to the hounds, I threw the mask, put the brush in my pocket and led Gay Minstrel down to where she was sitting on a boulder; we sat together looking off over countless miles of rolling country to where our horizon met the sky. Below us a group of whitewashed cottages clustered about a church spire. High up on the ridge a farmer's deep-mouthed hound was cold trailing the long afternoon away.

I was recalled to consciousness by vaguely noticing hounds drifting off in groups of twos and threes. Reluctantly I arose and called them to me. I put my companion up and we started our long ride home. They said it was twenty-one miles back to the kennels. Hounds had reached that comfortable degree of sobriety where stray cats and house dogs cease to be of interest and so come comfortably along. The back country was peaceful and of spectral quiet after the turmoil of so long and hard a gallop; the lengthening years have never dimmed the beauty of that ride. We traversed countless country lanes ankle deep in fallen leaves where horses' feet made pleasant rustlings, and long maple-edged avenues into which red and golden leaves were ever filtering. I seemed unconscious of saddle or distance, for truly my fates were busily weaving that which no man may ever entirely cast off. Until then I had been so engrossed in myself and in games and sport that I knew naught of the heart. I knew now, however, that I was very much in love.

We rode on for some time in understanding silence and I was glad, for I knew not what to say that would not have sounded inconsequential. I had my first lesson that day in the eloquence of silence, and learned that conversation is strangled by chatter.

Then, in response to a question she told me of her home in Paris, and of a diminutive Warwickshire cottage where she stayed during the hunting seasons, and we drifted on to favorite authors, to stories that we often reread, to cherished verses, and we revisited quaint niches and corners of the Old World.

We came at last to a crossroad and asked a country girl to direct us. As we moved on, my companion said, "I once lost my way while hunting in France, and stood at a crossroad just as we have done. A little French child came by and without looking right or left made me a prim little curtsey and started to pass on. I asked my way; gave her a small coin for directing me, and, being curious, asked her what she would do with it. She looked down at the ground, made a little pile of white dust with her bare toes, looked up at me very solemnly, and said, 'A part for Mother of Jesus, a part for my own mother,' and then, with just the semblance of a smile, 'something food for me,' and walked on." How strange it is, Pendleton, that after so many years her simple little stories should linger on in my memory!

When we reached Lesser Windover we stopped to gaze at its diminutive cemetery, a quiet peaceful place surrounded by a low gray wall. Years ago some country person of imagination had planted a fringe of cedars along the north which had grown into a feathery reredos. While looking at it she said,

"Do you remember how gay the flowers are in Swiss cemeteries? I once climbed a hillside there to look at a particularly charming little walled cemetery, and said to an old guide who was making hay close by, 'There are more flowers in your cemeteries in Switzerland than in any I have ever seen, and they're wonderfully bright

and full of color. Your people must spend much time and work to
make them so beautiful.'

"Putting down his scythe he leaned over the wall with me
and, gazing at the flowers and simple white stones, said, 'It is because of them that we are here, and Mademoiselle, surely you must
know that to be here in Switzerland is good. That is why so many
flowers.' He went back to his haymaking and I to my carriage."

On Athelling Hill we turned our horses to look at the lights
flickering in the cottages of Afton Village below us and saw the
evening star in the east. She asked me where we were, and I said,
"On the crest of Athelling Hill."

She sat with her hands folded on her knee, the reins hanging
loose on the mare's neck. As we turned from looking at the star
our eyes met and I reached forward and took her hand, and we
gazed off over the great stretches of darkening country, while the
hounds stood patiently around us in a circle.

On the far side of the road stood the gaunt ruins of a Revolu-
tionary house with its crumbling chimneys silhouetted against the
deepening sky. We could see the outlines of sheep grazing in and
around the ruins, and out of the stillness I heard a soft and beautifully modulated voice saying:

> "Where the quiet-coloured end of evening smiles,
>   Miles and miles
> On the solitary pastures where our sheep
>   Half-asleep
> Tinkle homeward thro' the twilight, stray or stop
>   As they crop—
> Was the site of a city great and gay,
>   (so they say)."

She did not finish it, and I asked her if she remembered Browning's last verse, and the concluding line: she said yes, commenced
to recite it, and then hesitated and said, "Isn't it your turn? Isn't that
a man's verse?" So I continued:

> "In one year they sent a million fighters forth
>   South and North,
> And they built their gods a brazen pillar high
>   As the Sky,

Yet reserved a thousand chariots in full force—
    Gold, of course.
Oh heart! Oh blood that freezes, blood that burns!
    Earth's returns
For whole centuries of folly, noise and sin!
    Shut them in,
With their triumphs and their glories and the rest!
    Love is best.

"Do you think it is?" I asked. "I know it is," she answered. She looked at her imprisoned hand and then up at me and said, "I'm terribly tired and it's quieting and comforting to have you hold it. There are times when the beauty of outdoors seems more than one can stand. We have had the sparkle of midday, the glory of sunset, the twilight, and now the evening star and," she hesitated— "Browning. I don't believe we know what days like this do to us. I have crossed the best countries of England and Ireland, but never had such adventures as we have had. I have thought of you as my knight of old piloting me on and on to the fair fringes of the horizon, and to a knoll at the world's end. Perhaps the big fence took something out of me, for it was such a hopeless place, and my poor little mare seemed so unequal to it. Will you ever forget being down in the water and looking up at those bleak unfeeling boards?"

Eight o'clock was striking as we rode through Oldfield and turned into the lane that led to the Kennels. I helped her down and saw her to her waiting carriage and said good night. As I moved away she called me back, and I thought her voice had a catch in it. When I reached the carriage she said, "Oh, never mind, it's nothing. Thank you, good night again and good-bye," and turned her head away.

I surrendered the hounds to Will Simpson, the huntsman, told him briefly of the day, saw our overtired horses done up for the night and, cold and hungry as I was, I sat some time on the club porch fearing any interruption to my thoughts.

When I telephoned her hostess the next afternoon they said she had sailed that morning for her home in Paris.

I followed to urge my suit. When I reached Paris they said she had gone to Capri. There they told me she had gone to Rome.

On the way up to Rome, I read the announcement of her engagement to the Marquis of Oldwick.

I have never seen her, nor until today even a picture of her, since I helped her to dismount that night at the Kennels.

The Colonel handed me the magazine and I looked at the portrait of a wistfully beautiful woman in a black velvet gown. She had snow-white hair. "Eleanor, Marchioness of Oldwick."

Trail's End

MARGUERITE F. BAYLISS

Of all the hunts of fact or fiction, this is surely the longest! It is slightly difficult to believe that horses, men, hounds and quarry could have had a continuous hunt from the upper regions of the state of Virginia into the upper regions of the state of New Jersey, but, if nothing else, we get a picture of different types of hunting country and good descriptions of the work of the descendants of St. Hubert's black hounds.

Sunrise—Christmas morning. I awakened in a sparkling world. It had cleared, according to last night's promise in the wind and sky. The air was still. The earth, frozen just enough to travel on with ease, lay laved in leagues of crystal light.

I awakened with a feeling of light-heartedness. The evening returned to my mind, and our fireside gathering,—Madame Farleigh, Nellie, Hugo, Hovon, Mr. Brann, the doctor, and myself. With Laura lying near us, sable and shining. Ah, yes,—we were giving a hunt breakfast this morning, and Madame Farleigh was to announce to the County her daughter's wedding in a week to Bois Hugo Bolinvar. This was the morning of the Christmas Hunt, and the Bolinvars hoped to take the Duke of Hovon hunting; a hunt to long remember in after days in England. The best horses in the Cavalier County were fresh and fit this morning; the black hounds were tuned to perfection; they were ready for the run of their lives. My mulatto boy had lit the fire; it flamed brightly on the hearth. I sprang up.

157

While I was dressing, I saw a little horse, his furry winter coat lustrous from the brushes of the grooms, who had polished him while he breakfasted, his snowy mane and tail tossing gently with his movements, his big eyes darkly deer-like, his head up, his ears a-prick, walking lightfootedly across the fallow turf where the summer house of tragic memory had been. Little Middy was abroad, playing in the Christmas morning sun.

I dressed with care; I wanted to start, at least, right to the last button, for Jersey's fame in foreign parts; if I came home in muddy rags, no matter. I found Hugo, turned out on the same theory, this time for the fame of Ole Virginny; Hovon was with him, and it was not Hovon who ever travelled too hurriedly or too lightly to have with him the ingredients for a hunt's or a ball's sartorial pomp; they wore both, of course, in scarlet, Hovon with canary collar.

A third man was present, Colonel Morgan was talking to Hugo. He had made good his promise to come early. As I approached, I heard the Firebrand filly mentioned. Morgan detached himself from the confabulation, put a hand on each of my shoulders, and shook me a trifle, fondly. He said, "Hugo has been telling me about your conduct from first to last in this miserable mix-up. It is what I should have expected of you, Dev. I was an admirer of your father, the first Devereux Bolinvar, in the old days. And you are his son, through and through."

I was both pleased and confused. "Call him off, Hugo," I implored. "Why do you stand there like a dolt, doing nothing to rescue me? Although I admit, Colonel Morgan, it makes me happy to be compared favorably with my dear father, whose foremost admirer I am myself."

"A wonderful thing to be an admirer of one's father," Hugo said sadly. "You make me jealous, Dev."

"Oh, damn!" I sighed. "I've managed to be tactless. I'm sorry, Hugo."

"Never mind," said Hugo, with a charming smile, "I have a certain claim upon your father, who was my next closest kinsman."

Morgan put one arm around me, and the other arm around Hugo, and drew us together and close to him. "Let an old school-fellow of both your fathers give you his blessing and his congratulations on this Christmas Day," he said. "For yourselves, I don't know which of you is more dear to me."

Once, when I spoke of Colonel Morgan, did I not say that I thought there was nothing half-hearted about his good-heartedness? Time, and acquaintance with him, had verified my opinion in that first meeting.

Before nine o'clock, the hall and the dining room were thronged, and the grounds were filled with coaches, gigs, and saddles horses. The driveways rang with hoofbeats, the rooms rang with laughter. Glasses clinked, toasts and greetings flowed on every side. All the people Hugo had interviewed yesterday were present, and all the mutual friends they had been able to annex in the interval. Everybody who had been at the hall was there. Everybody made cordial speeches, everybody drank to the bride. Nine o'clock came and went, the hunt breakfast, and the wedding announcement.

Madame Farleigh and Nellie were dressed for riding; they, and the Misses Selina, Lois, and Ada, and a fifteen-year-old Miss Diana, from the Bedloe party, the latter beginning young to live up to her name, were going to honor us with their presence in the field.

Morgan was telling about the mare he was riding today. She was a new hunter, lately brought up from Tennessee. Her name was Copper Queen, her sire a Copperbottom stallion. We had an argument about her because of her dam.

"You say her dam is out of the dam of the racehorse Potomac?" Hugo remarked. "Tell you now, Morgan, she won't go all the way with the four-milers, if we have a long run and a fast one."

"Why not? Potomac was a bang-up four-miler. You know he was. Why not his dam's granddaughter, by a Copperbottom horse?"

"In the first place, the Copperbottom horse has probably got a soft spot in his dam's line; I never heard of a Copperbottom yet that could show all six crosses, authenticated. But pass that, the Copperbottom stock deserves its fame. As for what we know about Potomac here in Virginia—we know that he was a freak. He had speed, he got it from Diomed. Anything by Diomed could run. Potomac couldn't breed speed. He was a disaster in the stud. He was mated with a lot of the best mares in Virginia, for the sake of his sire-line and his turf record, and he never got a really good one. His dam, your mare's second dam, was nothing but a cold-blooded cart mare. I warn you, don't bank on anything with blood of Potomac's dam close up."

"This is a grand looking mare," Morgan insisted. "Look at her, when we go out. You never heard of a Copperbottom that wasn't tophole, did you?"

"No," Hugo conceded, "I never did. But I don't believe that any horse with cart-horse blood inside three crosses will stand an extreme test with such horses as Rupert and Agrippa."

"I know. That's always been your belief, Hugo. Yet, some of us contrive to hunt a whole lot on horses not quite bred for Epsom Downs, or the Metairie Course. That sort are all right for you and Dev, but at my age I'll wager Copper Queen will stay in as long as I can."

Colfax and Bedloe, carrying their goblets, were edging their way through the merrymakers to a window which overlooked the park toward the highway. Something outside had attracted their notice.

"Hey, boys," the doctor hailed, as he passed us, "that's my Jed comin', ridin' bareback on old Sue, as if he thinks he's a Bolinvar himself. Look at my old mare leg it! We'd better head for outdoors, and meet him."

We followed the doctor, who pushed a path through the people, and got outside. The youthful darkey was tearing toward the house, twisting in and out among the terriers, hounds, horses, grooms, mounted and dismounted huntsmen, vehicles and loose pickaninnies, that obstructed his passage.

"Hi, Jed! This way! Here I am!" the doctor shouted. The boy kicked his steed in the ribs, and rushed to the front steps, where his master awaited him. Hugo, Bedloe and I were near him.

"Somebody dyin'?" Colfax inquired. "Betsy and the chaise are round by the stable; run fetch 'em."

"Marse Doctah! Hit ain't folks dying! hit's Prince, an' he done daid a'ready! De Fox just kilt him, an' Sukey, she tole me to run fo' you, an' Marse Hugo, and Marse Debereux, an' de houn's."

While the boy was still pouring out his message, Hugo was in action. He darted into the hall, where Mr. Brann was, and said to that surprised gentleman, "We are going after the Colfax Fox. You are appointed deputy host until we return."

He stopped one instant beside Nellie. "You heard what I said to Mr. Brann—expect us back when you see us. Good-bye."

He rejoined me. "Round up the foxhunters, Dev. Collect those who really amount to something to ride, and tell them what's up. I'll have the hounds and horses here by the time you've done it."

He was gone.

No need to tell Bedloe, he was present. He, too, began to seek riding cracks. I found Hovon, and Morgan, and a couple of other veterans; Bedloe came with two or three. We gathered at the front steps, in the frosty radiance of the morning. It was ten o'clock.

Bedloe mounted his horse, which he had ridden alongside the coach that brought the ladies from his house, except the gay young ladies who had ridden with him. Morgan got his mare, the yellow roan from Tennessee. As her blankets came off, she shone like gilt, and his confidence in her was easy to understand; but, even in our excitement, I looked her over sharply, and I did not entirely share his view that she was a grand one; there was a rounded prettiness about her that I distrusted.

A rushing cavalcade was on the driveway, coming from the stables. Hugo, and Adonis, and four huntsmen, and some led horses, and a pack of hounds were galloping up. Hugo rode Tirade, and led Agrippa; Adonis rode a breedy bay that was a favorite with him, and led Rupert. They slowed down; they did not stop. We sprang on, and sent the horses into the gallop again from the half-halt. Hovon slapped Agrippa's crest.

"Good horse," he said enthusiastically. "Do you remember me, sir?" Agrippa did, and with approval; he cocked his ears in answer to the hand and the voice, even while he was striking his stride.

Then we did not know it, but two of the trio of great hunters that Hugo and Hovon and I were riding were passing through the park for the last time; they did not return.

Out on the highway, we made the most of "hunting pace," we went to the doctor's house in a thunder of hoofs, the hounds at speed to keep with us. Bedloe wiped his brow as we turned in at the entrance.

"Whew!" he muttered. "I feel as if I have been in a horse race already. If you Bolinvars think you are going to take me far at this rate, you are much mistaken."

I looked behind us. Just coming into view on the road was a chaise, drawn by a wildly galloping sorrel nag, flecks and clods of kicked-loose road-dirt flying from hoofs and wheels. Dr. Colfax leaned over the dashboard larruping Betsy's tail with the ends of the lines. Whether or why, he meant to get home in time to see the black hounds take the trail of his fox friend.

Sukey met us, agitated, important, and calling upon us and high heaven with flattering impartiality. The mangled carcass of the shepherd dog attested her impossible story.

"Ah was right hyar in de kitchen do', jest comin' out to gib de peelin's to de pig, an' de Lawd dun show me de Ole Evil One, shaped jes' lik' a big, big fox, an' po' Prince runnin' to git home afore him. But hit wan't no use, he got kotched, an' Ah shut de do' an' hollered."

"Did you see where it went, after it killed the dog?" we asked her.

"No, sah. Ah didn't feel no call to look, sah. Ah jest hopin' dat hit didn't kotch sight ob me, an' bust right in de kitchen windah to git me. Dat no common fox, Marse Hugo."

"Evidently," Hugo agreed, with his usual cool sarcasm. "Do you know where it came from?"

"By hit's looks, say, hit come right out'n de brimstone pit."

Having a trail from that point, we started from the body of Prince, whose judgment was indubitably vindicated, for him, untimely. Sukey had a hit-and-miss idea of the direction from which Prince had come in his flight for refuge, and along that line we sent the hounds.

The hounds—those that Hugo called out of the kennel yard in the tumultuous departure—I noted them as they pressed forward. Three of the Trojans were here: Trailmaster, and Tireless, and Truthful. An even dozen of the black hounds were defiling past me —Lead, and Laura, and their sons Faust and Fatal, and Ranger IV, and Basso, and Stickley, and Shadow, and Speedwell, and Clinker, and Windhound, and Old Fire and Water. One more hound went with them, little, pedigreeless, Joseph in his coat of many colors.

Trailmaster knew the scent; his hair bristled when he found it. Lead looked up at Hugo and Adonis inquiringly. His noble, golden-brown eyes scanned their faces with human interrogation. This was a strange beast, to whose trail they had come; were the master and the huntsmen sure that they knew what they wanted? They were sure; they urged him on. Lead poked through the frozen grass a few yards, tacking slightly, snuffing vigorously, his long ears flopped forward in massy folds. He glanced once more at Hugo, to be positive that he was acting under orders, and sent his divine roar resounding across the Virginia hunting fields. The others followed him. The solo swelled into a chorus. The black hounds were on the line.

Just because he was an artist with the horn, and loved the chase's ancient melodies, Adonis raised his circular, sweet-toned copper horn, and sent a message "Gone away! Gone away!" floating with the wind for any belated member of our breakfast party who might have a second thought about riding with us.

As we passed the doctor, sitting in his chaise behind the blown but interested Betsy, where he had driven all the way into the kitchen dooryard, Hugo called, "Coming doctor? Will you try your luck in your Elijah's chariot?"

The doctor shook his head. "I'll be here waitin' fur you when you get back. Waitin' fur his head, to hang above my mantelpiece, as you promised me. Good luck to you, good luck."

"Go back and take care of those we left behind, who may feel like having a hunt for a conventional fox," Hugo entreated him, riding slowly by. "There are plenty of plain, everyday foxes in Virginia, and plenty of hounds and horses and huntsmen at home. See that everyone has a good time. Mr. Brann will help you."

For, from the minute we struck this trail, we were resolved not to leave it, or to be shaken from it, until we came to the end of it, and the maker of it—somewhere—sometime.

During the next half hour, in disorderly snatches of conversation, we gave Hovon an account of the wonderful Colfax Fox. He, totally unbelieving, shouted with laughter. "If you'd told me this last night at midnight, after all those wassails, I'd understand," he jeered.

We expected raking badinage from Hovon when we assumed responsibility for the existence of such an animal, and we patiently made the best of it for miles while we got it. All the while, our course was north of east; counting the huntsmen, there were twelve

riders at the start, all picked horsemen. From the beginning, Hugo
and I nursed our horses, riding them with all the skill we had, saving them, conserving their nerve force. This was not the time for
neck-or-nothing going. For all we knew, the Colfax Fox had come
from the brimstone pit, and we might have to ride there if he
headed for home.

Copper Queen was quick of foot, and always on the bit, but she
did not pull. She had pace, and she could carry weight. She was
both temperate and free, a rare combination, precious when found.
She was bold, she would jump anything. Hovon watched her ap-
praisingly. Presently, he said, "Hugo, you're a great judge of a
horse, but it looks to me as if you may have slipped a bit about
that mare. I don't know much about the stock you were discussing,
but the roan mare looks like a good 'un to me."

"Oh, there's enough Copperbottom in her to make a horse of
her," Hugo replied. "It is her descent from Potomac's dam that I
don't like. I wouldn't give that blood barn room. Don't bet on it,
Basil, don't bet on it."

Certainly, she went like a first flight hunter. But my instinct
for horses warned me that Hugo was on the right track. A strain of
cart-horse blood had taken the racehorse finish out of her. Perhaps,
since so wise a critic as Hovon was disposed to give her the benefit
of the doubt, it was my knowledge of the mare-line behind her
that implanted my misgivings. On performance, she was showing
them unjustified.

We plodded north by northeast. At times, the hounds were
very slow, although the scent seemed strong; groping for their line,
which often lay on exposed ridges, as if the wily layer had counted
on its dissipation by the wintry winds that whipped them, and had
avoided the hollows and the lowlands where scent hung longer in
the still air. Once, the hounds did a good deal of tacking, apparently
dissatisfied with the turnings of the trail. We were close to them at
all times, and we rode up then to encourage them; but they were
satisfied before we reached them, and went on. Hugo and I recalled the trails laid over trails the night we had run the Colfax Fox
in November, and we wondered if the hounds, this time, had cor-
rectly unravelled a similar booby-trap. It looked that way. They
gave tongue confidently, and the course seemed right.

Like a self-proving mathematical equation, the fact that they were running it steadily after miles proved that they had found the true line at the check. League by league, we passed through our familiar hunting country, where Hugo and I had ridden together while nature grew gorgeous around us and then dun and azure. The sun climbed the sky. Noon came and went. We entered the regions where I had not been before, and rode through terrain strange to me, and no longer intimate in every yard to the Virginians; we were beyond the boundaries of the home hunts. A river glistened across our course. We had reached to Potomac.

The hounds were swimming, streaming before us like onleading banners. While we watched from the shore, Lead and a few others clambered up the farther bank, and began to cast for the trail. We waited, absorbed in their quest. Lead's incomparable voice recrossed the river to us; he had it. The hounds went on.

"At my time of life, I can treat my bones better than by immersing them in that December river," Bedloe announced. "Good luck to you, and good-bye."

Both of the sportsmen who had joined our regular party returned with Bedloe for Christmas dinner, and one of our huntsmen, whose horse was tiring, went home with them. In the river, another huntsman had trouble with his hunter and had to turn back. The two remaining huntsmen, Adonis, and the gentlemen of the hunt— Morgan, Hovon, Hugo and I,—rode out of the Potomac into Maryland.

The Colfax Fox, then, must have been not far ahead of us. He had laid a shifty trail in our own hunting country, calculated to lose us; and he had not lost us. He had resorted to a wide river, believing that his enemies the hounds could not, or would not, follow him beyond it. He must have been, when we were landing, where he could hear the swelling baying of the black hounds, telling him that they had crossed where he had crossed, were coming on his line.

Within a mile from the river, the style of the hunt underwent an alteration; the pace increased, and increased. The Colfax Fox was trying to outfoot the black hounds, to leave them by his speed. It suited the hounds. They had speed themselves. The eyes of the Trojans glistened with fierce lights. The cry of the black hounds was a happy antiphony. They drove on, and drove on.

Hovon stopped chaffing us. He was beginning to realize that, whatever our quarry was, it was something out of the ordinary to chase. He was riding King Agrippa to hold his powers; the Duke of Hovon meant to go where the Bolinvars went. And the Bolinvars meant to follow as far as hounds could lead them, as far as hunters could carry them, until a kill or until they saw the Colfax Fox spring skyward in a pillar of fire or vanish into the earth in an earthquake clap.

Copper Queen came on. She was visibly tiring, but she was steady; Morgan had a right to be pleased with her.

But both of the under-huntsmen quit. Later, the good bay Adonis rode struck the top bar of a rail fence and hurt his knee. Adonis pulled up and got off. Hugo rode over to him, they looked at the horse briefly, they spoke together a moment, and Adonis regretfully handed Hugo his big, circular horn. We left him standing beside the injured horse. Morgan, and Hovon, and Hugo and I went on.

The pace eased again. We were glad of it, for the sake of the horses; we had no idea how far they might have to go. The shadows tilted from the westward, and the sun lowered; we were riding away from the sunset into the northeast by east. Christmas Day was waning. The land of our hegira was cultivated farming country, but it had abundant woodland cover for wild animals; we often had long views of beautiful rural reaches. From one hilltop, higher than most of its fellows, we could look across many miles to the rolling landscape; and in the distance, on our right, we saw the smoke and the spires of a city.

Morgan's mare was near the end. She travelled with sagging head. She stumbled when she changed gaits. She ticked dangerously at jumps. Morgan was over-riding her now. He had been mistaken when he estimated that she could stay in as long as he could. In his keenness, his years yielded; he was urging her when he should have been checking her.

Had it not been for the respite of pace, she could not have held on as long as she did; after we had passed out of sight of the far-off city, she stopped. She was done. She was ridden to a standstill. Morgan dismounted. We all halted and alighted. The hounds were out of sight ahead, their blending voices came back to us in a chant worthy of any monastery's choir. They were driving on.

We inspected the horses and took stock of the situation. Hovon had nothing to say. He loosened Agrippa's girth the minute he reached the ground, and while we held council, he was walking the big bay gently in circles. He was thinking that Agrippa, with his two hundred up, had the heavy end of the run. What he was thinking about the Colfax Fox he kept to himself.

Copper Queen looked ready to drop in her tracks. A queer thing struck us, as we surveyed her. The rounded prettiness had deserted her, and the class of Copperbottom too; in her extremity of fatigue, her very type had changed. She looked like a cold-blooded mare. Morgan stared at her.

"Lord," he muttered, "she looks like Potomac's dam! Never noticed the least resemblance before—strange. But I see it now, plain enough. Hugo, when somebody fools you about a horse, show him to me, will you?"

But she had done well. She had lasted for hours, some of them at forced pace. A yellow roan in Tennessee had sent her half way across the state of Maryland before the blood of her mother stopped her. So much had Copperbottom done.

Hugo made a comprehensive gesture toward the five counties she had hunted in, and the gesture was a salute to Copper Queen. "The next thing is to get home with her. For the present, whiskey will help. You'd better find a tavern, and lay over until tomorrow."

Morgan uncorked his flask and began to teach Copper Queen to take swigs from it. "Have you any money?" Hugo inquired practically.

Morgan explored his pockets. He carried some assorted silver, for the benefit of a hostler or a boy who might serve him while he was out; that was all. Both Hugo and I had had the foresight to put some bills in our coats when we were dressing in the morning; we supplied the Colonel, and he dolefully bade us farewell. The Duke, Hugo and I remounted, and sought the hounds.

They had gone on out of hearing, and twilight was upon us. Hugo and I rode side by side, and continued our confab. The hunt breakfast seemed a long, long way behind us, in miles and in time. The horses had had nothing to eat since the morning feeding. The prospect for being out until far into the night was first class. We considered the advisability of halting at the first decent inn we could locate, baiting the horses, and having a quick meal. Hovon took no part in the powwow. He was attending strictly to his hunting.

"Come on, Basil," I petitioned him, "aren't you hungry? Do you vote for beef and potatoes wherever we can find them?"

He glanced at me humorously. "Well—if you Yankees stop for meals, when you're hunting on a continental scale—anything that's customary—"

"We've lost hounds anyhow," Hugo said philosophically. "We can get back with them as easily in forty minutes as in twenty; we might as well stop."

So we pulled into the tavern yard at a hamlet near our course, and gave the horses in charge of the stablemen with promises of liberal reward for the best possible feeding and grooming in a short time. In the tavern we ate a meal to make an epicure shudder, one selected for its substance, and consumed without one moment's unnecessary delay. We filled our flasks and saddle wallets; we had left home with whiskey, but we had started so suddenly that sandwiches had not been provided, and we got them here. We also had the head hostler fetch us six quarts of oats for each of the horses, in small sacks which could be conveniently attached to the saddles; the weight was insignificant, and we thought it wise to anticipate the possibility of wanting to feed the hunters again before we had access to another tavern.

While the oat bags were being fastened, Hugo said to the man, "Less than ten miles back, from a hilltop, we saw a large town in the southeast. Can you tell us what it was?"

The stableman pondered our position, and the direction. "That'd be Baltimore," he hazarded.

The brief rest, the grain and the rubbing brought the horses out in fine fettle. They looked ready for anything as we mounted. The moon was tinging the dusk with elfin gold dust. The night would be ideal; it was a coon-hunting night: windless, cold, and golden.

We soon met a farmer jogging along the road in a rumbling wagon; we stopped him and asked him if he could give us tidings of our hounds.

"Was they yourn?" he queried, with interest. "I seen them, a while ago, runnin' that way," pointing to the northeast, "and after I couldn't see 'em, I heard 'em, keepin' on the same way."

We thanked him, and pressed into the northeast. Following roads that went our way as much as possible, to favor the horses, we made good time at a steady pace, but in an hour we heard no back-floating notes from the music we knew the black hounds were pouring around their passage, if all was well. The moon soared into nocturnal majesty, the world, early to bed in the country, went to sleep. Another half hour, still the silent night, giving back only the ringing hoofs of the horses, no voice of hound upon it. We were growing anxious. As Hugo had remarked, great Lead could cast his bell-canto half way across a Shire. Where was he? Why did he not speak? Where was Basso's noble peal? Where were the bells of Laura's throat? Where the heaviest boom in all the pack, the *de profundis* of Old Fire and Water?

We found out. We rode abruptly out of a thicket-fringed pasture upon the shore of a broad and shining water, so unexpectedly that the horses shied at the sight of it, almost marching headlong into it before we saw it. We stopped.

It was a large river, darkling in the shadows, blazing in the moonbeams, bordered by bush-grown banks that hid it from wayfarers who did not know it was there. We sat on the horses and listened. Only the rippling of the water, the murmuring of the nightwind. Had the hunt come this way? Had the Colfax Fox crossed this shining flood? Had our hounds crossed too? If so, they must be far, far ahead, for we heard them not.

After a short pause, Hugo raised the horn, and blew a signal on it; following immediately with a call— "Lead! Lead! Lead!"

Far down the river, far across the flood, a glorious hound voice replied. Lead had heard the horn, and recognized it; had heard the voice of his master, and answered it. We turned downstream, and rode as rapidly as we could through the pastures toward the point which we judged to be opposite the place from which Lead had spoken to us. We were close to the place when the silence was broken by a cry of discovery on the other shore. Immediately, the rest of the hounds joined in, all the flutes and bugles going. Away they went, bells and baritones. They were running due north, a variation in the course which we were quick to note; so far, we had come all the way from Loudoun County on a northeasterly line.

The undertaking next in order was aquatic. We had no idea whether a bridge spanned this river within fifty miles of us. Nor had we any ideas about its identity. Naturally, Hovon could not be expected to know anything about it; and it was a revelation to Hugo and me that such a body of water could be found in that part of the United States.

"By the looks of it, it might be the Mississippi," Hugo remarked, "but we can't have got that far, and anyhow, the Father of Waters is not in this direction."

As a matter of fact, it was the Susquehanna, but we had not realized that it was so big, and this unpreparedness deceived us when we met it. We learned, afterward, that we had encountered it at an exceptionally wide section.

The horses were used to swimming, with or without riders, and we had the hunting habit of fording ordinary streams as they came, on horseback. There was nothing to be gained by stripping for the crossing, for it would take us nearly an hour to construct a raft of branches which might ferry the saddles and our clothing over without wetting; we did not want to leave hounds so long. We discussed this, and decided to go on. The night was cold, but not cruelly cold, and since we were constantly in motion the sousing would not hurt us. So we swam the Susquehanna, with only minor adventures, quite as successfully as if we had known its name.

While we were in the river, and when we first emerged, we could hear the baying hounds, going north. Presently, the music stopped, a few minutes of silence ensued, then a tentative cry, then the baying in full volume again, once more bearing into the northeast.

Putting together the details of the past two hours, we could reconstruct the developments of the hunt almost as accurately as if we had witnessed them. A bold beast, and a worried one, the Colfax Fox had resorted to the wide waters a second time. This time, he was not so sure that the hounds that had followed him over the Potomac would not cross a broad river to run him. He had left a trappy trail for them to puzzle over. He had entered the river and descended with the current for a mile or more before he came ashore, leaving the two ends of his trail widely separated by a stretch of river that ought to stop hounds then and there.

But, he did not know the wise and tenacious black hounds; he did not know the ways of Lead and Laura and Old Fire and Water. He knew nothing about Shadow, who came right on forever. And Speedwell, the fleet and staunch.

Having satisfied themselves that he really had gone over, they went over too. Not finding his trail where they landed, they had fallen into the silence which had fretted us, while they hunted for the line, probably up the river as well as down. As they were hounds who had little to say except when they had something to say, we were not guided by their voices while this quest was in progress.

Evidently the Fox had in mind a particular route, to which he wanted to adhere; he ran north upon his exit from the water until he was abreast this position, then he turned at an angle and resumed his northeasterly line. The hounds had overrun his line where he turned, caught themselves, interrupting their music, circled, picked him up on the northeasterly line, and were driving on.

We were headed into the northeast. Before us, the black hounds were on their way to Kingdom Come, singing the song of the trail. The horses pricked their ears, and of their own volition regulated their speed to keep within earshot of hounds, faster or slower as they set the pace. With the curious knack of horses on a long road, they had settled down to a pilgrimage of unknown duration; probably, they understood the proceedings as well as we did; they acted as if they did.

The moon stayed with us until long past midnight. Some of the time, we rode through fertile farming country, where the going was good, and the visibility so excellent that we caught occasional glimpses of the pack, a dark blotch upon the luminescent landscape, moving steadily from brake to brake, through vale after vale, over ridge after ridge, in and out of woodlots, splashing through brooks and meadow water courses, often slowly, advancing yard by yard, with earnest conference about the trail, but never wholly stopping, and ceaselessly sending their anthem to meet its returning echoes. Oh, Hugo and I were satisfied with the way our black breed was hunting the Colfax Fox; glued to his line, never off it, never weary.

Between the setting of the moon and the rising of the sun, we rode a pearly half-light, night-time and tinted by the receding moonlight and the crescendent sunlight. It was beautiful, but it was a vexatious dimness for us poor wayfarers, reducing us to a laggard progress, unable to see what we were doing. So we chose this time to halt, to rest and feed the horses, and to eat our sandwiches. We thought that in this region of substantial farms and villages we should get news of the hounds at a barn or a cross-roads tavern, if they went beyond our hearing while we stopped.

For we were careful of the horses. They needed now and then a pause, a meal and a drink, as we did ourselves. We expected them to stick to this hunt as far as the hounds did, but not on the same terms. The canine carnivore is designed by nature to fast indefinitely and to eat erratically; not so the horses, for them, small feeds often. The hunters were taking drinks from brooks and creeks whenever they pleased; we offered them grain without hesitation, they were not heated, the cool weather and the moderate pace prevented that. We unsaddled them and gave them their oats.

We loafed near them, drinking water and whiskey, and eating the bread and beef we had brought from the Maryland tavern. We felt quite sure that we must be in the State of Pennsylvania, on the theory that Pennsylvania extended for hundreds of miles in all directions above the state of Maryland, and there was nothing else in that part of the world. We decided to ask the first people we saw to tell us where we were; the Colfax Fox, of course, was laying a trail that avoided inhabited places, so that we passed farms and hamlets widely and got little chance to ascertain our position.

"What is next, north of Pennsylvania?" Hovon asked.

"York State," we told him.

"Good hunting country?" from Hovon, tersely.

"Topping. Superb scenery, too."

"Sounds good," said Hovon.

After a while, when the cry of the hounds began to grow very faint, the horses fidgeted and looked after their distant comrades so interestedly, that we took the hint, and saddled them and rode on.

We passed out of the populated agricultural region sooner than we had expected to, doubtless by arrangement of the Fox; in midforenoon we were having a hunt like a hunt in the Black Forest, heavy timberlands were on all sides of us, and the hounds were often out of sight when they were only a short way ahead of us. We struggled through wretched going for three hours, then we got out of the timber, and presently to another river. It was by no means as large as the first one, and although its current was rapid in places, it was not very deep. We had reason to be thankful for these favors of fortune, for the banks of the river proved to be the scene of a booby-trap as neat as any ever laid for hounds to unwind.

The hounds had crossed when we arrived, we saw them on the other bank diligently snuffing for the spot where the Colfax Fox had left the water. Since they were getting along nicely by themselves, we let the horses stand, resting, while we watched the hounds and awaited their report. They scouted up the river until they were out of view, then they came back and hunted down the river a long way. Then they began a system of wide casting inland from the

bank, thinking that the Fox might have tried to get back to his northeasterly route farther on, as he had done before, and they might be able to strike his line without actually getting the end of it at the river bank. But their idea did not work; they cast in vain.

Although they did not need us, we decided to go to their assistance, or at least to their aid and comfort mentally. We pulled up our girths, and forded the river. We unsaddled the horses and turned them loose to browse on frozen grass, and have a roll if they wanted it; we explored the edge of the water for footprints, or other telltale signs where the Fox might have come out. The day was mild and pleasant, and the sun, past the meridian, had thawed the ground so that the margins of the river were muddy and would take impressions of paws. We did this thoroughly, and the hounds stuck to it patiently with their good noses; but we found no footprint, and they found no scent.

"I'm sincerely alarmed," Hugo said. "I fear that he took to the pillar of fire somewhere near here. The scent is getting stale, by this time—if he left a scent."

I did not blame him. I was on the verge of going over to the Devilists myself. Hovon looked thoughtfully across the river. He said slowly, "If he took the pillar of fire, he did so in the stream. The hounds ran him right to the water on that side. We saw them on the line to that point. So he left an earthly line that far."

The inferences were interesting, but somehow vague. We felt as if we had a clue, but did not know precisely what to do with it.

"Let's cross the river again," I proposed, "and try on the original bank. If he applied his bright ideas between the end of the trail on that bank and this bank, the evidence must be either where the trail stops or in the water itself."

We did not know what we were going to do on the first bank of the river, but there being nothing whatever to be done where we were, we called the horses, replaced the tack, assembled the hounds, some of whom were casting a long way from the river, and the whole party reforded to the first shore.

"We might as well do this systematically," said Hugo. "Let's split the pack. I take one section and go up the bank for a mile, you and Hovon take the other part of the pack, and follow the river down for a mile. When we think we have gone that distance we will return to within a quarter of a mile of the trail we have, and turn parallel to it, and to each other, one pack on each side of it.

"He certainly did not turn around in the river, come out on the trail he went in, and run on his back trail; if he had tried that, we should have encountered him. If he came out at a new point on this bank, we will catch it when we go up and down the bank. If he ran a little way on his back trail, and jumped it, we will pick up his line when we cast back parallel to the trail."

It was a good program, and we acted upon it. Hovon and I were turning, after a fruitless mile, to get back toward Hugo and the paralleling of the back-trail, when we heard—blessed sound—Lead's grand clarion. He had it. And then the horn, calling, "Gone away!"

We galloped across at an angle, guided by the baying, joined Hugo, and threw in our pack with his: the reunited pack went crying on the trail again. And we were going back to Virginia. Hugo gave us a hasty account of the trail finding.

"I have not figured out exactly the moves the Fox made," he said. "Off-hand, it looks rather as though he has the gift of making himself double when he wishes. The hounds struck a second trail, like the first one going into the river, a half mile upstream."

I studied this as we rode. We seemed to be on a bona fide line, some half mile off the one going in the opposite direction. Presently, I said, "How is this for what he did: he made use of the next big stream he reached, swimming, or trotting in the edge, up the river, in the water, until he reached a point he considered a safe distance from his original line; then, he came out of the river on the same bank from which he entered it; the trail you found is his place of exit. All he has to do now is to return to Colfax's back fields, leaving the hounds to hunt for his trail on the north bank of this river, where they naturally suppose it must be, until they are tired of it, and the one he is laying now is too cold to follow, if the hounds ever find it, which he considers unlikely."

"That sounds right," Hugo agreed readily. "It is much better than my first thought, that the second trail also entered the river. At least, it defers the hour when we succumb to Ole-Evil-One-ism. I catch at any straw which saves me from that."

Hovon remarked, "I have great respect for a brute that can

devise such a scheme. The Colfax Fox must be an intellectual animal."

"If he is a wolf, as we suppose, he is," I replied. "A fox is shrewd, but let me tell you, Basil, one of these big wolves is shrewder; and commonly shrewder than a man. A wolf has out-and-out brain power. Intellectual is the very word for him."

"This illustrates the drawbacks of hunting a wolf with foxhounds," Hugo added. "Wolfhounds, that hunt by air scent more than by ground scent, would detect the passage of a wolf on a parallel backtrack only a half mile distant. Unless the wind conditions were advantageous to the wolf. Whereas, these hounds are ground trailers of the bloodhound type, and under favoring circumstances, their quarry might pass them within yards, unseen."

"I never saw anything but bloodhounds run like them," Hovon said, "they never lift their noses off their line. They never look to right or left, or ahead or behind. Nothing rattles them, and nothing discourages them, and apparently a line never gets so stale that they can't work along on it. I haven't a doubt that they would have got on this same line eventually without human help."

"It is certain that they have a much stronger sense of smell than the Old Southern Hound breeds have," I said. "They require less scent. Remember that they, and their relatives the bloodhounds, are invincible on the trail of quarry far harder to scent than fox. And, I've repeatedly seen my hounds running glued to the line, never raising their eyes to look at something they had run down and were closing on within plain view in front of them. They don't finish with high heads on a breast-high scent as the Old Southern Hound types do."

"You'd think they'd run under the scent, when they get so close," Hovon observed.

"Apparently, enough scent sinks to satisfy them," Hugo answered. "They have some system of their own; they know when they are running up on the quarry, if they don't look up to see him."

"It's manifest," Hovon said, "that you can't lift these hounds and run around the country with them, just to cut a dash, as some of our professional huntsmen do at home. I'd like to see 'em! True, they did come along agreeably when you proposed to them that they re-try on this side; but they weren't settled on a line. I'd have to see you force one, let alone a pack, off his line before I'd believe it could be done."

"As a rule, it's not a strikingly successful experiment," Hugo assented. "You can clutch one, if you can catch him, by the loose skin of his neck, and hang on for dear life. If you can hold him, you can; he won't bite you. He won't notice you until you grab him, he howls mournfully when you do, and the minute you let go, or your arms weaken from fatigue and you lose him, he picks up his line within an inch of where he dropped it, and goes on."

We and the hounds had now gone some five or six miles toward Virginia; all at once the pace increased, and the course changed. The hounds began to bear to the left, swinging in a semi-circle; for minutes together they continued this sweeping curving.

"What now?" Basil mused.

We were going almost due east, and going fast. The hounds sang enthusiastically as they drove on. It was not long before we re-entered country we recognized as that through which we had passed when approaching the river; and presently we rode down to its bank for the second time virtually at the same spot where we had first forded.

We checked, jumped off, and stood beside the horses silently speculating what the Colfax Fox had done to us this time. Hugo and I were more confounded than Hovon was, for he, less familiar with the black hounds, dallied with the idea that they had made a mistake somewhere and got back onto the original line to the river. But we knew better. If the hounds had come here again, the Fox had come here again before them. These hounds were simply following the Colfax Fox; no more and no less.

Moreover, they were in haste. In their opinion, speed was worth while. They did not hesitate, but plunged into the river and swam over. We waited, to learn what they reported from the other shore. Neither was it a tedious wait. The hounds found a trail upon landing, where positively no trail had been on the previous occasion. Their matched chimes rang back to us; they vanished, driving on.

We forded the river for the third time, and settled down in the wake of the hound-cry. As we rode, we grappled with the tactics; finally, we concluded that this was what had happened:

The Colfax Fox, confident that he had shaken off the hounds by his manoeuvre at the river, and perhaps flagging and indisposed for superfluous exertion, had been making his way at his leisure toward his Virginian haunts when he was surprised, and startled, to discover the hounds coming on his trail as he travelled slowly southward. In his northern flight, he had had a method; he was not running aimlessly, he was going to a particular region. But, he preferred his southern location, if he could dispose of the hounds all this distance from it and return to it in security. He made the most of, or created, an opportunity to effect this safely. Finding himself still pursued as he went toward Virginia, he resumed his temporarily abandoned route of flight toward his other refuge. To this end he circled in a large loop back onto his first trail, joining it near the river, where he crossed, heading again on his northeast course. This explained the big loop we had encompassed, the repeated trail at the river, and the alteration in rate as the hounds came up on him and drove him faster. It probably explained the assurance of the hounds when they were fording again, for, no doubt, they were informed by some animal wisdom, which seemed slightly occult to the inferiorly endowed human hunters, that their game was not far ahead of them.

"Wolf or fox," Hovon said, "with a lead no more than we think that he had when he came from the water on this bank, he needs his time. I don't know as much about wolves as you two do, but I should think that these hounds will run three miles while a wolf runs two."

"Just about," Hugo told him.

"He'll concoct something to delay them here and there a few minutes," I said, "so, he will gain on them again. They can't use their speed against him, in a burst, as wolfhounds would. Wolfhounds might espy him, far away, and drop the line to run after him by sight."

But the faithful ground-trailers were having a good time, in their own way; the music of their attuned voices poured forth steadily. The country in which we followed them was uninhabited. It was, again, the hunt in the Black Forest sort of thing. We utilized logging roads, which cut through the woods to a considerable extent, and often we could ride on the open creek bottoms, where wild grasses lay thickly underfoot, grasses which in summer, before the frost wilted them, would have reached to the shoulders of the horses. We saw numerous clearings and slashes, where lumbering had been done, and occasionally a shut-up shanty of logs or slabs which had formerly housed the lumbermen. But we met no person, and passed no lived-in house.

The afternoon was turning into its last hours. If we wanted to find a place where we could bait the horses, and get even a make-shift meal ourselves, we had to be about it; another night was on its way. Lest we lose the hounds, we decided that Hovon and I should cling to their northeasterly route, while Hugo made a detour, as expeditiously as possible, in search of a settlement. He was to signal us with the horn when he was ready to rejoin us with news of any discovery he could make. Balancing transparent china cups or quaffing wine from stemmed goblets at Virginian tea or dinner tables, we had been flippant about the Colfax Fox, had joked about him as a wanderer from the vast Pennsylvanian wildernesses to the north and northeast of us; and now we had run him into that unopened country, and if the sun, moon, and stars did not mis-direct us, so that we were hunting in circles, we were driving him steadily through it to some nameless wilderness beyond it.

We plodded on for nearly an hour before we heard the horn; it was ahead of us; Hugo had thought we should advance faster than we did. We hailed him, and he let us know that he heard us by his answer on the horn; not the ordinary horn music of the chase, he was playing that favorite tune of the Duke's, which Hovon had once had the Prince-Regent's Guards' Band play in his honor, he was sending the catchy strains of "Ole Virginny Never Tire" over the long, long trail of the Colfax Fox.

He kept on playing until we came to him. He was standing beside his dark-grey mare, his back against her side, leaning on her, blowing his glinting horn like Pan blowing his pipe.

"There is no one in this whole region, unless there are Indians, whom I failed to find," he announced. "You are the first human beings I have seen since I left you. But I had Tirade wait for me while I climbed a small peak, from which I overlooked the land ahead, like Moses overlooked the land of his migration from the top of Mount Whatever-it-was. The country seems fairly open, and—"

He raised the horn, with laughter in his eyes, and changed his tune to "—there's one more river to cross, one wide river. . . ."

"That's interesting," said Hovon, who had an ear for music, and had an astonishing acquaintance with our native melodies, considering his opportunity. He recognized what Hugo was playing before I did.

It was sunset when we reached it. The country was, however, even more open than it had appeared to our scout from Mount Whatever-it-was the Second. The travelling was poky, but not bad. Neither was the river bad. It was smaller than the one we had almost made a habit of fording, earlier in the afternoon, and as it flowed south we presumed that it was a tributary of that river.

This time, profiting by sad experience, the hounds had stopped to explore the near bank before crossing, a sensible precaution. We counted them. Not one hound was missing. The stern-eyed Trojans, the dozen black hounds, and Joseph—all were there. Several of the blacks postponed their occupation to do something by the civilities; they came up, smiled at us with their handsome gold-brown eyes, wagged their tails, and hurried back to their snuffing. Joseph came too, and we paid him some pretty cordial compliments. For a little hound with no pedigree, who had despised rabbit hunting, he was doing very well—very well, Joseph.

They forded the river, satisfied that the Colfax Fox had forded it before them. They found his line, where he had emerged. Here, he had not stopped to try tricks. Was he a frightened beast, at last? Was he fleeing desperately, directly, for some far-off secret haven which had never failed him of old? Did he believe, now, that the hounds on his trail were hounds his tricks could not baffle, hounds as tireless as himself, hounds as persistent as the Norns, hounds that would ferret out cooling scents, hounds that would cling to stale lines? Did he fear, at last, that this unending baying on his trail was the last sound his ears should hear, a sound they should never cease to hear until they heard no more? The glorious voices rose, bells and bugles, cymbals and drums; the hounds departed, driving on.

We followed them. The bank of egress was matted with bushes, but, luckily, was not steep; we struggled through ourselves, with the reins thrown over the horses' heads, and helped them out after us.

The district on this side of the river was inhabited, as we saw soon after we mounted. We passed furnaces, where local mineral deposits were mined; they were idle, whether from the winter season, the demands of the Holidays, or permanent disuse, we could not guess. We also passed more of the boarded-up lumbering shanties.

These buildings presently were replaced by arable land and farms, but on most of them houses and barns were built of crude logs, and were small, and poverty-stricken in aspect. We rode by several of these dwellings, for in each one the people were so uncouth, and stared at us so sullenly, that we hoped for better luck the next time.

"Not a very prosperous community through here," Hovon commented.

"Nevertheless, we would be wise to pocket our fastidiousness, and halt," Hugo counselled. "We ought to provide for the horses, and it will soon be dark."

Realizing the good sense in this advice, we turned in at the least objectionable farm in sight, and after an undue amount of dickering, we obtained hay and grain for the hunters, and engaged a couple of shambling big boys to rub them down, except Tirade, who was decidedly more fastidious than we were, and would not have the boys near her. Hugo attended to her himself, and I helped him, while Basil wrangled with the woman in the house about preparing some supper for us. Perceiving that her dialect was too much for him, and his accent too much for her, Hugo and I hastened our task with Tirade and added our efforts to his; among us, we got her to boil some milk and give it to us hot, and to furnish a meal of corn bread and bacon, the most edible food the establishment could produce. Everything we had was paid for three times over, and delivered with surly manners. We were rather more than an hour there, for we felt obliged to let the horses eat some hay in peace.

"E'gad! What a nest of ugly peasants," Hovon said candidly, when we finally escaped, and got back to the sweet cleanness of the woods and the creek bottoms.

"Yes," I agreed. "We should have fared better had we located an encampment of Indians."

We were somewhat relieved to find that the place at which we had stopped was near the farther edge of the colony, and we were soon leaving it behind, for we were not armed, and the rough men of the settlement all had muskets, and few of them looked too virtuous to commit murder for the sake of the valuable horses. The horses stepped along willingly, and Tirade even pulled at first; she had no use for her late hostelry, and was for putting a good distance between it and herself as energetically as possible. She was still fuming disgustedly when the place was five miles in the rear.

The quietude of the lonely land was majestic under the rising moon. Far, far borne upon it, we heard the cadence of our deep-mouthed hounds. Their unrivalled baying led us on. Across the intervening miles, it told us that the hounds from the greatest strain the English Middle Ages knew were still St. Hubert's breed.

Since Christmas Day in the morning, Hovon had outgrown whatever insular opinions he might have held, privately, prior to our Odyssey, concerning hounds and hunting; he rated the black hounds as Hugo and I did, because now he knew them as we did.

"I'faith, I'd rather have the Hounds of Heaven on my trail," he said.

They were more dogged than swift tonight. Whether the scent, among the most mysterious of the natural elements, was less good than it had been last night, whether the Fox had succeeded in throwing enough obstacles in their way to retard their progress, or whether they had merely settled down to an unending, unhurried, driving him, until they drove him to doom, we could not know. But, gradually, we drew nearer to them, and we did not press the horses.

At ten o'clock, the chorus of the black hounds was so much closer that we could distinguish the individual voices in it. There was Laura, hers was clear and bell-like. There was Lead, master of mellow recitative. There were the royal young voices of Faust and Fatal and Ranger IV. Shadow—not often did we hear him; Shadow was a queer genius; his voice was good, but he was sparing of it. He ran mute for long stretches. But genius has its own prerogatives; Shadow was his quarry's shadow, silent and inseparable. There was Old Fire and Water, with his heavy bass. And Basso, one range higher. And Windhound, still young, whose voice, in its own time, would mature until, after Old Fire and Water was with his noble sires, we should think we heard him once again booming down a line, when we heard his son. Every hound voice, we knew it. Every voice, it spoke to us.

Toward midnight, a panther screamed wildly, in answer to the baying of the hounds. But they altered not a note for his noise, and we did not heed him; we were not hunting panthers. Later, we frightened a wintering herd of deer out of their yard, and they went scudding from us, with terrified whistlings; but neither had they cause to fear us, we were not hunting deer.

After this, the country became more rugged and more difficult, and coincidingly, a cloudiness edged between the moon and the earth, cutting off our light, so that we passed, by degrees, from the luminous glow which had served us so well to a darkness which reduced us to leading the horses.

We could see only a few yards around us. It was wooded enough to add the darkness of forest to the failure of the moonlight, and we were distressed hunters indeed. We bumped into tree trunks. We boggled through brooks we could have stepped over if we could have seen them. We felt our way around, and up and down, steep places where we feared the horses might come to harm, proceeding step by step. We scrambled through leafless bushes, switched by the branches. Briars, hardy souls, not winter-killed, scratched us. We were tripped by roots, and we stumbled over rocks. Through everything, we crept on, "By guess and by gosh," as Ash Drake would have said.

For, all the time, in the dead of night as in the shine of noon, out there in front of us old Lead was plainly telling us the chronicle of a winning hunt. His great voice proclaimed, "We're on his line. He went this way. We go too. Are you still coming? He veered here . . . we have his line. We're driving him. Are you with us?"

At intervals, Hugo communicated with the hounds by horn. All our animals were trained to the horn, and understood it well. Hugo, from time to time, sent a few bars of the French music of the chase, or the Old English calls, assuring the hounds that where they went, we followed.

"I'm certain," Hovon remarked once, with his witty inflections, "that my British mind never properly grasped the dimensions of North America. How spacious it is!"

The maps did leave something to be desired, come to think of it, in the matter of indicating its size.

"Are we still in Pennsylvania?" Hovon asked, later. We could not tell him. We had no idea where we were.

Quite suddenly, we found such an improvement in the going that we thought we must have come to a prosperous agricultural neighborhood. We may have passed not far from farmsteads. At that hour no light shone in any window, and we could have almost ridden into the buildings before discovering them. We found two fences by the process, which, presumably, the horses saw better than we did, for they jumped without mishap after we had examined them as well as possible.

For about one hour, I think I was never abroad in a darker night. It was all but pitch black, and we groped out our course with woes it would be hard to magnify. This hunting was not whirlwind hunting; oh, no. In the midst of the Stygian adventure, we fell in with, and nearly fell into, an exceptionally impenetrable belt, or band, of something close to the horses' feet and also out in front of our faces. Naturally, we stopped. We heard the lapping of water.

"My word, it's another river." Hugo's voice spoke gently in the nearby blackness.

In such a cold, caliginous pre-dawn winter hour, the ceremony of entering a strange river, the size of which we could not discern, the character of it and its shores equally unknown to us, ought to have been accompanied, or even preceded, by a few pertinent reflections whether we did or did not expect to get out alive. But we were too pre-occupied with the future of the Colfax Fox to worry about our own; and anyway, on the other shore, by the sound not a long distance away, the pibroch of the pack was calling us on. The Fox had crossed. The hounds had crossed. We intended to cross.

The cold was the worst of it. I shall maintain to my dying day that no worse circumstances for going in swimming can be imagined. The flow of the current, and the cry of the hounds, easily gave us our bearings; we got ashore, after a fairly brisk engagement with a network of bushes on the bank.

"That wasn't so bad," said Hugo, gamely, if not truthfully.

It was not cold enough to freeze our clothes, but it was cold enough to freeze us, our very blood in our veins, unless we did something about it. We started on at a sharp trot, leading the horses. Hovon backed Hugo up to the extent of remarking,

"It was no such fresh-water English Channel as that first one we swam, last night."

But it was a pretty good-sized river, at that. We left it to roll along in the darkness, while we got ourselves and the horses thawed with active exercise, and partly dried. But it was not de luxe fox-hunting; it was not.

At any rate, the going was fine. The country was open and out-spreading. We fancied that if we could see it a grassland galloping country equal to our Virginian hunting fields surrounded us. We were fortunate enough to find a road which took us after the hounds, and for quite a while we made the most of it, thankful to be out of the necessity of getting over or around badly seen or unseen obstructions in our course.

Ahead of us, the hounds were giving tongue to music with the syncopation of a martial band's. Their cry chanted, "We are running a strong scent. And it is growing stronger. We are driving him hard, gentlemen, driving him hard. We're not only running him, we're running him down. It won't be long until we get him. We're very well pleased."

A break in the night-dark foretold the approach of morning—the second morning since we had left Virginia. The clouds were ruptured, and were dissipating, and dawn was not far off.

"Unless I am mistaken," Hugo said, trying to study the sky, "there has been a change in the course since midnight. The last time I saw the stars, we were still heading into the northeast. If that is a morning streak on the eastern horizon, we must be going straight into the east now."

Basil and I looked also. It was so. Directly in front of us, a moving spear of silver in the clouds announced a sunrise there, bye-and-bye.

And, if we were not to be balked, after following our hounds so far, we had need of daylight. For, suddenly, the going became very difficult, and a few minutes afterward, impossible. For the first time since we had struck the trail to the Colfax Fox in the Doctor's yard we encountered geographical conditions which brought us to a total standstill. We had got into a place that made the rugged wilds of

Pennsylvania, which had vexed us variously, seem, by comparison, like a late, lost, happy hunting ground.

A little way ahead, the hound cry was reverberating in a medley of glens that replied to the baying with ten echoes to the note. There were thousands of trees, if not millions. There were thickets like the thickest in Central American jungles; not only the horses could not penetrate them, it was miraculous that the hounds had. There were rocks up to and including cliffs, which we were, luckily for our bones, butting into at their bases instead of tumbling off of from their tops; and between and on all sides of all the rocks of all sizes such a labyrinth of holes as Theseus never saw, ranging from holes a hoof could slip into, with the breaking of a leg, to holes the horse himself could slip into, with the poorest of prospects of ever getting out of alive. We halted, and for a short time we were motionless, not daring to start the horses in any direction, and wondering how we could even withdraw to safer footing.

Hugo, slightly in front of me, was saying quizzically, "We seem to have arrived. This is, if not the brimstone pit, for which we started, certainly the outer wall of fortification guarding it."

Rupert felt his way inch by inch along a rock ledge that towered over his head and mine; my stirrup clanked as it grazed the granite. I did not interfere with him; I was obsessed by an impulse to put my hand to my head, to push my thoughts back to sanity. What fantastic notion had seized me? We had come here through darkness which precluded seeing the outline of any natural feature against the inky sky. I could not distinguish a single landmark. I was so tired that I was hazy anyway. But the idea was real, and it stayed.

The multiplying echoes that rolled through these highlands were echoes that I knew. The relations to each other of the last river we had crossed, the splendid upland galloping country in which we had ridden, and the Tartarean region which had stopped us finally, suddenly fitted a system of things in my mind. Even the clicking of my stirrup iron upon the rock beside me was familiar; knowledge akin to the occult knowledge of the animals possessed me. I knew where we were. No night was so dark that I did not know when I stood upon the sides of Sor'land. No weariness so hazed me that I did not recognize the voice of Sor'land, speaking in its thousand echoes.

I extended my hand, groped for the rock, ran my fingers along it. I touched what I thought was there. I smiled: I knew that rock, too.

"Hugo, Basil. I remember something. Turn your horses carefully, and follow me." I backed Rupert cautiously away from the pitfalls while I was speaking. For some ten minutes, it was rather less than easy to act upon my instructions to follow a conductor they could not see over a terrain they could not determine; but we kept together, and I led them slowly forward. Then, it grew lighter, all at once. The very heavy, low-scudding clouds made it seem more night-like than it really was; they began to break up, and as they did so the greyness of dawn appeared. Soon, there was light enough to show the others what must have looked to their unaccustomed eyes like an ultimate frontier of untamed nature; it showed me what I expected to see—an obscured, crooked path disappearing into a confusion of bushes. But I knew that it did not end among the bushes that swallowed it; it went on, up, up, up, up—it pierced the wilderness of Sor'land to its heart on the inhospitable plateau, the prodigious solitude of sunbright, broad, high barrens, girt by netty shades.

"God's sake, Dev!" Hovon ejaculated. "You came straight to this—er, road. How'd you do it?"

"Knew it was here," I said succinctly.

"The deuce you did!" said Hugo.

I jumped off to lead Rupert. Seeing that we were going into a place that was no place to ride horses, they got off likewise.

"The gees could carry us up," I said, "but we are apt to need their speed on the tableland. The hounds will go up faster than we do, and will gain on us accordingly. We had better save the horses."

As we breasted the break-neck ascent, I explained. "The river in the dark was the Delaware. The fine country, which we compared with the Virginian hunting country, is very similar to it; it is High Hunterdon. It will interest you, Hovon, that it is one of the best locations on the globe for the breeding of blooded horses. It is superlative 'horse country.' Some of the greatest horses in the world are in the studs of the Hunterdon land-kings. It is bounded on one side by the wilderness where we are, which is not a rampart of hell, although some do fear it as such; it is my favorite hunting ground, the Mountain, Sorrel Land."

"It is a godsend that you know it," Hugo said, "for, my word, lacking a guide, we should be unable to find our way through it to be with the hounds at the kill."

"I have a theory about the Colfax Fox," I added. "Do you want it?"

They did. "Hugo will recall a conversation, prior to your arrival, Basil, in which I alluded to a story, current in West Jersey, about a race of fox-colored wolves, bigger and more savage than any other wolves, that were native to this wilderness years ago. They are supposed to be all gone. But, I believe that there remains one Mountain-born survivor of that ancient breed, not seen here because he had strayed far from his birthplace. I think that when he found these fatal hounds upon his trail, he turned homeward in his last flight. I believe that our hounds and the beast we have called the Colfax Fox are close to the trail's end, yonder on the lonesome upland where the Fox was bred, and has returned to die."

So did the hounds believe it. With the rhythm of the big drums and the soaring of the trumpets of an army with banners marching, their cry arose from the dark-grey, desolate Mountain to the sombre, riven sky. All the welkins poured the echoes clashing back upon their source, all the craigs flung the echoes changing in confusion each to each. From Amwell to Hopewell, old Sor'land resounded with the triumph-song of the hounds from St. Hubert's England.

Up from another world, a music swelled, which well I knew— the baying of the black hounds at Lowmont, aroused by the cry they knew to be the cry of brothers, never seen.

To meet the hounds, we were going at an angle to the advance of the hunt, thrusting diagonally up, and up, and up the flanks of Sor'land. Toward the tableland where the Colfax Fox was spending the last of his speed, the last of his strength, to reach the rocky fastness which had sheltered him in the days of his chubby cubdom. I was all but Mountain-born myself. I led my comrades on the hidden paths the Indians had used, and the narrow ways the deer had trodden. I found the openings that thickets masked, that gave on other openings. I turned to our account a hundred experiences with the lay of the glacial moraines. We said nothing; we had no breath to waste on words. They followed me steadily, silently, confidently.

We gained the top, and mounted the horses. Our care for them had about brought us to the point where they were better able to go than we were; especially Hugo, whose heart should have been considered more than it had been. In fact, the horses were not pumped-out. Their heads were up, their ears working; they still listened, eagerly, to the carillon that had led them so far.

We rode in a world in the sky. A world cut out of the Creation Story. Paleolithic forest bounded every lonely heath. The solitude of geologic youth still kept the stronghold of the Sor'land. The sounds that broke the stillness of Silurian time, broke the stillness here. The gone Ages congregated on the heights of Sor'land; this was their Valhalla. The Old Gods—the Very Old Gods, those that stole away when the skin-clad mammals came whose races afterward invented the worships and the Worshipped that most of their descendants know—those Gods retreated to the Sor'land, still walked and talked in the heart of Sor'land. All that had been, was, on Sor'land.

Now, another prehistoric sound was sonorous on the Mountain. The sound that set the Greenwood Forest ringing when the huntsmen of the long-bow followed black hounds there, the sound that the most ancient winds wafted to the hearing of other huntsmen long before the land of England was the prize of Goth or Norman, a sound as old as the alliance of hunting man and hunting dog. Not far ahead of us, the black hounds were closing.

"We'll have to ask the horses to raise a gallop!" Hugo exclaimed, "or we won't be in at the finish!"

"By Peter and Paul, I believe the horses will raise it," from Hovon. "What horses!"

They did raise it. They responded keenly when we asked for "hunting pace, please." But hunting pace was not enough. We had to call on them for the full gallop. The duel of Kingdom Come between the hounds of black St. Hubert's breed and the Colfax Fox, the last giant of the red-wolf race, had come to Kingdom Come. A strident, savage, snarling tore the daybreak bleakness, mingling with great Lead's heaven-filling cry— "Here he is! Here he is! We have him! Are you with us, gentlemen?"

Rupert was running like a stag. Over on my left, King Agrippa came, as if those leagues on leagues of trail had been a warming-up canter. On my right was Tirade—ah, Tirade! Some dark, sanguineous primordial theme in the war-cry upon the gloamy waste, under the wild-wracked sky of the winter dawn, called to her. Called, and she heard. Centuries and ages of domestication were banished by that calling undertone. She reverted to type long lost, a type not seen since Once Upon a Time.

—A battle was on a barren heath—

Amid the black hounds and the raging Trojans a huge gaunt beast was fighting. Its stentorian snarling was the swansong of a monster and its kind; this was the death of a demon, and the death of the zoologic era which had started toward the production of this animal and the consummation of this moment before the time of Man in North America.

It looked, indeed, like Mammy Sukey's Ole Evil One, shown her by de Lawd. It was big with the bigness of a Pleistocene experiment. No wolf of modern breed rivalled it in size. And, it was strangely fox-like in build, no less than in color. As if, somewhere, in some forgotten past, its ancestors had been as much related to foxes as to wolves. It was the yellowy-red of the fox, shaded and marked like the fox coat. Reddish hue, matching the reddish land of its nativity, with the sorrel of the Mountain bred into its hair. One good look we had at its fearful visage, as it looked in life, with blazing beams outstreaming from its red and yellow eyes.

No wonder the doctor's watchdog had scuttled from its menace. No wonder his catch-as-catch-can hounds had refused to own its trail. No wonder it had brazenly taken a baby from its mother; wonder, rather, that it had not taken the woman too. For certainly, nothing but a very unreliable disinclination would prevent this brute from taking any unarmed human being it wanted. Bedloe had been right in mistrusting that it might run—towards him. We could not guess what fell acts might be justly chargeable to the Colfax Fox, in the course of its career, if the whole truth were known. That it had done no more tragic damage in our section of Virginia was doubtless due to the ease with which it had lived on the fat of the land, sparing it the bother of attacking people.

We sprang from the horses. Not that the hounds needed our encouragement. They remembered Christmas Day in the morning, in the doctor's dooryard, when Trailmaster had uttered his cry of recognition at the trail of the Colfax Fox, when old Lead had looked again to be sure that we wanted our foxhounds to run this unfoxly fiend. They knew why they had pursued him in the Cavalier Country, and to its bounds, and beyond them. They knew for what they had made four States their hunting field; for what they had chased him out of meads and woodlands; and over meads into hogbacks, and thence to meads and woods again; for what they had forded wintry waters, and climbed scathing steeps; for what they had run him from fen to glen, and from glen to fen; for what they had swum the wide rivers he had put between himself and them; for what they had hunted him, by day and by night, unrestingly, across unreckoned miles. The hounds needed no urging.

Hugo had dropped Tirade's rein. The other horses hung around interestedly on the outskirts of the fray; but not Tirade. She looked above the heads of the combatants, as if she recognized her enemy of the Virginia covert, the animal that had attacked Hugo on her back, that she had kicked with such a lusty will. Tirade of the grey Viragos, Tirade whose relations were Tantrum, her full sister, and Terrible, her brother, and Fury, and Terror, and two Sharks, and Spiteful, and several Snaps, and both Viragos, and Crazy, and Tiger, horses whose names told their tale—Tirade went to the war. The hounds accepted her as an ally. They opened their ranks for her.

How many have seen a mare or stallion of the Only Blood go into battle? How few realize that such a horse, in full action, and especially if steel-shod as Tirade was, is one of the most dangerous fighting animals the Age of Mammals bred and bequeathed to modern times. Out in the open, fair and free, not even the grizzly of the Rockies has a chance to do better than escape alive from a horse like Tirade.

She seized the red wolf. She took it. She gave her head and her long muscular neck a twisting flip—and hurled the wolf some ten feet into the air, straight up. The snarling, which had been momentarily shaken into silence by the onslaught of the mare, came back in a mortal scream. The form of the wolf sprawled darkly against the darkly turbid sky; then it fell. The mare half-reared; she lashed out with her front feet; she hit the descending carcass with the lightning's stroke, and the lightning's sureness. But we thought she gave the wolf its death-blow when she threw it upward; it was then she snapped its neck. The mare and the hounds clustered around it. It was a limp mass of wind-stirred fur, neck broken, ribs broken, spine broken. The Colfax Fox lay dead upon the moor in Sor'land where he had disported when a whelpling. One of the Mountain's Own was back home.

For Speed and Endurance

Some Statistics on Speed and Endurance Records

THEODORE AYRAULT DODGE

The following interesting statistics on endurance riding were taken from the book Riders of Many Lands. *In these days when our idea of an endurance ride is to ride one hundred miles in three days, it is interesting to see that both horses and riders are capable of very much more, even under exceedingly trying conditions.*

Let us look at some good distance riding, for it is in this that our men (U.S. Cavalry) especially excel.

But to do this calls out another side issue by reminding us of the celebrated ride between Berlin and Vienna, and we may as well recall its incidents. There has been much honestly severe criticism of this noteworthy performance.

> "But what good came of it at last?"
> Said little Peterkin.
> "Why, that I cannot tell," said he,
> "But 'twas a famous victory."

Let us view it from every side.

Imprimis: so far as the endurance of the riders is concerned it counts for nothing. The best time was three hundred and fifty miles in three days—a mere trifle. Why, in 1858, J. Powers rode one hundred and fifty miles in six hours and forty-three minutes in San Francisco; in 1868, N. H. Mowry rode, on the San Francisco racetrack, in the sight of gathered thousands, three hundred miles in fourteen hours, nine minutes; and one Anderson, in the same city, rode one thousand three hundred and four miles in ninety hours. The fact that these men frequently changed horses only adds to the splendid character of the feat, so far as the man is concerned. But this is not all there is to the Berlin-Vienna ride. . . . The ride of these ten-score army officers between Berlin and Vienna has two interesting aspects; the amount of endurance of the animals ridden, and the judgment of the riders as to the capacity of their horses to perform. How these two items compare with what our cavalry is daily experiencing on the plains is a fruitful subject of inquiry.

As the crow flies, it is three hundred and twenty-five English miles from Berlin to Vienna. By the road it is variously called three hundred and fifty to three hundred and seventy; it is certainly short of the latter distance. Count Stahremberg, the winner, covered the distance from Vienna to Berlin (which, owing to the mountainous section being crossed in the early part of the ride, is easier than the course from Berlin to Vienna) in some minutes less than three days. Three other men came in within three days and three hours. The best German rider, Lieutenant Reitzenstein, took a trifle over seventy-three and one-half hours. This sounds like a set of wonderful performances. Are they really so?

The race was go-as-you-please. The riders successively started from Vienna or Berlin at different hours, and rode at any gait or speed, and by any road they chose. The horses were the very best; no one not owning a horse noted for unusual endurance would have been fool enough to enter. There were many thorough-breds, many native horses, Prussians, Hungarians, some ponies from Carpathian and Transylvanian uplands. The animals had all been prepared by weeks of careful training. They carried the least possible weight— the winner, *e.g.*, rides but one hundred and twenty-eight pounds, plus saddle and bridle. The roads were the very best. Under these most favorable conditions the winner rode one hundred and twenty miles a day for three consecutive days; the others less.

There had been a disposition among Anglo-Saxons to underrate this performance. The large number of horses killed or foundered, with good right, distresses our sense of pure sport. But for all that it was a famous ride, though open to serious criticism. Any horse ridden one hundred and twenty-five miles in twenty-four hours performs a great feat; one ridden two hundred miles in forty-eight hours, a greater; to ride three hundred and fifty miles in three days or a bit over is little short of marvelous, if you bring the horse in free from permanent injury. But there's the rub, and it is on this point that there is a word to say.

Comparisons may be odorous, as Mrs. Malaprop avers, but they are interesting and useful. Few people out of the Army know just what our cavalry is capable of, and this ride affords an opportunity, not to be lightly neglected, to point a moral and adorn a tale.

The nearest approach to the Stahremberg ride by an American which we can at the moment recall is that of the pony which Colonel Richard L. Dodge personally knew, and which I have already mentioned. His owner was a professional express rider, who carried the mail from El Paso to Chihuahua, thither once a week and back the next. As the country was infested by Apaches, the man had to ride by night and hide by day. His practice was to ride the distance, three hundred miles, in three consecutive nights, and rest his pony four days between trips. "Six months of this work had not diminished the fire or flesh of that wonderful pony," says Colonel Dodge. It is true that three hundred miles is not three hundred and fifty, but this pony, probably not over fourteen hands, and the rider, mail, and the usual plains trappings, carrying at the lowest two hundred pounds—used to make the three hundred miles in some sixty hours (*i.e.* three nights and the intervening two days), an equal average rate of speed as that of Stahremberg and a much higher rate while going, no one pretends that the Count or any other of the Berlin-Vienna riders could have turned round and done the same thing over again the succeeding week; whereas this little marvel kept on doing it every week for six months, and no one knows how much longer, over a country having no roads deserving the name, by night, and feeding only on bunch-grass. Which of the two is the better performance? This one cannot perhaps be equalled; but to ride and repeat nearly as great distances has never been and is not to-day considered an exceptional thing on the plains.

And if this pony outdid the winner of the great German race, by how far does he outrank the losers? The horse ridden by Count Stahremberg was brought in in fairly good condition, but died within a day or two. The horse of the German winner died. A very high percentage of the others either died or broke down midway, or were ridden home moribund or ruined. They were kept up, *on dit,* by all kinds of stimulants and nostrums on the road. No accounts have reached us showing the condition of the horses' backs under the saddle, always a prime proof of careful or unintelligent treatment. In fact, the number of dead or maimed animals seems to be purposely suppressed. That it was the ponies which came in with the least injury will not surprise our Western men. While a thorough-bred may outpace a pony, a ride which will kill him will not permanently disable the little runt of the prairie. The latter's ancestry had had to struggle with too much hardship to be easily killed, while the thorough-breds have been warmly housed and artificially handled. The pony's heritage is to do and endure; the thorough-bred's to make pace.

. . . Now, it may be interesting to give a few rides of our own cavalry on the plains, not as a contrast, but as a matter which all horsemen should be glad to know.

In 1879 several single couriers with the news of his imminent danger rode from Thornburg's "rat-hole" to General Merritt's column, one hundred and seventy miles, in less than twenty-four hours. The exact time of each was not taken. Rescue was more important than records. In 1891 two troopers of the Eighth Cavalry rode with despatches one hundred and ten miles in twenty hours, and one hundred and ten miles in twenty-three. In 1876 Colonel Lawton rode from Red Cloud Agency, Nebraska, one hundred and twenty-five miles, with despatches for General Crook, in twenty-six hours. Rides of from one hundred and twenty to one hundred and fifty miles have repeatedly been made within the day and night by our ordinary troop-horses when not specially prepared for the work, and over very bad ground, and it is extremely rare that they have suffered serious injury.

There are few three-day rides by single horsemen which can be readily equated; but other performances may be given, which are akin to this one. We put aside all mere hearsay rides. Of these there is no end; but it is well to put on record only such rides as are proven by official reports, and of which the distances can be measured by clear evidence.

It is plain that one man or horse travelling alone can go much farther or faster than two travelling together, and the more the individuals the slower the speed. The speed and endurance of a troop is that of the poorest horse. Extra weight infinitely adds to a horse's task and diminishes his course, and his capacity to go depends upon the chance to feed, water, and care for him suitably on the road. It is in marching detachments over great distances, under exceptionally difficult conditions, that our cavalry officers show peculiar success. Perhaps a knowledge of pace and the instinctive feel of the horse's condition is the highest grade of horsemanship. Civilians are wont to think that to play polo, or hunt, or win a race over the flat or over sticks or perform high-school arts demand the highest skill; but let any one undertake to ride a horse, or, better, to lead a troop one hundred miles in twenty-four hours, and despite all he may have learned in peaceful sports, he will find his knowledge of real horsemanship distinctly limited. Not all our cavalry officers are equally gifted, but some have made rides which are unsurpassed.

It must be remembered that our cavalry horse is, *ab origine,* a very common fellow. He is bought by the Government at a price which brings out mainly those animals which are not quite good enough to command the top of the market, and are held for sale at a rather low figure. They go out to the plains, and are there got into condition while at work. They are not, as abroad, raised in studs boasting sires of the highest lineage. On the march the troop-horse carries very little less than two hundred and fifty pounds—eighty-eight pounds for equipment and baggage, and, say, one hundred and sixty for the rider. In camp he is well fed; on the march he cannot always be, and he is watered at irregular intervals. All these things tell against him.

In 1873 Colonel Mackenzie rode his command into Mexico after Lepan and Kickapoo Indians, beat them in a sharp fight and returned across the border, making one hundred and forty-five miles in twenty-eight hours. In 1874 he again rode his command into Mexico after horse-thieves, making it there and back, eighty-five miles, in fifteen hours. In 1880, Captain A. E. Wood, Fourth Cavalry, one of the most thorough horsemen I have ever known, rode, with eight men, in pursuit of a thieving deserter, one hundred and forty miles in thirty-one hours. Let him tell his own story. It shows just how the trick is done:

"In the month of September, 1880, I was stationed at Fort Reno, Indian Territory; the paymaster had visited us, and in those days, after such a visit, some desertion was expected.

"About noon one day the latter part of September, the post commander sent for and astonished me by stating that the first sergeant of his company—Twenty-third Infantry—had deserted, taking with him a considerable amount of the company fund, and he wanted me to catch him if possible. He had discovered that the sergeant had bought one strong Indian pony and stolen another.

"The direction taken by the sergeant was not known, but under the circumstances I thought that he intended to reach the railroad as soon as possible. The nearest railroad was in Southern Kansas— the nearest point Arkansas City, one hundred and forty miles as the trail then went. I took a detail of two non-commissioned officers and six men from G Troop, Fourth Cavalry.

"The detail was taken from the roster, except the first sergeant of F troop who asked to go with me; the horses belonged to the riders; none were selected as especially qualified for the trip. I rode the same horse that I had been riding for months.

"I took two pack-mules with the men's rations; they were loaded with about eighty pounds each. We left the post at 1:35 P.M. The day was quite hot, and knowing what was before me, I did not push the animals very hard for the first twenty-five miles, which distance we had made by 6 P.M. This distance brought us to King-fisher Creek, where we halted for one hour—unsaddled, got something to eat, let the horses roll and graze, then groomed their backs and legs, saddled up and started at 7 P.M.

"We started and walked for thirty minutes, then took a trot for fifty minutes, when we dismounted and rested for ten minutes; adjusted the saddles, mounted, and took the trot for fifty minutes, dismounted and walked for ten minutes, until 12 P.M. when we halted and rested for twenty minutes. We then mounted and kept up the trotting for fifty minutes, dismounting and walking for ten minutes, until about 4:50 A.M. a little after daybreak, when we were so overcome with sleep that I allowed the men to dismount, unsaddle, and sleep for about an hour. My mind was so busy that I could not sleep much, so I awoke the men. We groomed the backs and rubbed the legs of the horses for a short time and resumed the journey as before. When we had gone about one hundred and twenty miles we again halted, unsaddled, let the horses rest, and made some coffee. This rest took three-quarters of an hour, after which we started and travelled as before until we reached Arkansas City at 8:30 P.M.— thirty-one hours. Men and horses were extremely tired; one horse was quite lame in front. We rested the remainder of the night, the next day and night, and then marched to Caldwell, Kansas, thirty-five miles, the succeeding day. We remained at Caldwell two nights and a day, and marched back to Fort Reno, a distance of one hundred and fifteen miles by ordinary marches. All but one horse seemed to be rested when we reached Caldwell. This horse was unserviceable when we reached Fort Reno, the others apparently were good as ever. The above is a record of the hardest ride I ever undertook. The fatigue was very great; but a good night's rest completely restored all of us.

"At that time our mounts were purchased in Missouri and Kansas. The horse I rode was twelve years old; the others were a little younger. I think that the horse that was rendered unserviceable was made so by bad riding. His rider was not a very good horseman and rode too heavily forward. I tried to correct this but it is impossible to teach the niceties of horsemanship on such a trip."

In 1870 four men of Company H, First Cavalry, bore despatches from Fort Harney to Fort Warner, one hundred and forty miles, over a bad road—twenty of it sand—with little and bad water, in twenty-two hours, eighteen and a half of which was actual marching time. The horses were in such good condition at the end of the ride that after one day's rest the men started back, and made the home trip at the rate of sixty miles a day. In 1879 Captain Dodge, with his troop, rode eighty miles in sixteen hours, and Lieutenant Wood, with his troop, rode seventy miles in twelve hours. . . .

General Merritt in 1879, with four troops and hampered by a battalion of infantry in wagons, rode one hundred and seventy miles to the relief of Payne in sixty-six and one-half hours, and reached the scene in prime order and ready to go into a fight. Very long distances have been covered by cavalry regiments at the rate of sixty miles a day. Colonel Henry, an expert on this subject, speaking of hardening the men and horses of a command by month's drills of from fifteen to twenty miles at rapid gaits, aptly says, "A cavalry command thus hardened, and with increased feeds, ought to be able to make fifty to sixty miles a day as long as required; and to such a command one hundred miles in twenty-four hours ought to be easy. The horse, like the athlete, needs training, and when this is done his endurance is limited only by that of his rider."

An Endurance Ride in the Year 1704

PHIL STONG

This delightful description of a journey from Boston to New York told in the words of Madam Sarah Knight should some day be used in a study of the comparative comforts of traveling today and yesterday. How many of those who blithely make in hours, by jet, the trip that took the little schoolmistress weeks, would be willing to undertake her adventure?

Madam Sarah Knight, Benjamin Franklin's schoolmistress, kept a journal of an odyssey accomplished between Boston and New York. It took her within an hour of five days to ride on horseback from Boston to New Haven; after a visit of some weeks there she completed the trip, Dec. 9, 1704, in three days. The modern automobile distance is 234 miles via New Haven; it would be impossible to guess whether Madam Knight's route was longer or shorter—a horse path is usually nearer a crow's flight than the route of an automobile road—but it is evident that about thirty miles a day was the usual speed between Boston and New Haven and New Haven and New York at the beginning of the eighteenth century. No thought need be given to the fact that Madam Knight was a gentle lady because she was traveling—"travailing," she says—with "the Post," certainly at the best rate of speed the roads and nags permitted.

Still the gentle lady made the journey in an elapsed "travailing" time of eight days over the same route that had taken the first Post two weeks, twenty years before. The road was better, of course, though "on each side the trees and bushes gave us very unpleasant welcomes with their branches and bow's." If the broad highway between Boston and New York was still uncomfortable for a horse-back rider because of "branches and bow's" it could not have been greatly better than it was when the Pequots tramped out sections of it in America's pre-European times.

The second day out, at the Post's second stage, they met the Western Post from Heaven knows where—possibly Worcester—and the two Posts exchanged mail. The two gentlemen concerned were almost the earliest approximations of the American mail clerk. The route then ran over the Pequot Path through Providence and Say-brook to New Haven.

The third Post "rode very hard; and having crossed Providence ferry, we came to a River *wch* they generally ride thro'. But I dare not venture; so the Post got a ladd and canoe to carry me to tother side, and hee rid thro' and led my hors . . . rewarded my sculler, again mounted and made the best of my way forward . . . But the Post told me wee had near fourteen miles to ride to the next stage, where we were to lodg. I asked him of the rest of the rode, foreseeing we must travel in the night. Hee told me there was a bad river to ride thro' *wch* was so very firce a hors could sometimes hardly stem it. I cannot express the concern of mind this relation sett me in; no thoughts but those of the dangerose river could entertain my imagi-nation; and they were as formidable as varios, still tormenting me with blackest ideas of my approching fate—sometime seeing myself

drowning, otherwhiles drowned, and at the best like a holy Sister just come out of a spiritual bath in dripping garments."

It seems possible that this boiling torrent may have been the Pawtuxet; at any rate the lady got to New Haven safely and later to Rye, where "down I laid my poor carkes, . . . and poor I made but one grone, which was from the time I went to bed to the time I riss, which was about three in the morning—"

The next day she got farther from "Connecticoot" and provincial New York and into the City. The danger and discomfort of a voyage from Boston to New York were finally celebrated by Madam Knight with a piece of doggerel scratched on a window pane:

> Through many toils and many frights
> I have returned, poor Sarah Knights.
> Over great rocks and many stones
> God has preserved from fractured bones.

A Rugged Ride

A . T . T S C H I F F E L Y

*Beginning in Buenos Aires, for two and a half years Mr.
Tschiffely rode through the deserts, the jungles, the plateaus
and the mountains of South and Central America, then crossed
the United States, ending his incredible feat in the City of
Washington. He did not know the country, spoke Spanish but
not the Indian dialects. He found his way for the most part
alone, though occasionally he hired a native guide where necessity demanded it. His horses, Mancha and Gato, were members of that hardy race, the Creoles. Their ancestors, of the
finest Arabian and Barb stock, were brought to the Argentine
in 1535 by Don Pedro de Mendoza, who founded the city of
Buenos Aires. The centuries have altered their physical type,
but not their spirit, sagacity or hardiness. As Mr. Tschiffely
himself says, one of his main reasons for attempting the trip
was to prove that it could be done by native Argentine horses.
One horse was fifteen and the other sixteen. Together the three
friends started this trip and together they finished it. The following gives a sample of some of the difficulties they faced
and shows how they overcame these difficulties mainly through
the courage and willingness of the two horses.*

Landslides and swollen rivers made it impossible to follow the road
and compelled me to make a large detour over the mountains to the
west. Natives who knew these regions advised me to take a guide,
for alone I should have difficulty in finding the direction among the
numerous little Indian footpaths.

With the mayor's assistance I found an Indian in a village who agreed to come with me, but unfortunately the man could neither speak nor understand Spanish. I bought provisions, and without losing time started out. The guide, like most Indians, preferred to go on foot, and even when the horses went at a trot he kept up with us with ease. After some time he led us into very rough country, and often he made a sign to me to go ahead. He took a short cut, and later I found him sitting somewhere far ahead, chewing coca while waiting for us.

We had crossed some giddy and wobbly hanging bridges before, but here we came to the worst I had ever seen or ever wish to see again. Even without horses the crossing of such bridges is apt to make anybody feel cold ripples running down the back, and, in fact, many people have to be blindfolded and strapped on stretchers to be carried across. Spanning a wild river the bridge looked like a long, thin hammock swung high up from one rock to another. Bits of rope, wire, and fibre held the rickety structure together. The floor was made of sticks laid crosswise and covered with some coarse fibre matting to give a foot hold and to prevent slipping that would inevitably prove fatal. The width of this extraordinary piece of engineering was no more than four feet, and its length must have been roughly one hundred and fifty yards. In the middle the thing sagged like a slack rope.

I went to examine it closely. The very sight of it made me feel giddy, and the thought of what might easily happen produced a feeling in my stomach as if I had swallowed a block of ice. For a while I hesitated, and then I decided to chance it, for there was no other alternative but to return to Ayacucho and there wait for the dry season. I unsaddled the horses, and giving the Indian the lead line I made signs to him to go ahead with Mancha first. Knowing the horse well, I caught him by the tail and walked behind talking to him to keep him quiet. When we stepped on the bridge he hesitated a moment, then he sniffed the matting with suspicion, and after examining the strange surroundings he listened to me and cautiously advanced. As we approached the deep sag in the middle, the bridge began to sway horribly, and for a moment I was afraid the horse would try to turn back, which would have been the end of him, but no, he merely stopped to wait until the swinging motion was less, and then he moved on again. I was nearly choking with excitement, but kept on talking to him and patting his haunches, an attention of which he was very fond. Once we started upwards after having crossed the middle, even the horse seemed to realise that we had passed the worst part, for now he began to hurry towards safety. His weight shook the bridge so much that I had to catch hold of the wires on the sides to keep my balance. Gato, when his turn came, seeing his companion on the other side, gave less trouble and crossed over as steadily as if he were walking a trail. Once the horses were safely on the other side we carried over the packs and saddles. When we came to an Indian hut where chicha and other native beverages were sold we had an extra long drink to celebrate our successful crossing, while the horses quietly grazed as if they had accomplished nothing out of the way.

. . . Between two distant settlements part of the trail had been swept away by a landslide, and I was warned that a man and his mule had fallen down trying to cross. This meant making a detour of two or three long days, and as I had my doubts about the truth of this report, I decided to go and see for myself. After several hours we came to the spot, and a glance at the broken off piece of rock, some eight feet, convinced me that it would be running too big a risk to try to jump the gap. There was no alternative but to return all the weary distance we had covered that day, and make the detour. Mancha was the saddle-horse that day, and was going in front, and as the pack needed readjusting, I went back to Gato to do this before starting to return. I had been working for a while when I happened to look up. To my horror I saw Mancha moving towards the spot where the trail was missing, and before I could stop him he jumped—and landed safely on the other side. My joy at this ticklish feat soon changed to consternation when I realised our real situation. Here was I on one side with Gato, whilst Mancha was on the other, as unconcerned as if nothing had happened, as if he had only jumped across an arroyo in the pampas, and not across a gap where he would have fallen several hundred feet had he hesitated or slipped. We all know that an eight-foot jump is not much for a horse, but then the place and uneven nature of the trail had to be considered, not to mention one's nerves.

There was no time for much thinking, so I tied the pack-horse to a loose rock, and jumped across to do the same with the other, lest he continue his dangerous wanderings. Now the question was as to whether it would be safer to bring back one animal or to cross the other. After a good look at the trail I thought the latter way would be safer. I unsaddled Gato, who jumped like a goat, after which I brought the pack and saddle over by means of a rope, having to cross from side to side several times to accomplish this primitive and ticklish piece of engineering. Another fright, a good lesson, and many miles saved.

A Discovery and a Chase

CHARLES DICKENS

Mr. Pickwick at his best. This story depicts very clearly the hazards of travel in Dickens' day, but a traveler unaccustomed to such hazards would make very much more of them than our author-host. We complain if, on a smooth road, our vehicle goes over a slight bump. Here we witness Mr. Pickwick and Mr. Wardle cooped up in a tiny box of a chaise, rocked back and forth and thrown from one side of it to the other while the horses gallop over roads which today would be considered impassable. They end up with their carriage quite overturned, yet the general tenor of the tale is to accept these as normal conditions. Verily, times have changed!

The supper was ready laid, the chairs were drawn round the table, bottles, jugs, and glasses were arranged upon the sideboard, and everything betokened the approach of the most convivial period in the whole four-and-twenty hours.

"Where's Rachael?" said Mr. Wardle.

"Aye, and Jingle?" added Mr. Pickwick.

"Dear me," said the host, "I wonder I haven't missed him before. Why, I don't think I've heard his voice for two hours at least. Emily, my dear, ring the bell."

The bell was rung, and the fat boy appeared.

"Where's Miss Rachael?" He couldn't say.

"Where's Mr. Jingle, then?" He didn't know.

Everybody looked surprised. It was late—past eleven o'clock.

Mr. Tupman laughed in his sleeve. They were loitering somewhere, talking about *him*. Ha, ha! capital notion that—funny.

"Never mind," said Wardle, after a short pause, "they'll turn up presently, I dare say. I never wait supper for anybody."

"Excellent rule, that," said Mr. Pickwick, "admirable."

"Pray, sit down," said the host.

"Certainly," said Mr. Pickwick: and down they sat.

There was a gigantic round of cold beef on the table, and Mr. Pickwick was supplied with a plentiful portion of it. He had raised his fork to his lips, and was on the very point of opening his mouth for the reception of a piece of beef, when the hum of many voices suddenly arose in the kitchen. He paused, and laid down his fork. Mr. Wardle paused too, and insensibly released his hold of the carving knife, which remained inserted in the beef. He looked at Mr. Pickwick. Mr. Pickwick looked at him.

Heavy footsteps were heard in the passage; the parlour door was suddenly burst open; and the man who had cleaned Mr. Pickwick's boots on his first arrival, rushed into the room, followed by the fat boy, and all the domestics.

"What the devil's the meaning of this?" exclaimed the host.

"The kitchen chimney ain't a-fire, is it, Emma?" inquired the old lady.

"Lor', grandma! No," screamed both the young ladies.

"What's the matter?" roared the master of the house.

The man gasped for breath, and faintly ejaculated—

"They ha' gone, Mas'r—gone right clean off, sir!" (At this juncture Mr. Tupman was observed to lay down his knife and fork, and to turn very pale.)

"Who's gone?" said Mr. Wardle, fiercely.

"Mus'r Jingle and Miss Rachael, in a po'-chay, from Blue Lion, Muggleton. I was there; but I couldn't stop 'em; so I run off to tell'ee."

"I paid his expenses!" said Mr. Tupman, jumping up frantically. "He's got ten pounds of mine!—stop him!—he's swindled me!— I won't bear it!—I'll have justice, Pickwick!—I won't stand it!" and with sundry incoherent exclamations of the like nature, the unhappy gentleman spun round and round the apartment, in a transport of frenzy.

"Lord preserve us!" ejaculated Mr. Pickwick, eyeing the extraordinary gestures of his friend with terrified surprise. "He's gone mad! What shall we do!"

"Do!" said the stout old host, who regarded only the last words of the sentence. "Put the horse in the gig! I'll get a chaise at the Lion, and follow 'em instantly. Where"—he exclaimed, as the man ran out to execute the commission—"where's that villain, Joe?"

"Here I am; but I han't a willin'," replied a voice. It was the fat boy's.

"Let me get at him, Pickwick," cried Wardle, as he rushed at the ill-starred youth. "He was bribed by that scoundrel, Jingle, to put me on a wrong scent, by telling a cock-and-a-bull story of my sister and your friend Tupman!" (Here Mr. Tupman sunk into a chair.) "Let me get at him!"

"Don't let him!" screamed all the women, above whose exclamations the blubbering of the fat boy was distinctly audible.

"I won't be held!" cried the old man. "Mr. Winkle, take your hands off. Mr. Pickwick, let me go, sir!"

It was a beautiful sight, in that moment of turmoil and confusion, to behold the placid and philosophical expression of Mr. Pickwick's face, albeit somewhat flushed with exertion, as he stood with his arms firmly clasped round the extensive waist of their corpulent host, thus restraining the impetuosity of his passion, while the fat boy was scratched, and pulled, and pushed from the room by all the females congregated therein. He had no sooner released his hold, than the man entered to announce that the gig was ready.

"Don't let him go alone!" screamed the females. "He'll kill somebody!"

"I'll go with him," said Mr. Pickwick.

"You're a good fellow, Pickwick," said the host, grasping his hand. "Emma, give Mr. Pickwick a shawl to tie round his neck— make haste. Look after your grandmother, girls; she has fainted away. Now then, are you ready?"

Mr. Pickwick's mouth and chin having been hastily enveloped in a large shawl, his hat having been put on his head, and his great coat thrown over his arm, he replied in the affirmative.

They jumped into the gig. "Give her her head, Tom," cried the host; and away they went, down the narrow lanes, jolting in and out of the cart-ruts, and bumping up against the hedges on either side, as if they would go to pieces every moment.

"How much are they a-head?" shouted Wardle, as they drove up to the door of the Blue Lion, round which a little crowd had collected, late as it was.

"Not above three-quarters of an hour," was everybody's reply.

"Chaise and four directly!—out with 'em! Put up the gig afterwards."

"Now, boys!" cried the landlord—"chaise and four out—make haste—look alive there!"

Away ran the hostlers, and the boys. The lanterns glimmered, as the men ran to and fro; the horses' hoofs clattered on the uneven paving of the yard; the chaise rumbled as it was drawn out of the coach-house; and all was noise and bustle.

"Now then!—is that chaise coming out to-night?" cried Wardle.

"Coming down the yard now, sir," replied the hostler.

Out came the chaise—in went the horses—on sprung the boys —in got the travellers.

"Mind—the seven-mile stage in less than half an hour!" shouted Wardle.

"Off with you!"

The boys applied whip and spur, the waiters shouted, the hostlers cheered, and away they went, fast and furiously.

"Pretty situation," thought Mr. Pickwick, when he had had a moment's time for reflection. "Pretty situation for the General Chairman of the Pickwick Club. Damp chaise—strange horses— fifteen miles an hour—and twelve o'clock at night!"

For the first three or four miles, not a word was spoken by either of the gentlemen, each being too much immersed in his own reflections to address any observations to his companion. When they had gone over that much ground, however, and the horses getting thoroughly warmed began to do their work in really good style, Mr. Pickwick became too much exhilarated with the rapidity of the motion, to remain any longer perfectly mute.

"We're sure to catch them, I think," said he.

"Hope so," replied his companion.

"Fine night," said Mr. Pickwick, looking up at the moon, which was shining brightly.

"So much the worse," returned Wardle; "for they'll have had all the advantage of the moonlight to get the start of us, and we shall lose it. It will have gone down in another hour."

"It will be rather unpleasant going at this rate in the dark, won't it?" inquired Mr. Pickwick.

"I daresay it will," replied his friend drily.

Mr. Pickwick's temporary excitement began to sober down a little, as he reflected upon the inconveniences and dangers of the expedition in which he had so thoughtlessly embarked. He was roused by a loud shouting of the post-boy on the leader.

"Yo-yo-yo-yo-yoe," went the first boy.

"Yo-yo-yo-yo-yoe!" went the second.

"Yo—yo-yo-yo-yoe!" chimed in old Wardle himself, most lustily, with his head and half his body out of the coach window.

"Yo-yo-yo-yoe!" shouted Mr. Pickwick, taking up the burden of the cry, though he had not the slightest notion of its meaning or object. And amidst the yo-yoing of the whole four, the chaise stopped.

"What's the matter?" inquired Mr. Pickwick.

"There's a gate here," replied old Wardle. "We shall hear something of the fugitives."

After a lapse of five minutes, consumed in incessant knocking and shouting, an old man in his shirt and trousers emerged from the turnpike-house, and opened the gate.

"How long is it since a post-chaise went through here?" inquired Mr. Wardle.

"How long?"

"Ah!"

"Why, I don't rightly know. It worn't a long time ago, nor it worn't a short time ago—just between the two, perhaps."

"Has any chaise been by at all?"

"Oh yes, there's been a shay by."

"How long ago, my friend," interposed Mr. Pickwick, "an hour?"

"Ah, I daresay it might be," replied the man.

"Or two hours?" inquired the post-boy on the wheeler.

"Well, I shouldn't wonder if it was," returned the old man doubtfully.

"Drive on, boys," cried the testy old gentleman; "don't waste any more time with that old idiot!"

"Idiot!" exclaimed the old man with a grin, as he stood in the middle of the road with the gate half-closed, watching the chaise which rapidly diminished in the increasing distance. "No—not much o' that either; you've lost ten minutes here, and gone away as wise as you came, arter all. If every man on the line as has a guinea give him, earns it half as well, you won't catch t'other shay this side Mich'lmas, old short-and-fat." And with another prolonged grin, the old man closed the gate, re-entered his house, and bolted the door after him.

Meanwhile the chaise proceeded, without any slackening of pace, towards the conclusion of the stage. The moon, as Wardle had foretold, was rapidly on the wane; large tiers of dark heavy clouds, which had been gradually overspreading the sky for some time past, now formed one black mass overhead; and large drops of rain which pattered every now and then against the windows of the chaise, seemed to warn the travellers of the rapid approach of a stormy night. The wind, too, which was directly against them, swept in furious gusts down the narrow road, and howled dismally through the trees which skirted the pathway. Mr. Pickwick drew his coat closer about him, coiled himself more snugly up into the corner of the chaise, and fell into a sound sleep, from which he was only awakened by the stopping of the vehicle, the sound of the hostler's bell, and a loud cry of "Horses on directly!"

But here another delay occurred. The boys were sleeping with such mysterious soundness, that it took five minutes a-piece to wake them. The hostler had somehow or other mislaid the key of the stable, and even when that was found, two sleepy helpers put the wrong harness on the wrong horses, and the whole process of harnessing had to be gone through afresh. Had Mr. Pickwick been alone, these multiplied obstacles would have completely put an end to the pursuit at once, but old Wardle was not to be so easily daunted; and he laid about him with such hearty good-will, cuffing this man, and pushing that; strapping a buckle here, and taking in a link there, that the chaise was ready in a much shorter time than could reasonably have been expected, under so many difficulties.

They resumed their journey; and certainly the prospect before

them was by no means encouraging. The stage was fifteen miles
long, the night was dark, the wind high, and the rain pouring in tor-
rents. It was impossible to make any great way against such obstacles united; it was hard upon one o'clock already; and nearly
two hours were consumed in getting to the end of the stage. Here,
however, an object presented itself, which rekindled their hopes,
and re-animated their drooping spirits.

"When did this chaise come in?" cried old Wardle, leaping out
of his own vehicle, and pointing to one covered with wet mud, which
was standing in the yard.

"Not a quarter of an hour ago, sir," replied the hostler, to
whom the question was addressed.

"Lady and gentleman?" inquired Wardle, almost breathless with
impatience.

"Yes, sir."

"Tall gentleman—dress coat—long legs—thin body?"

"Yes, sir."

"Elderly lady—thin face—rather skinny—eh?"

"Yes, sir."

"By heavens, it's them, Pickwick," exclaimed the old gentleman.

"Would have been here before," said the hostler, "but they
broke a trace."

"It is!" said Wardle, "it is, by Jove! Chaise and four instantly!
We shall catch them yet, before they reach the next stage. A guinea
a-piece, boys—be alive there—bustle about—there's good fellows."

And with such admonitions as these, the old gentleman ran
up and down the yard, and bustled to and fro, in a state of excitement which communicated itself to Mr. Pickwick also; and under
the influence of which, that gentleman got himself into complicated
entanglements with harness, and mixed up with horses and wheels
of chaises, in the most surprising manner, firmly believing that by
so doing he was materially forwarding the preparations for resum-
ing their journey.

"Jump in—jump in!" cried old Wardle, climbing into the chaise,
pulling up the steps, and slamming the door after him. "Come
along! Make haste!" And before Mr. Pickwick knew precisely
what he was about, he felt himself forced in at the other door, by

one pull from the old gentleman, and one push from the hostler; and off they were again.

"Ah! we *are* moving now," said the old gentleman exultingly. They were indeed, as was sufficiently testified to Mr. Pickwick, by his constant collisions either with the hard wood-work of the chaise, or the body of his companion.

"Hold up!" said the stout old Mr. Wardle, as Mr. Pickwick dived head foremost into his capacious waistcoat.

"I never did feel such a jolting in my life," said Mr. Pickwick.

"Never mind," replied his companion, "it will soon be over. Steady, steady."

Mr. Pickwick planted himself into his own corner, as firmly as he could; and on whirled the chaise faster than ever.

They had travelled in this way about three miles, when Mr. Wardle, who had been looking out of the window, for two or three minutes, suddenly drew in his face, covered with splashes, and exclaimed in breathless eagerness—

"Here they are!"

Mr. Pickwick thrust his head out of his window. Yes: there was a chaise and four, a short distance before them, dashing along at full gallop.

"Go on, go on," almost shrieked the old gentleman. "Two guineas a-piece, boys—don't let 'em gain on us—keep it up—keep it up."

The horses in the first chaise started on at their utmost speed; and those in Mr. Wardle's galloped furiously behind them.

"I see his head," exclaimed the choleric old man. "Damme, I see his head."

"So do I," said Mr. Pickwick, "that's he."

Mr. Pickwick was not mistaken. The countenance of Mr. Jingle, completely coated with the mud thrown up by the wheels, was plainly discernible at the window of his chaise; and the motion of his arm, which he was waving violently towards the postillions, denoted that he was encouraging them to increased exertion.

The interest was intense. Fields, trees, and hedges, seemed to rush past them with the velocity of a whirlwind, so rapid was the pace at which they tore along. They were close by the side of the first chaise. Jingle's voice could be plainly heard, even above the

din of the wheels, urging on the boys. Old Mr. Wardle foamed with
rage and excitement. He roared out scoundrels and villains by the
dozen, clenched his fist and shook it expressively at the object of
his indignation; but Mr. Jingle only answered with a contemptuous
smile, and replied to his menaces by a shout of triumph, as his
horses, answering the increased application of whip and spur, broke
into a faster gallop, and left the pursuers behind.

Mr. Pickwick had just drawn in his head, and Mr. Wardle,
exhausted with shouting, had done the same, when a tremendous
jolt threw them forward against the front of the vehicle. There was
a sudden bump—a loud crash—away rolled a wheel, and over went
the chaise.

After a very few seconds of bewilderment and confusion, in
which nothing but the plunging of horses and breaking of glass
could be made out, Mr. Pickwick felt himself violently pulled out
from among the ruins of the chaise; and as soon as he had gained his
feet, and extricated his head from the skirts of his great coat, which
materially impeded the usefulness of his spectacles, the full disaster
of the case met his view.

Old Mr. Wardle without a hat, and his clothes torn in several
places, stood by his side, and the fragments of the chaise lay
scattered at their feet. The post-boys, who had succeeded in cutting
the traces, were standing, disfigured with mud and disordered by
hard riding, by the horses' heads. About a hundred yards in advance was the other chaise, which had pulled up on hearing the
crash. The postillions, each with a broad grin convulsing his countenance, were viewing the adverse party from the saddles, and Mr.
Jingle was contemplating the wreck from the coach-window, with
evident satisfaction. The day was just breaking, and the whole scene
was rendered perfectly visible by the grey light of the morning.

"Hallo!" shouted the shameless Jingle, "anybody damaged?—
elderly gentleman—no light weights—dangerous work—very."

"You're a rascal!" roared Wardle.

"Ha! ha!" replied Jingle; and then he added, with a knowing
wink, and a jerk of the thumb towards the interior of the chaise— "I
say—she's very well—desires her compliments—begs you won't
trouble yourself—love to Tuppy—won't you get up behind?—drive
on, boys."

The postillions resumed their proper attitudes, and away rattled the chaise, Mr. Jingle fluttering in derision a white handkerchief from the coach-window.

Nothing in the whole adventure, not even the upset, had disturbed the calm and equable current of Mr. Pickwick's temper. The villainy, however, which could first borrow money of his faithful follower, and then abbreviate his name to "Tuppy" was more than he could patiently bear. He drew his breath hard, and coloured up to the very tips of his spectacles, as he said, slowly and emphatically—

"If ever I meet that man again, I'll—"

"Yes, yes," interrupted Wardle, "that's all very well: but while we stand talking here, they'll get their license, and be married in London."

Mr. Pickwick paused, bottled up his vengeance, and corked it down.

"How far is it to the next stage?" inquired Mr. Wardle, of one of the boys.

"Six mile, ain't, Tom?"

"Rayther better."

"Rayther better nor six mile, sir."

"Can't be helped," said Wardle, "we must walk it, Pickwick."

"No help for it," replied the truly great man.

So sending forward one of the boys on horseback, to procure a fresh chaise and horses, and leaving the other behind to take care of the broken one, Mr. Pickwick and Mr. Wardle set manfully forward on the walk, first tying their shawls round their necks and slouching down their hats to escape as much as possible from the deluge of rain, which after a slight cessation had again begun to pour heavily down.

The Race Run

The Hambletonian

DWIGHT AKERS

Dwight Akers has made the most careful study of the ups and downs, details and full panorama of harness racing ever to be attempted. And he gives it all to us in clear and simple style in his great book Drivers Up! *Few others could have presented the picture of a day at the Goshen track as blood-stirringly as has this trotting historian.*

It was on August 12, 1937, that the curtain rose on the twelfth annual renewal of the Hambletonian. The parking places at Goshen's Good Time track were filled, but late-coming cars, pouring in over the table-smooth white roads from Manhattan, from Kentucky, from Massachusetts—the license plates were a roster of the states—found an afternoon's shelter on the elm-shaded streets of the little town. For the three days of the meeting that had already elapsed the ordinarily quiet routine of Goshen households had been interrupted by social engagements—luncheons, dinners or teas for visiting guests, gatherings of "home folks" who were attending races together. Race-week hospitality is a Goshen tradition. Today, however—Hambletonian Day—was an occasion on which all humanity, like sparrows flocking in from the four quarters of the world, seemed to be alighting at Goshen. At the track, the crowd overflowed the stand, overflowed the bleachers and lined up along the stretches.

From their stalls, smelling of straw and leather, horses looked with cool, unpuzzled eyes on the hustling human parade that

223

streamed up from the gate, a scene that after their weeks of racing "on the Grand" had in it no new thing to excite their interest or surprise. On lawns before the sheds other horses, on leading straps or under blankets followed the steps of their grooms back and forth like slow-swinging pendulums or round-about like the hands of a clock. Of all visitors to this rural theatre, only the actors seemed unconcerned with the answer to the question of the day— "Who gets the money?"

There was a full card of racing events and it was late afternoon before the stars were called for the big act, their contest for the thirty-five thousand dollar Hambletonian stake. But at last they came, America's fastest fleet of three-year-olds—parading before the stand behind a high-stepping saddle horse: DeSota, Twilight Song, Hollyrood Audrey, Delphia Hanover, Farr, Shirley Hanover, Europa and Earl's Spencerian.

After their warming-up spins to the turn, a gong sounds from the judges' box. Crimson and blue, orange and green, black and white and gold—today as in old times—from the seats of a dozen sulkies the emblems of a dozen great stables throw a rainbow band of color across the track as the horses, wheeling at the starter's signal, fall into line. After a trial or two they are off to a flying start —a double tier of them, DeSota at the pole. "Go!" Horses and drivers have taken the word and are off. The pounding of hoofs on clay, a sharp clatter as they pass the stand, is only a muffled drumming as they take the turn.

The fast brush for position is over, they have fallen into line and are making for the quarter post. Shirley Hanover, a five-to-one shot in the betting, leads the field and sets the pace. At the half-mile post, she is still ahead. Farr, another horse that was sold for a song in the betting, is at her heels. DeSota, the favorite, is close behind.

The time of the half-mile is 1:02. Far out on the backstretch the horses, seen from the stand, are moving with the wooden earnestness of toys shifted by a child's hand, but practiced eyes behind the field glasses note every change in position and stop watches record the quarter seconds.

They are at the three-quarter post in 1:32½. Shirley Hanover is still in the open, taking the air on her nose, but the field is bunched close behind her. They blaze away at last into the stretch and spread across the track for the brush home. *Here they come! Watch 'em, people!*

The scrambled field of horses, seen from the stand as a flying cloud, looms larger as it bears down to the wire and breaks apart. The roll of hoofs, putt-putting on hard clay, has become a clatter again. *Watch this, folks! It's a horse race! It's a horse race!*

Glimpses of flying manes and lathered flanks! A play of summer lightning over the ears and along the flanks of the sweating browns and bays as the drivers—whips flying—lift their tired but fighting horses home.

Brown and bay horses! Drivers in coats of crimson and blue, orange and green, black and white and gold! They have passed the wire. Driven by Henry Thomas, Shirley Hanover from Lawrence B. Sheppard's kindergarten of colts at Hanover, Pennsylvania, has won the heat. Shirley Hanover—a five-to-one shot! And little Farr —Goshen's home horse! Who would have supposed, seeing her little prancing step before the race, that Farr could stay in the field with DeSota and Twilight Song and Delphia Hanover, and—second horse in this heat!—give the winner a race?

A second heat confirms Shirley's victory and divides second and third money between Farr and DeSota. There she stands, after her jog back to the judges' box, nervously shifting her feet—Shirley Hanover, 2:01½, receiving about her neck a wreath of flowers, while bursts of white light record her image on the camera plates so America tomorrow may see her picture in the papers. Who's happier than Henry Thomas, holding his filly and keeping his grin while he takes the light in his eyes? If anybody, it is three youngsters who play about the stall that is Shirley's home. Alma, Charlotte and Sonny Sheppard—solemn-faced in the presence of a battery of cameras! Young Americans coming up with the game!

Overcoat Meeting

GEORGE AGNEW CHAMBERLAIN

This excerpt from the book by the same name gives a pretty good picture of what went on at the trotting tracks, in the days when finding a race that wasn't fixed would have presented quite a problem.

Jeddo had missed his chance. Thinking of a way to get the horses home had been fine, but why couldn't he have saved out enough sense to grab Mit before she got into the cart? He could have held her as she had held him on that day so long ago and could have cried as she had cried, "I love you—I love you!" As it was, he had only offended her beyond forgiving, treating her worse than a drunk kicking his dog. No wonder that the encounter in the depths of the Barrens became a wall. Behind it was their joint childhood, on this side a new beginning. They met every day at the track, and spoke whenever necessary but that was all, for Mit wore the air of a cat with ready claws waiting to rake him at the first chance. But something happened to take Jeddo's mind off Mit. Keen Garret, returning from down Maine, and Ep from the Lexington Trots reported that during their summer wanderings they had been able to cause the itch for an Overcoat Meeting to spread like wildfire. Not only was the fixture all set but the only change from the good old days would be a plentiful sprinkling of dashes. The date was for the second week in October as Jeddo had figured, barely a fortnight away.

226

Excitement rose steadily at the Daretown track. Everybody seemed to sense an approaching climax and small incidents could take on absurd proportions. The truant officer nabbed Zed and the ensuing screams of rage, soon followed by a man's howl of pain, brought Jeddo on the run to force Zed's jaws open and release the officer's ear. Jeddo carried Zed aside and whispered to him so effectively that he not only consented to apologize but went meekly off to school. Mit realized the pay-off was at hand and caught Jeddo by himself.

"Who's going with our horses to the Overcoat Meeting?" she asked.

"Ep and me and Zed," said Jeddo, "and shouldn't wonder Beef would go in his truck and take Keen along."

"When do you start?"

Jeddo gave her a steady look. "About dawn come Monday."

"Day after tomorrow?" exclaimed Mit.

"That's right," said Jeddo.

"Of course I'm going," said Mit, "though you didn't bother to include me."

"No sense to that," said Jeddo, "your folks wouldn't stand for it."

"Ain't Ep most the same as my uncle?" said Mit. "He's as good as two married women and safer than six old maids. I'll be here early."

"Don't forget your overcoat," said Jeddo.

"And the red flannels," said Mit, unsmilingly.

She showed up as promised with the family Gladstone bag. Already Bingen Blue and Spring Hanover were standing side by side in the horse-van with the two sides of its roof flaring up like butterfly wings. The trough thus formed was packed with a single tack trunk, bedding, bags of feed, a jumble of harness and across the strong iron rods were strapped the two sulkies. There wasn't a nook left for her bag, so Jeddo placed it on the back seat of the sedan. Ep was already settled in front, but there was no sign of Zed. She got in beside her bag. Slap piled in after her and with Jeddo at the wheel they started off. Five miles up Commissioner's Pike, bordered with flaming marsh maple and reddening oak, a tiny figure popped out of the woods. It was Zed. He tried to push

Ep over to get the window but Ep wouldn't have it and jammed him in the middle. By noon they had covered half the distance and drew up at the roadside to feed. Ep fished out a skillet.

"You won't need that," said Mit. "Mother fixed us plenty."

Jeddo threw up his head and Ep looked around with a relieved smile. "That sets right good with me, Mit," he said. "I was sort of fretting over that there kidnap law."

Jeddo was the only one who couldn't eat. Strangely enough the problem of how to put himself right with Mit had left his mind entirely, pushed out by his single purpose to shoot for the whole pot. What was worrying him now was how to tackle Zed. They started off again and traveled several miles before he decided to make a start. "Ever hear me say it takes brains to take orders, Zed?" he asked.

"About a dozen times," said Zed.

"Well, Ep and me are going to hand you a few orders before we get to the farm near to the racetrack where we're going to leave you off."

Zed's skinny body straightened into a ramrod. "Alone?" he moaned.

"Yep," said Jeddo. "Alone with Springer and Slap." Zed settled back, completely relaxed, and Jeddo continued. "From the farm there's a road goes through a woods will land you bang at the entrance to the track. Racing starts at one o'clock tomorrow but horses will be out doing their walk from around eleven in the morning. Don't you dast to groom Springer but come ten o'clock you hitch him, drive to the track, jog him his two miles, then take him back to the farm. Now here's where you got to begin to listen good. From the minute we leave you off this afternoon you don't know Mit nor me nor Ep and we don't know you."

"Why not?" asked Zed, bewildered.

"There's a lot of things that's none of your business and that's one of 'em," said Jeddo. "Day after tomorrow Spring Hanover is entered in the third race, a Classified trot. You bring him to the track around eleven, warm him up, feed him light, hitch again, come out at the call bell and race him."

"Me?" breathed Zed.

"I wouldn't of told you so soon," said Jeddo, "save that it'll be on the racing card—Spring Hanover, owner Deep Creek Farms, driver Zed Buckalew."

"Who's kidding who around here?" said Mit, echoing Zed's remark of weeks ago.

"Yeah, that's what I want to know," said Zed.

"You both got the wrong idea," said Jeddo, "and if you don't drop the notion I'm fooling it will likely cost this outfit all we hope to make. There's one more thing. Remember the name of the owner. Should anyone ask you, it's Deep Creek Farms and Deep Creek Farms is me and Mit.

"I'll remember," said Zed. Then he murmured, still dazed, "So I'm honest going to race the Old Man!"

"That's the size of half of it," said Jeddo, "and here's the other half. I'm betting that somewheres, most likely it'll be going or coming through the woods, a guy with the eyes of a weasel and the smell of a skunk will probably stop you, talk soft and offer you a chunk of money to pull your hoss. When that happens, what you going to do?"

"Spit in his face!" said Zed promptly.

"Wrong, dead wrong," said Jeddo. "You're going to take the money, give him your word to pull the race and keep your word. If you don't—"

"That's slimy," interrupted Mit furiously. "Teaching a kid to cheat. Telling him to take a bribe. Wanting him to pull a race!"

Jeddo slowed the car, studied the side of the road, pulled off, came to a full stop and faced around. "Shut that mouth," he whispered. "Sew it up. Who's running this game?"

Ep laid a hand on Jeddo's shoulder and pulled him around. "It makes a lot of difference, Mit," he said. "Jeddo's shooting for a whale of a pot and you could help him plenty if you'd go along instead of raring back on the bit. Seems somehow you got on a train going the wrong way. Where we're headed if you was to shoot into the crowd with a scatter gun, chances are every pellet would hit a crook, but you can take my word for it Jeddo wouldn't be amongst 'em."

"When we drop you off to the hotel at Hartford," suggested

Jeddo, "why don't you stay there and read a book, not bothering with the track at all? That way you wouldn't have to suffer and we'd have a better chance."

"That's a proposition fair to both sides," said Ep. "Because if you can't take orders you'll sure be in the way."

"I'm tired of all of you making out I've got no brain," said Mit angrily. "Jeddo's told you something he won't tell me."

"He ain't," said Ep promptly, "because he didn't need to. But that part of it don't enter neither here nor there. What Jeddo's ordered me to do I've done it from the start, and me an old man. What's more I aim to keep right on."

Strange sounds were coming out of Zed and at each gulp his scrawny neck looked as if it was trying to swallow an egg with the shell on. He raised pitiful eyes to Ep's face. "Mister, you want I should not groom Springer and pull him on the top o' that?"

"Son," said Ep, "you do just like Jeddo tells you. If you don't you'll be double-crossing all of us, including Mit."

It took only a few minutes to settle Zed at a farm belonging to a friend of a friend of Ep's and half an hour later Jeddo stopped in front of the Hotel in Hartford. "How about it, Mit?" he asked.

"I'll take orders from now on," she answered. "How'll I get to the track?"

"Bus," said Ep, "loads of busses."

"Taxi," said Jeddo, "and it's on the house."

She was so early at Cherry Park the next morning that the grand-stand was still quite empty yet a surprising number of people were floating around, mostly men but here and there one of them would be dragging along a woman. In spite of two overcoats, one over the other, she recognized the stranger who had driven Old Walt clean off his bean with his offer of five hundred for Bingen Blue. When she ran into Ep she told him about it and he heaved a deep sigh.

"That let's me out," he said, "and I'm double glad you come to your senses, Mit. Jeddo's going to need you bad tomorrow."

"Is he?" said Mit eagerly. "Why?"

Ep merely stared and at that moment a sprinkle of laughter grew into a roar. They looked around and saw a face go by, the scaredest face east or west of the Mississippi. It was Zed, doing the splits behind Springer's rumpled rump. He was barefoot as usual and his toes curled around the make-shift leather stirrups he himself had devised so many months ago.

The stranger in the two overcoats shouldered Glowboil Willets, named for his nose, into a safe corner and whispered excitedly. At the Overcoat Meeting it isn't the purses that count but any chance for a build-up into wild and furious betting. Glowboil studied the racing card for the next day. He struck off a mental balance sheet of the performances of all the horses matched against Spring Hanover and agreed with the stranger that here was a natural. Promptly he looked for Harry Flint, nicknamed Skin. He gave him instructions backed by four hundred dollars in cash and when Skin had departed he went around proving to anybody who cared to listen that on his standing Spring Hanover couldn't lose.

"Classified trot nothing!" he would sneer. "They give him a gift."

The next day as Zed, on the way to the track, entered the darkest bit of the woods, Skinflint stepped out of his parked car. "Hi-ya, kiddo. Ain't that Spring Hanover you're driving?"

"Yep," admitted Zed in apparent terror, but he was sad inside, for the man had eyes like a weasel and emitted a sour smell.

"I see how you're driving for Deep Creek Farms. What does that stand for?"

"A couple o' kids," said Zed.

"Kids, eh? Will they treat you any better than this?" He opened his fist. "Know what it is, bub? Ever seen one o' them before?"

"Hundred-dollar bill," said Zed, grief adding its touch to his look of fright.

"Take it," said Skinflint. Zed did. "Now it's yours, see? And you'll get two more like it if you do just like I say."

"What?" asked Zed, listlessly.

"All you got to do is not to win. Though I can't see how it would happen, somehow you might find yourself up in front. If you do, lose the race. Pull the hoss or let him break and gallop his head off. It's easy. Are you on?"

"I guess so."

"No guessing about it," snarled Skinflint. "Yes or no?"

"Yes," muttered Zed.

The fix had been so soft that Skinflint began to wish he hadn't wasted one hundred of the four Glowboil had authorized him to spend. Something troubled him but he didn't know quite what. As Zed started off he yelled after him: "One more thing, you punk—if anything goes wrong I'll wring your guinea neck. Get me?"

Zed didn't bother to answer, for an abandoned feeling was gnawing at his insides. Two hours later, waiting for the call bell, it grew worse. Ep was nowhere around, neither had he seen Beef, Mit or anybody else and when Jeddo went by with Bingen Blue he didn't even give a nod but kept on to the track to limber up. Zed decided to tag along though well behind. The betting tent was three quarters of the way around and when Jeddo with Bingen Blue reached it he slowed to a walk and then to a stop. Zed couldn't help catching up.

Oh, shades of a fading day and a dying epoch. Once it took a driver twenty years of learning and all a man's guts to get in there and score against the other rogues in a major race, him a rogue along with the rest, all out to steal the start. The clang of the recalling bell. "Now, gentlemen, go back, go way back. And you, Mr. Balagher, if you can't respect the horse in pole position—" Etcetera, etcetera, and louder and louder, again and again. No more, not at the big tracks. The betting public won't stand for it. So they tuck you to bed in a moving gate and bring you down all in a row and nine times out of nine you're off. But that's only the half of it. Consider the pari-mutuel, the darling gadget of the moron mind. Any glamor moll can totter to the window on her spike heels, dangle a bill from her lacquered fingernails, get a ticket and go find somebody to read it to her.

Not so in the betting tent of yesterday or of the long yore before that. On a big day it was a maelstrom, a cross between a bargain counter and a massacre. With near-blind Mussy on the rostrum, flanked by spotters and clerks, you might start out just nodding, but you'd end up waving your arms and yelling your head off. Why? Say there are seven horses in a given heat. There's the board with the chalked-up odds. For the plungers they might read 200 for the favorite, 100 each for a couple of others and 200 for the field. A spotter favors you. You get a ticket. You've bought your choice out of the named horses or the field. The winner will snag that individual pool, $600 less commissions. Another pool is offered and another and another. As soon as the plungers lag, the price comes down but not the proportion. Now it's 100, 50, 50 and 100, or it can keep on dropping till it hits bottom. When the betting fades out or when the start of the race is called, whichever comes first, that's the end. How many tickets did you get? All you wanted? All you could pay for? Not necessarily. It all depends how loud is your voice or how winning your ways. With Mit as winning as they come, Keen so well-known and Beef a friend to all the world, Jeddo had picked himself a good team.

Inside the big tent, jammed to capacity, the auctioneer, two ticket writers and a couple of spotters were feverishly engaged in selling pools on Spring Hanover's race, a Classified trot. Forget that word auctioneer, because he doesn't really auction. Once a pool is announced its total price is a fixed sum, but the odds inside it can change. Hence the bedlam, sometimes demoting the favorite and often erupting a dark contender out of the field into individual prominence. Each pool was numbered and grossed the total of what was bid for the individual horses plus the field, a system that beats any pari-mutuel hollow for excitement—no place, no show, the winning ticket to take all that pool less commission. Jeddo's ears tingled to the hum, roar, ban dang "Sold!" The pools were moving so fast that the ear could almost beat the gavel to that final "Sold!" He longed to abandon Bingen Blue and bore his way into the tent, for Keen was in there on one side and Mit on the other with Beef Boulder somewhere in between. Each had a thousand dollars in cash of Jeddo's money and their instructions were to bet the field and keep on buying it as long as Spring Hanover was in it. If by any fluke he should emerge, they were still to buy him, going and coming, up to the clang of the starting bell or down to their last red cent. Only Ep was missing from the team, driven into hiding by the presence of the stranger with the two overcoats who might recognize him and promptly smell a rat. Jeddo itched to know what odds his buyers were averaging and how they were making out. For it wasn't nods the auctioneer was recognizing—it was screams and clawing upheld hands. Finally he heard the call bell and he had to go.

Zed caught up with him. "Jeddo," he murmured mournfully, "ain't that the bell for the start?"

"Don't know yet," said Jeddo without looking around. "Get down there and tie into scoring."

With six entries in the race, Spring Hanover had drawn third position and Bingen Blue fifth. All horses were old campaigners and got the go at the third score. Jeddo had only one object, to kill off the speed for Spring Hanover's benefit; better than anybody he knew what Zed's Old Man could do for a single heat and how he would do it. He shot Bingen Blue for the lead at the turn and made it, all the field piling after him with the sole exception of Springer. Zed couldn't make it out; the old horse seemed to be trotting fine yet there was a three length gap between him and the bunch and it seemed to be getting wider. Zed had another distinction, he was the only driver unfurnished with goggles. He thought of the hundred dollar bill in his hip pocket. That man had been a fool after all, it looked he could have saved his money.

It was toward the end of the first lap of the half-mile track that something happened to wake Zed with a jolt. A clot of mud from the damp track banged him on the forehead, followed by another that half blinded his left eye. The field had come back to him, he was on top of the bunch. He forgot all about his promise, both his promises. What should he do—pass on the turn? He drew on the right rein, but Springer paid no attention; only when they entered the clear of the backstretch did he sidle out and start to plow ahead. First he passed Bingen Blue, completely pooped, and then the next horse and then the next. No longer did clots of mud rain against Zed's face, for Springer was traveling wide of the only trotter left ahead.

Betting in the tent had kept on until the very start of the race; consequently Mit had had no time to reach the stands. But scarcely had she got outside than she spotted Ep, hugging the rail nearby. She pushed in side him and dug her nails into his unfeeling wrist.

"Give me all your tickets," he said without taking his eyes off the track. "I got Beef's and Keen's already."

"Poor Zed," she groaned as the horses passed for the first time. "You didn't even give him goggles!"

"On purpose," muttered Ep.

"Why," exclaimed Mit. "How can you expect him to drive without out goggles?"

"He ain't driving," said Ep.

"W-w-what?" sputtered Mit.

"That's Jeddo's big idea you been fretting yourself sick to know, Mit, no harm to tell you now. All Zed weighs is ninety pounds and the best his string-bean arms can pull is just enough to keep Springer from falling on his nose. That's who's driving—Springer. Same as he did the day Zed took Ed Munyon while you and me and Jeddo was looking on and only Jeddo had the brains to parlay his hunch up to twenty thousand dollars."

"Oh!" breathed Mit in a diminuendo that let all the wind out of her lungs. At that moment Springer's big head came into view in second place. "Look!" she screamed, "Oh, look!"

"Watch now," groaned Ep. "Watch close!"

Again Zed thought of the hundred-dollar bill, but in a different way. As he felt Springer give another surge, lengthening his stride, he remembered the solemn promise he had made to his friends. He started to pull, but all that happened was that Springer seemed to like it, he clamped his teeth solidly on the bit and surged with greater confidence. He was still traveling wide and on the turn into the stretch the lead driver opened out to force him up the bank and out. Zed bore down hard on the right rein, hoping to avoid a crash. Instead Springer shot inside to the left and grabbed the pole.

"He took him," bellowed Ep. "Oh, Springer," he yelled at the top of his voice. "I kiss you front and back! Look at them ears. See that belly hunt the ground. Wah-hoo! Wah-hoo!"

"Mother!" wailed Mit. "Oh, mother, mother, mother!"

Far down the stretch a small boy was being put to the torture, stabbed from the right by the red-hot poker of Skinflint's wrath and from the left by the reproachful eyes of his friends, while in between moved the blur of the pal of his heart—Springer. The Old Man was battling neck and neck. He was edging ahead. He was passing! Zed snatched a double wrap on the reins and dragged himself as upright as the stretch of his legs would permit. He honestly believed that all he had to do to check Spring Hanover was to sink back suddenly with all his weight. But he didn't. He couldn't. Instead he opened his arms wide.

"Old Man!" he screamed. "Old Man! You and me! Take him—and to hell with everybody!"

Spring Hanover shot under the wire, winner by a length. Zed flopped back in the sulky seat. Tears streamed down his cheeks for only the third time since last he bawled for his mother's breast. He had cheated Skinflint, he had double-crossed every friend he had in the world. Springer slowed and turned as though handled by a master and popping out from nowhere Jeddo was running along beside the bike. He led the horse to the stand for the judges' announcement and then out through the gate into the paddock where Mit and Ep were waiting. Zed was still crying.

"Quit that," said Jeddo. "What you crying for?" He turned to Ep. "Have you figured out the take?"

"We averaged nigh eight to one," said Ep. "Near as I can come, it's over twenty thousand and under twenty-one."

"Hear that, Zed?" said Jeddo. "We were betting on you all the time."

"Huh?" said Zed with a wet stare, freeing his feet.

"You heard me."

Zed leaped from the sulky and it wasn't a small boy that landed on Jeddo; it was the clawing, biting, snarling and spitting essence of bobcat. There was no holding the fighting demon in that scrawny body and out of it came words that would have curdled the blood of a loggerhead. Reduced to basic English their intent inferred that

anybody tried to make a fool out of him, the whole lot of 'em, were a bunch out of an unmarried she-coon mother crossed with a skunk.

It was Mit who rescued Jeddo from Zed's teeth as she had done once before, back at the beginning of time. Kneeling she wrapped her arms tightly around him and waited patiently for the stream of curses to run itself out. Then she talked to him and what really turned the trick was her proving that she had been played for a bigger fool than he.

"That's the way it had to be, Zed. If you'd known, could you have looked and acted the way you did? And the same thing goes for me because instead of a brain I've got a mouth could spill a barrel of apples. Besides, it seems to me in a race like that the driver's share is five per cent of the winnings."

"Sure is," agreed Jeddo. "You get a thousand dollars and out of it you can buy me a shirt and a new pair of pants."

Ep tapped Zed on his hard skull. "Get going, son. Think we're going to stay in Connecticut after dark with what'll be in my pocket?"

He went off to settle at the betting tent and Jeddo picked a sure way to make friends with Zed. "You give the Old Man a good grooming, Zed, while I start packing the van."

"What about the guy give me a hundred bucks?" asked Zed. "Do I give it back?"

"Not on your life, you don't. You pulled, didn't you?"

"Yeah, but he promised to wring my neck."

"Don't worry," said Jeddo; "I'll lend you Slap."

Thomasheen James and the Dangerous Age

MAURICE WALSH

The irresistible Thomasheen James appears here in a story with all the accoutrements of folk comedy, including the unlikely combination of romance and betting at the track.

An afternoon late in August I sought out Thomasheen James in a shady corner of the garden. I found him sitting on the tail of his empty barrow, and old pipe of mine in his teeth, and his chin propped on the handle of his sweeping-brush.

"Just after takin' a small piece of a rest to dry the sweat out o' me," he explained.

I ignored that.

"We're off in two days' time," I said.

"Who? Me an' you——?"

"No! My wife and I—Kerry this time, for all of September."

His eyes lit up.

"Ah! I was feart it might be Scotland! Kerry! You'll need a safety-pin in your pocket, an' you better take me along to guard you from the rear."

I swept a hand round the garden.

"You will give the lawn and the hedges two final clippings, lift and pit the last of the second-early potatoes, give the celery a third earthing, pull the keeping onions for drying, plant out four rows of savoy, strip the plums, store the carrots in sand-boxes, tidy away the pea-stakes, keep watering the tomatoes, gather the refuse for burning, and—well! that's about all!"

"Just as you say," he said agreeably. "Anything else at all at all?"

"You can take your own holidays then," I told him unwisely.

"Like the birds o' the air, an' grow fat on daylight an' spring wather! Let it be! I'm used be this to subjugation."

I let it be, and in two days we left house and garden to the mercy of Thomasheen James. He might do none of the things that I had enumerated, but the house and all in it would be perfectly safe in his charge. Plain, petty pilfering was never within his compass; rather was he in the diplomatic class of scoundrel, for he always had a stake on the board and generally lost it—or I did.

The first morning in the last week of September found my wife and me at our final brief anchorage at Ballybunion on Kerry coast. In the shade the air had a crisp edge, but the sun was comfortably warm and the water had that wonderful tang and perfume that comes with the ripening and bursting of the bladder wrack.

My wife was lounging and reading on the ruin-crowned promontory that noses out into the bathing-strand, and I, after a swim, was taking a sun-bath on the dry sand below. Under the leaf of an old panama I looked down my nose and over my bare toes at the sun-shimmering green waters of Shannon Mouth, and at the bold black cliffs of Clare six miles away across the estuary: and, for no reason at all, the thought of Thomasheen James leaning on a hoe in the arid suburbia of Dublin came into my mind. I was lazily sorry for him.

A shadow fell across my feet, and a voice that I knew made insulting speculation.

"Cripers! I wonder is there a touch of the Chinee in him? The sun couldn't do that to no man."

I lifted the flap of the panama. Yes, that was the satan of my thoughts, Thomasheen James himself, aslouch within three paces. He was wearing a cast-off, but sound, homespun suit of mine, and his deepsea-pilot cap was set aslant over one eye. His lean face was as speckled as a brown trout; his china-blue eyes were alive, youthful, bold, and wary; he was in the very pink of hard condition, but I knew it had not been acquired in any garden of mine.

Having given me one quick appraising glance, he turned his

eyes aloofly towards the cliffs beyond the Lady Strand, and got the first blow in.

"I'm on me holidays—same as you told me."

After years of experience I was wise enough not to bandy words with Thomasheen James on work not done. He was no chattel of mine, and the tie between us, while close enough, was never that of employer and employee. He carried freedom under his hat, and came and went like the rain or the wind or a visitation of Jehovah. And secretly I was a little flattered that he had sought me out in the wilderness of Kerry.

I let my head drift back on the sand, snuggled my shoulders into ease, and enquired nonchalantly:

"How did you get this far?"

"Be me usual method—perambulatin' on me two round feet."

"Not all the way?"

"Every dang foot—except for a short bit of a lift I got between Ard-na-Righ and Castleinch."

That short bit of a lift covered at least five-sixths of the total two hundred miles.

"Oul' Matt Shurridan the tinker an' his Kildare band o' chicken-stealers was bringin' down six vans for the Listowel Races," he went on to explain. "I picked them up at Ard-na-Righ an' dropped 'em at Castleinch. Matt is a dacent oul' puckaun in his own way."

"You were in good company—one tinker with another."

"And that's not much of a lie for you," he agreed surprisingly. He sank cross-legged at my side, turned one shoulder to me, watched a handful of dry sand trickle in a yellow spray through his bony fingers, and went on half-musingly. " 'Tis true enough. I have a drop o' the tinker blood in me, as you pointed out more than wance, usin' strong langwidge. Me gran'father was a Ward from the County Wicklow, tinker to the core. That was on me mother's side, an' we'll leave me unknown father rest at peace in his own hell. Oul' Matt Shurridan says that wan drop o' the blood sinds a man to the road or airly, an' mind you, 'tis a life I could be doin' with. A tilt van painted green, white and yalla, with a stove an' a couple o' bunks, no work to speak of, and food in your mouth reg'lar! What more could a man want?"

"A woman to cook the stolen food."

"An' that's the bloody snag, I admit," agreed Thomasheen James. "A woman to cook and wash, an' her oul' granda attached, mendin' tin cans through the country an' liftin' a chicken here an' there. I know tinkers, for I lived with 'em many the day an' night, an' you only think you know them because you wrote about 'em. Thim tinkers o' yours never spit in a man's eye nor tanned a woman's hide for divilmint. Moreover, I never cared for the red hair you're always draggin' in be the gory locks."

"Nor the black hair?"

"I never said nothin' agin black hair," he protested too warmly. "Since that time in the Big War beyant in Stamboul I have a prediction for the brunetty wans in a gineral way. You know the sort? Black as a crow's wing in the hair, an' blue-black in the eye, an' the dusk o' the sun redd'nin' her cheeks. An' shapely bones well padded —if you get me?"

"That sort does not exist."

"I seen her."

"Not amongst the Sheridans," I led him on, marveling. "I know that tribe of tinkers. Lean as a pole and ragged as a bush—"

"You never seen Peg Kate, oul' Matt's gran'daughter. You'd be puttin' her in a book an' changin' her past knowin'." He lapsed into his half-muse. "An' there's no dam' need to change her neither. Risin' twenty an' nice in her ways. I used to be cuttin' sticks for her, an' fillin' her can o' water—an' watchin' the white hound's teeth an' I gettin' a laugh out o' her. Young, young! an' 'tis a pity o' the world to see her gay at the beginnin' o' the road the tinkers travel. Aye! an' her own cousin sidling up to her every chance he gets. A black pug of a lad an' a mean streak in him—Mick Andy. May the divil meet him!"

I lifted the flap of the panama and considered Thomasheen James from a new angle. His gaze was lost in the shimmering green sea, and the blue of his eyes was hazed with dream. I was filled with wonder. Was the dangerous fire of autumn aglow in him? Had Romance, to show her dominion, tackled her most unpromising subject? Never once, in all our dealings had he failed to rail contemptuously at woman with or without provocation, and here he was dwelling fondly on the attractions of one Peg Kate! And at his age! But what was his age? He hid his years well, but he must be approaching forty.

Forty! No, that was not old. It was worse. It was the dangerous age. And at that dangerous age had Thomasheen James done one of the really dangerous things: made advances to a tinker maid? A maid of the wild gypsy tribes that ramble and riot over the roads of Ireland, mending cans and pans, huckstering donkeys, coping horses, drinking, fighting, stealing only occasionally, going to jail often, and beginning again the same old round. A tinker maid! Lovely at twenty, draggled at thirty, dead at fifty, worn out by child-bearing and man-handling! My poor Thomasheen James!

His eyes came down aslant to mine and looked hastily away, and, as I live, the rare flush of embarrassment came to his lean face. He changed the subject hastily. Like most Irishmen, he hated to be caught in his own secret dreamings.

"You was easy traced. A word in a hotel bar or a Guard barracks, an' there was your trail leadin' on dead straight with a coupla o' bends on it. One week you was at Glengariff an' a second at Sneem, an' a week fishin' at the back o' Waterville, an' you caught a fi'-un trout—be a stroke-all so 'twas said—an' here you are takin' the say at Ballybwingan. How's the missues? I see her up on the Castle Green watchin' us."

"Fine. Were you looking for me all these weeks? My garden—"

"I was not. Our circulation co-opted be accident. Tell me, are you goin' to the races at Listowel tomorrow?"

"Ah! I'm getting you. You're going?"

"I'll be somewhere contag'ous."

"And you're dead broke?"

"Don't misdoubt me. I've a mornin's job sellin' racecards for oul' Matt Shurridan, an' later twirlin' a rowletty wheel. 'Tis only pure fri'ndship directed me footsteps to your vicinity. Are you goin' to the races, I axed you?"

"Too much racing in Dublin."

"But manalive! Listowel! The best three-day meetin' in all Ireland!"

It was one of the best certainly, a nice blend of fences, sticks,

and sprints. Listowel was only ten miles away, and we were going
the first and second days; but on the third day I had an appointment
at Killarney that I would have to keep.

"O' course you're goin'," said Thomasheen James. "I'll have
something good for you—an obsolete dead-sure snip."

"Same as Davy Hand had at the Curragh?"

"I knew you'd bring that up agin," said Thomasheen James, regretfully. "You keep on doin' it. An' blast it all! Haven't I worked
off them few shillin's in blood an' sweat an' abuse."

"You'll need the lives of a cat to work off some things," I said.
"What is this absolute dead-sure snip?"

"I haven't it yet— Wait! Wait, won't you? Gi'e me time to
eluciate! Comin' down through Kildare we called in at the Curragh
an' dug up a piece o' information."

"How dead was it?"

"Will you listen to me or won't you?"

I listened. The Curragh is the headquarters of Irish racing, and
any real information therefrom is worth considering.

"Oul' Matt's sister has a great-gran'son a stable-boy with Tom
Kent the trainer. Turn up your nose if you want to, but a cute lad
of a stable-boy knows more about the capacity of a horse an' the
misintintions of a trainer than the owner himself. It stands to reason.
So oul' Matt had a talk with Seumaseen in passin'. Seumaseen is
the lad's name. Look here! Did you ever see a tinker lose money
on a bet? You did not. I know—I know! But I'm only a fraction of
a tinker. Did you ever get a tip from a tinker? You did not. They
keep it betune theirselves. Listen to me, now! Tom Kent, the trainer,
is bringin' down a string o' four horses to Listowel, an' wan o' them
is earmarked to win; an' whin Tom Kent earmarks a horse to win,
that horse retaliates be winnin'. It'll be wan o' two, but which wan
will depind on the state o' the goin'. Are you attendin' to what I say?
Tom Kent will win a good race an' the race will be in me pocket
on the mornin' on the day—or maybe the evenin' before. That's all."

"Not quite. How much are you demanding in advance?"

"Betune me an' you? The Lord forgive you! Listen! Tomorrow,
up to the first race, I'll be sellin' race-cards at the near end o' the
foot-bridge across to the Island Course. You'll see me an' I'll see

you, an' if any information is goin' you'll be welcome to it—so long
as you keep your thumb on it. The meetin' is now adjourned. I'll be
seein' you."

He got limberly to his feet and started to move quickly away. I
sat up and called after him:

"Wait! Sure you're not broke?"

He made a lordly gesture with his hand.

"Keep your money—this time. I'll make me own killin'."

He went on three paces, wavered, paused and turned back, his
eyes on the ground. I had expected this sort of tactic before the final
inevitable touch. But his words surprised me, and their hesitating
diffidence.

"I'm often wonderin' what wan o' thim caravans 'ud run a man
in for. You might know?"

"You mean the price? A motor-van?"

"No dam' fear! A horse for me. I'd want to navigate slow an'
rencounter the resources o' the native. A green, white, an' yalla van,
with a stove and a bunk—or two bunks—you know?"

"I know. A horse—you'll need one with a full set of legs—say
thirty pounds; the van about eighty; fittings, twenty—"

"Cripers! that's a power o' money—"

"But there's a final item much more expensive."

"What the hell could that be?"

"A dark-haired tinker girl named Peg Kate."

Thomasheen James did not explode; he did not even protest
mildly. His eyes met mine and his mouth opened.

"You was takin' it all in," he said gloomily. "Amn't I the bloody
fool at my age?"

He turned and plodded away head down, and this time he kept
going. His hard-bitten misogeny was fighting hard against the
autumn fire in his blood.

My wife and I went to Listowel Races on Tuesday and Wednesday. The weather was perfect, the track in fine order—if on the hard
side—and the racing first-class. I am not describing that racing, or
the crowds, or the games, or the daredevil gambling cheerfulness of
the men of Kerry. This chronicle is devoted to Thomasheen James.

I purchased two race-cards from him on Tuesday morning at the foot-bridge crossing the Feale River to the Island Course. I looked the card over while my wife, who is a born gambler, questioned Thomasheen James for a gambler's tip. He gave her two horses that might have "a chance an' a half."

"Tom Kent has a horse in the third," I suggested.

"Put your shirt on it an' be arrested for inclemacy," said James deridingly. "Don't touch a horse o' Tom Kent's till I say the word!"

Nevertheless I put a small bet on that horse and lost it. My wife, plunging on Thomasheen James's two horses, had no better luck.

On Wednesday I ignored Thomasheen James, or, rather, he ignored me. Again Kent had a horse running, and again I lost a little on it. I am more interested in horses than the gamble thereon, and never bet heavily—a good rule for a man unlucky in gambles. Still, I had some of the luck that was going at Listowel, and at the end of the second day was ten pounds to the good. My wife, who does bet, had varying fortune and was five the other way—which was better than her average.

"That finishes Tom Kent as far as I am concerned," I said, "or need we go to Killarney tomorrow?"

"We must," my wife said, and added slyly, "You could make Thomasheen James your agent?"

I maintained a dignified silence and we left it at that.

We were slowly shouldering our way across the crowded foot-bridge when I saw a well-known deepsea-pilot cap ahead. Thomasheen James's sandy-red poll was below it. He was not alone. A girl was holding his arm. He is a tallish lath of a man, and her bare black head barely reached up to his limber shoulders. Black, indeed, was her hair, and the sun of twenty summers had not rusted the gloss of it. Over her shoulders and low on her neck was the hay-tartaned tinker shawl, and her neck, between hair and shawl, was round and the perfect color of old ivory. She was busily, gaily talking, and when she turned her head up to her swain I saw the dusky richness of her cheeks, the impudent tilt of her chin, the side-glint of white teeth.

I remembered Thomasheen James's words: "The dusk o' the sun redd'nin' her cheeks, an' the shapely bones of her well padded." That described her. She was as bonny as—as a tinker lass. For half a minute I commended Thomasheen James—perhaps envied him—

in my own mind, and then I remembered her breed and was sorry for him.

At the bridge exit, where the crowd splayed out, he turned his head and saw us. He said a quick word out of the side of his mouth to the girl, and I saw the unaccustomed blood touch his cheek-bones. At once she dropped his arm and, never turning a glance in our direction, twisted her lithe tinker's way through the crowd; and as she went she called back encouragingly:

"Never you mind, Tommy boy! Tomorrow for luck!"

"Goodness!" exclaimed my wife. "What a lovely girl! That is never our Thomasheen James?"

"Only the end of him," I said.

He waited for us. He glanced at my wife shamefacedly and touched the peak of his deepsea-pilot cap.

"I want a word with the boss, beggin' your pardon, ma'am."

"Too late, Tom!" she said. "We are not racing tomorrow."

"I'd like a word with him all the same, ma'am," he said stubbornly, "if 'tis no incommodation to you."

She looked at me firmly.

"We are going to Killarney tomorrow," she said. "I will wait for you at the *Listowel Arms*. Do not be too long." And she in turn made her more sedate way through the crowd.

Thomasheen James led me away, and I went without protest. He did not pause till he had me round the quiet flank of the old Desmond Keep that towers over the placid reaches of the Feale. It was the last keep in Ireland to fall to Cromwell.

"Let me show you," said Thomasheen James briskly.

He extracted from breast pocket the race-card for the following day, thumbed two leaves over, and brought his hand smack on a page.

"There it is! The fifth! For three-year-olds and upwards that never won a race value 100 sovs.! Weight for age. That's right! Put on your specks. See that wan! Number 2, *Caroline Hot*, owner an' trainer, T. Kent. An' down here below, No. 11, an' bottom weight, *Rushes Green*, trainer T. Kent. This is our wan—*Rushes Green*."

"Why not Kent's own, *Caroline Hot*—or is it hat?"

" 'Tisn't hot, anyway, an' I'll tell you why. 'Tis only a mudlarker. An' that's Tom Kent's cuteness. He has a double string to his bow

an' arrow. *Rushes Green* runs only on top o' the ground, the harder
the better, an' tomorrow the ground'll be as hard as that oul' castle
wall—barrin' the sky falls, an' it won't. We have it in the bag, I tell
you."

"You heard what my wife said?"

"I wasn't payin' no attintion," he lied. "What was it?"

"We are not racing tomorrow."

"What differ is that?" said Thomasheen James with a confidence that I knew was superficial. "Can't you trust me to put your
money on for you? Wo—wo! Keep your hair on! This is straight
from out of the horse's mouth, I tell you."

"All right! You back it. I'm not interested."

He sighed deeply, and came to his real object.

"Very well so! I've another engagement, an' I'll not waste your
time. Will you advance me two quid?"

"Advance!—"

"Call it anything you like. I'm broke as bread."

"You've been broke all the time?"

"No, only a bloody fool same as always. I had five quid in me
hip this mornin', all me own an' won honest, an' I'm after backin'
five losers with it wan after the other."

"And you want me to finance that sort of luck? You are mistaken. Cut your losses and run—and run hard. You know what I
mean, you poor moth."

"Cripers! You got a new name for me agin. Alludin' to the two
quid—"

"You'll find them waiting for you in Dublin," I said, and strode
away.

I strode a dozen paces and looked over my shoulder. Thomasheen James was standing forlornly, head down and a hand rubbing
the cropped hair at the back of his neck. I should not have fallen; it
might have been better for him if I did not. I probably did owe him
a pound or two, and I had some winnings on me. Having beaten
him into the last ditch—for his own sake—I walked straight back
and pulled him out of it.

"Here! It is Bookmaker's money and unlucky."

"Becripers!" exclaimed Thomasheen James in warm surprise.
"Two fi-pun notes! I always knew you were a man back of all."

"Five o' that is yours, and you can, put it to any foolish use you like. The other five is mine and you will put it for me on *Rushes Green*."

"What else would I do with it?"

"Many things. I know you. Absolutely no explanations accepted. That fiver goes on *Rushes Green* and on nothing else."

I had no faith in that horse, and I had no faith in Thomasheen James. I knew that he would not cheat me directly, but I knew from experience that he might change his mind, with or without reason, and back another horse for me. So I insisted on *Rushes Green* to save my future.

"On his nose it will go," proclaimed Thomasheen James with finality. "Dog, god, man, or divil will not make me swop that bloody bet. 'Tis as safe a'ready as the Bank o' Ireland. I'll be seein' you tomorrow night, me pockets full o' tin."

I knew that I was a fool, and I left him without another word.

We went to Killarney next day. I did not want to go, but I went.

The weather had changed overnight, as weather does change in the South, without warning. There had been no rain for three weeks, and any weather sign that I knew was set fair, but I was waked very early on Thursday morning by rain pelting on my window. And it pelted and poured and cascaded and sheeted all day. The sky fell indeed.

But we went to Killarney, and all the lovely hills were shrouded to the feet, the silken waters were gray, and the trees drooped and dripped chillily; but we kept our dull appointment, and ate dull food, and talked dully of dull things. And in between whiles I looked out at the pouring rain and wondered what the going was like on the Island Course at Listowel, and what chance *Rushes Green* had of racing on top of the ground. Now there was *Caroline Hot!*

The rain was turned off as by a stop-cock before set of sun, and we motored home through a perfect evening with the mountains royal in purple, and the waters serene in their silken sheen, and all the leafage brighter than emerald and ruby in the glow of the west.

At our hotel in Ballybunion I went straight across to the desk-clerk, an old friend.

"What won the fifth, Bill?"

"The fifth! Were you on it too?"

"I had a small interest on *Rushes Green.*"

"So had I—the bastard!" said Bill feelingly. "So had every man, woman, an' child with a tanner to bet. Favorite at six to four on."

"And lost?"

"Mind you, he might have won," said Bill with deliberation, "if they turned on their tracks half-way round. He'd have a forty-length start the second half. Came in some time before the sixth race, slithering in the mud."

"What did win?"

"His stable-companion, *Caroline Hot.* Larruping home in the mud—at tens, and you could have got twenties till some stable-money went on at the end."

"Ah, well!" said I resignedly. "A good thing to have a double string to your bow and arrow."

"What? Had you a saver on *Caroline Hot?*"

"No, Bill. I very carefully cut that second string last evening. To hell with it, anyway!"

I did not see Thomasheen James that night—his pockets full of tin. I did not see him next day either, because next morning early we left for Dublin. When I saw my garden I really did want to see Thomasheen James—to immolate him in his own autumn fire.

I did not see Thomasheen James for four weeks. Often enough in the past he had disappeared for longer periods, and I had never given him a thought; but now I discovered that I had a friendly interest in the scoundrel. I was worried about him. The wild strain in his blood might send him back occasionally to the gypsy life without much harm, but if the autumn fire had really immolated him on the altar of Peg Kate, the tinker girl, that would be harm in plenty. There was in him too much tame blood ever to mix adequately with the tinker strain. The blend could only result in disaster to Thomasheen James and the girl—to a moral and physical degradation. And Thomasheen James was not yet degraded. So I was worried about him.

And then, one brisk afternoon at the end of October, Thomasheen James turned up. It was a clear, brilliant day in the fall, with the sun shining brittle as glass, and a brisk breeze blowing and veering. I was in the vegetable patch burning garden refuse—a job I like, for it is pleasant to watch the flames flicker and lick, to dodge about the curl and eddy of acrid smoke, to sniff the fine earthy perfume of burning weeds. And Thomasheen James turned up.

I had got a wisp of smoke into my eyes and was giving utterance when a voice that I knew made remark close at hand:

"Cursin' won't help without you have sinse to keep win'ard."

I wiped the tears out of my eyes. That was Thomasheen James. He had been away for a mere month or so and was now back. That was all, and there was nothing to do but behave according to code. Already he had a spare fork in his hand, and a single dead cabbage leaf impaled for sacrifice. I cleared my throat carelessly and said:

"Had a nice long holiday?"

"If you'd call it that, an' me trampin' the roads of Ireland like a sowl out o' hell."

Here, as well I knew, was an indirect intimation that he was prepared to be questioned and had all his answers ready. While busily forking I took occasion to consider him out of the side of an eye. At the end of September he had been brown-freckled and lean and fit; but now the brown and freckles had paled, his cheeks had grown sallow under tight-skinned cheek-bones, and his eyes were washed to a colder blue. His old homespun showed stains of wind and weather, his shoes, that used to shine with my polish, were scuffed grey as the grey dust on them; but his deepsea-pilot cap still retained a little jauntiness. Wherever he had been for the last month he had not enjoyed life, and now he wanted to tell me about it for some purpose of his own. He would too, and I could not stop him; nor would I aid him, for all my curiosity.

The fire was going well now, and I leant on my fork handle, out of the smoke but near enough to get the pleasant warmth. Thomasheen James shuffled to my shoulder.

"Hot work!" he said. "I'm not used to it yet. I saw you calculatin' the weight on me mind."

"Can't weigh the imponderable," I said.

"That don't mane nothin' to me no more than to yourself," he said, sighing patiently. "Do you know? the divil out o' hell is timptin' me the whole week to tell you a straight honest lie. 'Keep your trap shut,' says he to me. 'I never could,' says I. 'I'll ha' to tell him somethin'.' 'All right so!' says he. 'Tell him what he'll believe.' 'He'll not believe it,' says I, 'after I tell him.' An' so we went. No, sir! I never told you no lie—not never."

"Not never is hardly right, though you never told me much else."

"You know what I mane. Them bits o' lies be way o' business or divarision don't matter a ha'porth. Don't you live be lies yourself an' you callin' it ficshun? Haven't I caught you twistin' me own little prevaricatin's? That's nothin'. But when it comes down to the rock, an' what's expected from you to me, I have cause often enough to curse the tinder nature o' me own honesty. Listen, while I have the spunk! Do you remimber bein' at Listowel Races—an' may the divil drown the same Listowel an' ten miles round it?"

"I believe I was there—one day, or was it two?"

" 'Tis the third I want to forget. An' you well remimber handin' me a fiver to put on the bastar' called *Rushes Green* in the fifth? You remimber that?"

"I do."

"An' you remimber shovin' your fist under me nose warnin' me that I was to back *Rushes Green* an' nothin' else?"

"Well?"

"I didn't do it."

"Didn't do what?"

"Didn't back *Rushes Green*," said Thomasheen James, and sighed. "I got it out at last—but don't you have no hopes, I'm warnin' you."

I grasped his arm and stopped him.

"I'll have no fears either," I said forcefully, "and I am warning you. As far as I am concerned, that fiver went on *Rushes Green,* and I refuse to be responsible for its later adventures."

"Just as well," said Thomasheen James, brightening up a little. "I ran away meself. I better tell you all about it."

"Be brief!"

"If I had a stem o' sinse," cried Thomasheen James bitterly, "I'd be brief to the p'int o' extinguishment."

He went round the fire forking furiously at half-burnt twigs, and then quieted down. All during the subsequent narrative he emphasized his misfortunes in the same way, and in his calm periods I collected more material for his fork.

Aye! I'd be dam' brief (went on Thomasheen James). Me privit divil says to me: *"Rushes Green* lost, so keep your trap shut!" But could I? I can't—damn'd if I can! The Lord knows, maybe I am a fool, but I respecks the footin' on which both of us stand an' fall. It gi'es me a sort o' place in me own mind, a sort of a feelin' that I'm a peg above all them heirs to the throne except the heir himself. If I done the dirty on you on the heads of a measly fiver I couldn't never look you in the face agin. I'd be as bad as a politeecian. Thim's my sentiments, take 'em or leave 'em!

Gi'e me time, me dear man! for this is comin' out o' me with a corkscrew twisted in me interials. Where was I? The third day at Listowel. Yes, becripers! It started to rain after the turn o' the night, and in bucketfuls it came down. The weather set out to quinch hell, and the course went along. Two horses came down at the regulation fence first time round in the steeplechase, an' in the third—a flat mile —the jockeys came in mud to the eyeballs. "If this bastar' *Rushes Green* goes on top o' the ground 'tisn't in Listowel he'll go it," says I to meself, an' I whirlin' the rowletty wheel.

I had your fiver in me inside pocket ready to slip on when the time came, an' I was grossly concerned for it, an' a bit for me own as well. So I bundled up the wheel—'twas too wet for play anyway—an' took a quick turn round to get a hould o' Peg Kate. You didn't hear me mintion Peg Kate—Peg Kate Coffey, oul' Matt Shurridan's gran'-daughter? Oul' Matt the Kildare tinker— Oh! you did? You'll hear more of her from this on. I knew where to find her.

"Peg Kate, *agrah*," says I, "is *Rushes Green* still the goods?"

"I couldn't rightly tell you, Tommy," says she, for she has an honest drop in her. "Me gran'dad is away round to see Seumaseen" —that was that stable-boy o' Tom Kent's.

"Will the Oul' Wan tip us the wink?" I asks her.

"He'll tip it to me, anyway," says she, "and I'll pass it to you, Tommy, but they mustn't see me doin' it."

You know the underground way thim tinkers has. Their infromation stays at home. Though I was a piece of a month with thim, an' thick as thieves with wan or two, divil a word I'd ha' known about *Rushes Green* only for Peg Kate, an' it took me a week to ameliate her be collogin' in a corner.

"Where could I meet you on the quiet, Tommy?" says she.

I knew the spot. "Down below at the las' turn, Pegeen," says I. "You'll see a bit of a hedge flankin' the post at the river-side. We'll meet under it out o' sight while the fourth race is on. Run now an' find the oul' puckaun!"

Off she wint, an' as I turned round there was Mick Andy givin' me a dirty look close at hand. He's her own first cousin. I told you about him! An ugly thick pug of a lad, an' makin' up to Peg Kate.

I met a fri'nd then, an' we had a pint in a markee an' another on top, for I needed courage to decide not to obey orders, as it might be. Wan thing an' another, the fourth race was over whin I got down to the hedge. Peg Kate was not there. There was no wan there, though they was millions round the corner. I wasn't none disturbed at first. There was lashin's o' time, and I could dipind my life on Peg Kate. I gave her five minits. Thin I gave her two more, an' began to bite me tongue.

"Blasht her! the rashpeen!" I says out loud.

An' at that I heard a squeak at the other side o' the hedge. A

choked kind o' squeak—like a rabbit in a brass loop, but with a
touch o' the cat an' the female about it. There was a hole in the
bottom o' the hedge, and through it I wint like a fox. Behind, there
was a tree or two growin' on a narrow patch o' grass, an' then the
bank o' the river fell straight down five or six feet; an' below was a
spit of stones an' gravel with the shallow water washin' the edge of
it.

Listen! As sure as I'm tellin' you, Peg Kate was down there, an'
so was her cousin Micky Andy. He had her throttled agin the bank
with wan hand, an' th' other hand was over her mouth; an' she was
doin' her dam'dest with her teeth an' her feet, an' gettin' an odd
squeak out betimes. He was as strong as a wake mule, an' she
couldn't do much, the crathur.

"Aisy! Aisy there!" says I up above, an' he let her go an' jumped
clear. An' she jumped th' other way an' let a screech out of her.

"Tom! Oh, Tommy! He's after tryin' to break me windpipe so I
couldn't pass you the word."

"Mick Andy, you tinker's scut," says I, humorin' him for the
occasion. "You shouldn't man-handle no woman less she's your
wife."

"Near enough," he yelps at me in a timper. "Come down here,
you Dublin Jackeen, an' I'll l'arn you man-handlin'. Come on
down!"

"I don't want no trouble with the likes o' you, Mick Andy," I
says, peaceable be intent, "an' far be it from me to shame you before your own cousin, Peg Kate."

He hopped on the ground like a magpie, an' his coat was off in
a twist.

"Come down!" he bawled, "an' I'll show Peg Kate the color o'
your liver. Come down, you deludherer! Or I'll come up."

I don' mind admittin' that I was a bit discreetly frightened of
him. Tinkers is dirty fighters—kick an' gouge an' bite—an' he was a
thick, strong-built chunk of a young lad.

Clear out o' here, you chicken-stealer," I says, doin' me best
to pacify him. "You heard what happened the last man I hit?"

"I did." He let a bellow out of himself. "He got two months for
mistreatin' a—a snotty nose."

Wherever he got that approbious name I don't know, but he hadn't it out o' his gob before I landed on top of him an' scattered him to the gravel. An' as he come up under me I gev him the right. You saw that blow I hit Barney Doony in Ard-na-Righ? You did not! I mane the blow I hit him whin you wasn't lookin'! That's the wan I gave Mick Andy—from me heel up. It turned him round like a tee-toe-tum an' I stopped him with a left under his ear. Aye! but he was indured to corporeal beltin' an' he comes at me, his head betune his shoulders an' both hands thrashin'.

"I'll take you to bits, you so-an'-so," says he.

But I circulated away from him, jeldy-footed, an' he near wint into the river. I abetted him with a root in the right place, an' he wint in knee-deep. He come out agin be main force, an' we had it.

I had a couple or more inches on him in reach, but he had it in weight be a stone, an' me eyetarnal sowl depended on the way I could stand off an' bombinate him with long fire. I did that, an' hot an' heavy for five minits. Peg Kate enj'yin' herself hoppin' round us an' gettin' out o' the way. An' then the drink began to tell on him, young as he was, for he was full o' bad porther an' had been for three days. I had him gaspin' for breath in no time at all, an' then I set about returnin' him proper to his native mud. I would, too, in another minit, only me foot turned on a stone, an' he got his hands on me. It done him no good. He was too done to get me down, an' whin he tried to get his thumb in me eye I propped his head agin the bank, an' started to gi'e him the double roll o' kettle-drums in the short ribs. At that he let a final yell out of himself.

"Peg Kate, don't let him kill your cousin! Hit him a chroosht with a lump o' stone."

Busy as I was, I saw her out o' wan eye leverin' up a lump o' rock as big as me head, an' I tried to shake meself loose; but he had the strangle-clutch o' death on me. You know what tinkers are, or do you? Did you ever insinuate yourself betune two o' them in a puckin' match? You did not, an' don't never. 'Tis dead fatal eleven times out o' ten. They jine forces an' rip your hide off.

I remimbered that with Micky Andy tangled on me, and Peg Kate comin' in at us with the stone up in her two hands. An' I could do nothin' but dodge me head down an' shut me eyes—an' I had no

time to think o' the falsity o' the sex. An' then! Ker-r-lump! An'
Mick Andy wint limp in me arms an' slipped to the ground under
me. Think o' that, will you?

"Did I kill him dead, Tommy?" she screeches, pullin' me off him.

"You did," says I, "less his head is iron."

"I better hit him another to make sure," says she. "I'll never get
a better chance."

But I held her off. The three C's fits me to perfection—calm,
cool, and collected. In all the ruckus the business in hand never took
a back seat, the same bein' the investment o' two fi'-pun notes to
the advantage o' the oul' firm—me an' you.

"Peg Kate," says I, shaking her, "what's the latest?"

"The latest what, Tommy?" says she, the sinses scattered on her.
So I gev her another good shake to settle her.

"Rushes Green? You onshuch!" says I.

"Oh!" says she. "Seumaseen says the bastar' has no chance no
more—not in the mud."

"What has, then?"

"Things is betwixt an' between, I dunno, Tommy! The goin' is
too soft for wan, an' maybe not soft enough for another, but
Seumaseen says that *Caroline Hot* is the best out o' the bag as things
are."

"Best out o' the bag is good enough," says I, an' I made a drive
to top the bank. But she caught me.

"You can't, Tommy!" she schreeches.

"Le' me go, you rip," says I, me hand up to her.

"But if you saw yourself? Like a stuck pig you are, your nose
the way it is. An' where's your collar an' tie? Put your head round
the corner an' you'll be arrested for manslaughterin' Mick Andy."

She was right too. No man can fight a tinker for five minits an'
come out of a band-box. I felt wan eye shuttin', an' me own blood
tasted salty in me mouth. But did I lose me sagacity? No, sir! There
was only wan thing to be done an' I done it. Me hand in me hip, the
two fivers slapped into Peg Kate's hand, an' her fingers down on
them—like that!

"Run, you divil!" says I, givin' her a shove towards the bank.
"Run! an' put thim two fivers on *Caroline Hot* at any price you can
get. Our bit of a van is in it." We used be talkin' of a van all to our-

selves an' we alone together. "Run!" says I, givin' her a hoist, "or I'll tear every hair out o' your head. Meet me at the usual place at the fall o' dark." We got into the habit o' comin' together for a bit of a collogue in a quiet place in the back of oul' Matt's van. "Run, me darlin'!" says I, "an' remember our own nate bit of a van an' our travelin' shop. Run, you imp o' hell!"

I thrun her on top o' the bank in a last heave, an' she wint through the hedge prompt as a cat in haste. After that I turned round to Mick Andy. He was sittin' up blinkin', an' rubbin' the goose egg that was laid be the rock on the roof o' his skull.

"We'll raysume the argyment where we was interrupted," says I.

"The conclusion is clinched for the time," says he.

"Only wan nail to drive home," says I, liftin' me foot—an' he lay down agin.

I left him there watchin' me out o' wan eye, an' after gettin' a bit o' the blood off me face an' shirt I circulated round be the river an' got off the course. . . .

You know what won? You do! *Caroline Hot* at tens. Me good intintion was to meet Peg Kate in the usual spot, collect our spondulicks, take the last bus out to Ballybwingan an' heave a rock through your winda to joyful awakement. No, I didn't heave no rock. I wasn't in Ballybwingan at all. I'll tell you. 'Tis all I can do.

That evenin' comin' on dusk I wint round to the back o' the tinker's camp a mile outside the town—in a bit of a plantation. There was a nice shady sally bush there between two scarths o' briars—only it was damp be that time. Peg Kate wasn't there yet. I waited for her. I waited an hour. I got a start of a fright wonderin' if she was late gettin' our money on, an' maybe herself afraid to face me now—an' well she might. I waited on. There was no Peg Kate.

I crept close in an' looked through the wheel of a van. There was a big fire in the open, an' a melodeon goin'. The tinkers, men and women, had had a good day be all appearances. Some o' them dancin', an' some singin', an' two o' them havin' a quiet puckin' match to theirselves in a corner—an' the kids scurryin' like chaff—an' all o' them takin' turns at a slug out of a five-gallon jar. But there was no sign anywhere of Peg Kate, or oul' Matt—or Mick Andy aiether. I daren't go in. Desprit an' all as I was, I had sinse enough to keep out. Go in among a band o' tinkers ravenin' in drink, an' me after malafouxterin' Mick Andy! You could bury me remnits in a cigar-box.

I crept up on me belly as near as I could to oul' Matt's van—the green, white, an' yalla wan I told you about. He had a brindle dog, a cross betune a bull an' a hound, that slept under the van, an' that same brute-baist 'ud tear the throat out of his own mother after the fall o' night. The van was dark an' the curtains down, but in betune the varses of a song beyant by the fire I thought I heard snorin'. That would be oul' Matt, blind drunk. Pegeen, as I knew, had not reached the maturity for sich wholesale music.

I wint a bit closer in an' gev a small whistle, an' the dog growled. I stuck me ground an' whistled agin—louder—an' after that I left there knockin' sparks out o' the ground, an' the dog hell-for-leather after me. I bate him to the road an' turned him with a rock hoppin' off his rump. I gev in for the night.

I slept in a horse-box with two stable-boys, an' waked up nex' mornin' the sun shinin' bright into me good eye; an' me heart in me boots. What would you do then? Curse your bellyful an' cut your losses, an' maybe you'd be right too. I cursed sure enough, to break an ass's back, but I did more.

I know tinkers, an' you don't, for all your talk in print. I wint up to the camp an' marched straight in, drums batin' an' colors flyin'. It was on in the mornin' then, an' most o' them were at a late breakfast round the fires. You'd 'a been in bed with a could bandage on your head, but the tinkers, after a tearin' night, was wolfin' down bacon an' sausages an' eggs an' strong tay. The perfume made me mouth water, an' me stomach agin me backbone.

Let no man miscall a tinker where I am. In their own camp, an' sober, they are the fairest, hospitablist set of bastar's in all Ireland, an' a few belts an' kicks given an' partook in drink is only considered as a bit of diversion—till next time drink is in 'em. I knew that, an' staked me carcase on it.

They hurrooed when they saw me an' gathered round to speculate me black eye, for, as I soon l'arned, they knew 'twas me busted Mick Andy. Did they mind? Not thim! His own brother slapped me on the back. "I'd give the sight o' wan eye," says he, "to be able to trim him so han'some. He's beyant in the tilt, a poultice on his head an' a yard of stickin'-plaster holdin' his ribs on. You're a ragin' terror, Thomasheen James."

I ate with them an' kep wan eye liftin', for, as you may guess, there was no sign o' Peg Kate anywhere—or of oul' Matt. An' all the time I was wonderin' how many o' the facks was known to the band; for I caught some o' them grinnin' an' winkin' behind me back. So after a last cup o' tay I says sort o' careless:

"Where's the Oul' Wan?"

"Over in the van," says a lad, "havin' a late sleep to himself."

"I'll over an' bid him good-mornin'," says I.

"Why not you?" says he agreeable.

So over I strolled, an' becripers! if the whole crowd didn't follow me, nudgin' an' showlderin' each other. The van door was shut at the top o' the steps, an' before I could climb up, the whole jin-bang o' them, men and women and childer, let a yell out o' themselves to wake the dead.

"Ould Wan! Ould Wan! Here's Thomasheen James to bid you good-mornin'."

At that the door opened, top an' bottom, an' there stood oul' Matt, mild as milk, sober as a judge, an' his beard white as the dribblin' snow. An' oul' man he was, an' noble-lookin' as a bishop; an oul', white-livid puckaun with a white smeg in a caroline hat, an' you'd think to look at him that butter wouldn't melt in his mouth; but he had a weight o' sin an' expayrience behind him to sink a battleship. In all Ireland there wasn't the likes o' oul' Matt Shurridan.

Tinkers haven't no leaders—they won't stand for no leaders—but in every band you'll find a charackter that goes be the name th' Oul' Wan. He hasn't a ha' porth o' power, maybe, but nothin' worth mintion is done till he vets it, an', even then, it might not be done or done contrairy. 'Tis a dam' quare office.

Oul' Matt was the Oul' Wan o' the Shurridans. I seen him at work. A lad might have a turn-up with his wife a batin' wouldn't settle, or a double-crossin' bargain on the tape, or a difficulty about a horse or a girl, or a thing like that, an' he'd sidle along careless-like in Matt's gineral direction an' start a indifferent collogue; an' the two o' them would go at it talkin' about an' along an' over an'

under the subjeck in hand, an' not wan plain word o' the subjeck
direct; an' after a while the lad 'ud withdraw himself cursin' the
oul' divil his head moidhered; but after another while a word here
an' a word there might come to his mind, an' puttin' two an' two
together he'd have a hell of a notion o' his own smartness.

Oul' Matt sat down to the top step above me, an' never let his
mild deceivin' ould eyes rest on me down below. He looked out over
all our heads an' started to cut a plug o' tabbacy for his pipe, an' I
tried to get a peep up into the van behind him. I took him judicial
to start with.

"Me hairy oul' puckaun!" says I, "where's Peg Kate this
mornin'?"

He took no notice at all but went on sawin' at the plug. I kep'
me timper.

"Do you want me to come up an' take the whiskers off of you
like I'd pluck a goose?" I says reasonable. "Where's Peg Kate, I
asked you?"

An', at that, the pack o' divils behind me let a yowl out o' them.

"Where's Peg Kate? Come on out, Peg Kate!"

An' becripers joe! Peg Kate herself came out of a corner o' the
van, an' stood up above the Oul' Wan. You saw her wance. She's
nice. She was nice then, her mouth all atrimble an' her eyes big with
the tears she unsh'd. An' her voice trimbled as well.

"Tommy! Oh, Tommy!" says she. "They done it on me."

I didn't ax what they done on her. I wint up three steps, an' the
Oul' Wan stopped me with the p'int o' his knife firm agin me
breast-bone.

"Peg Kate," says I soft over his head. "Did you do that?"

"I did," says she, "every farthin'. I got twelves, an' a minit
sooner I'd 'a got twenties."

"An' what then, you tinker's brat?"

"Wo—wo!" says she. " 'Twas all your fau't, Tommy, not to let
me hit Mick Andy another peg. He was only half-kilt, an' heard
every word. An' whin I got me winnin's—the full o' me two stockin's
—off of Jack Larry the bookie, an' before I could move a foot, I was
surrounded be Mick Andy an' the crowd o' them there."

"They took it off of you?"

"Not where it was, but they ran me home to camp."

"An' that was th' end of it?"

"No, Tommy, no! Me gran'da here has it—every penny. Don't be hard on him, Tommy, an' he mightn't see us wronged."

I looked up at him, an' he wasn't lookin' at me, but over me head, and the p'int o' his knife not movin' agin me breast-bone. I wasn't none hard on him outside plain tinker langwidge.

"You sepulchrous oul' ruffeen!" I said. "That's me honest-won money—wan hunder' an' thirty solid quid—and I'll have it out of you if it was hid in your gizzard itself. Come on you—!"

The p'int o' the knife bit me, an' I took a buck of a jump backways that landed me on me heels with agility.

The lads gave a hurroo, an' the Oul' Wan lifted his hand to stop them, an' they hurrooed agin before givin' him silence. Not once, mind you, did he let his deceivin' oul' eyes come down my way.

"A strange thing," says he, addressing his remarks to a tree across the way. "A strange thing how a drop o' the blood'll tell! I mind as well as the day before yesterday the mornin' this girl's father"—he put a thumb over his shoulder— "Black Tom Coffey, a dacent man, God rest him, but wake in the skullbone, he was kilt be the kick of a jinnet at Puck Fair. I mind that first day he come into me camp near Scartaglen. His great gran'father, a farmin' man, poor fella, on the Cork border, stole away wan o' the black Carty rips out of a band o' Kerry tinkers, and here agin was the wild drop comin' out in the third gineration—"

"Will you shut up, you oul' gandher," I roared, "an' talk turkey?"

"I mind the day well," he keeps meandherin' on calm as a jail, "when in walked Black Tom in desp'ration. A prosperous travelin' tinsman I was at that time with two vans o' me own an' me only child Kate growin' up around me. 'Matt Shurridan,' says he, 'I can't sleep no longer under a thatched roof an' the moon shinin' in at the winda; I can't get up at five in the mornin', day in day out, to milk the cows an' wather the horse; I can't sit down to three square meals a day at the same kitchen table. Damn your sowl, Matt Shurridan!' says he, 'will you let me go the road with you for a piece of a year, an' I might come to me sinses an' marry a thick-hocked agricultooral girl from the North o' Kerry.' I was a soft-hearted man, an' I did it—"

"I'll soften it agin for you, you ould blatherskite," I roars up at him.

"Kill or cure I did it. Man dear! he took to the life like a duck to the wather, an' in no time at all I made a good tinsman out of him. He could bottom a can with a nateness of judgment so it wouldn't leak a drop till our next round was due. An' after a time he saw me daughter Kate for the first time—an' he after seein' her every day for months, an' she lookin' at him her eyes like a dyin' duck. She scatthered the sight on him, I tell you, for she was a purty armful. But he was a honest *bosthoon*. He comes to me. ' 'Tis this way,' says he stutterin'. 'I know,' says I, 'you want Kate, can you keep her?' 'If she'd stay—' 'You blockhead!' says I. 'I mane can you feed her an' the mouths to come?' 'There's me bit o' land on the Cork border,' says he. 'She'd die on it,' says I, 'but if you had a van of your own or the price of it—' 'I could sell the bit o' land,' says he. 'Very good!' says I. 'Listen! when you meet her tonight in that bunch o' sallys betune the scarth o' briars tell her that you are ready an' willin' to jump the budget with her. I won't have her wronged,' I says. He did, he told her an' they jumped the budget in front o' me eyes, an' I gave the pair o' them me second van at a bargain. Ah, well! they are both dead now, God rest them, an' I won't see their daughter wronged naither."

That was all he said. He got up on his lively ould feet, and turned towards the door. I let a yell out of me.

"What about me money, you white-liveried oul' finaceer?"

He turned agin an' looked over me head.

"I never wronged no man," he says, "an' I'll not begin now, wan foot in the grave. A gran'daughter's best is a gran'father's bet till she has a man of her own an' a van of her own. I am wrongin' no man, an' I will not. I will not tear any man's windpipe out be the roots as long as I have a dog to do it. Here, Paddo!"

An' there was Paddo, the half-bred bull, on top o' the steps, grinnin' down at me, pleased with anticipatin' me windpipe.

Oul' Matt turned into the van, pushin' Peg Kate in front of him, but not before she took two handfuls o' wool out of him. The whole band hurrooed me in a mockery, an' for wan' desprit minit I had a notion of assailin' the dog. But me madness evapirated observin' his bare teeth.

I made a silent retrate. What more could I do? I wint down to the river bank an' considered su'cide an' murdher an' a bit of arson on the quiet, an' after a while I raycalled a few o' the scatterin' remarks the Oul' Wan had vintilated. There was the van at a bargain, an' jumpin' the budget—which is the tinker's method o' matrimony —an' there was that sally bush in the scarth o' briars. How the divil did the oul' puckaun know o' the sally bush an' meself an' Peg Kate circumspeck as weasels? That stuck in me mind, an', be way o' investigation, I crept round there that evenin' at the fall o' dusk.

You guessed it! Peg Kate was there before me, an' her arms round me neck like a—a octopus.

"The luck o' the world we have, Tommy darlin'," says she, makin' me ear tickle. "Everything is right agin. Look what I have for you."

I thought 'twas me money she was rubbin' agin me cheek, an' me heart lepped; but it was only a square o' white paper with writin' on it—she could write handy—an' a stamp at the foot.

"What the hell is that?" says I jumpin'.

"A receipt," says she.

"A receipt?" says I, an' you could knock me down with a feather.

"Yes, Tommy," says she happy. "A receipt for wan hunder' an' twinty quid marked be me gran'da be his own mark. We're grand, Tommy! He sold us the van horse, budget an' fittin's for wan hunder' an' twinty—a dead bargain. All he asks is a shakedown in a corner an' a bite now an' then—an' he says he'll taich you to bottom a can for nothin'. But we'll ha' nothin' to do with a tinker's life no more, Tommy darlin'. We'll have our own little travelin' shop. Isn't it grand?"

I swallowed me heart an' palate, an' tongue an' tonsilatus, an' after a while I coughed up me tongue.

"They was another ten pounds," I said in a wake voice.

"Here it is," says she, "an' th' Oul' Wan said it was for our honey-moon—Killarney an' the bed of honor itself. We can jump the budget tomorrow if we have to, an' then go off be ourselves an' get married decent be a priest, for I'll be a tinker no longer."

An' she shoved the two fi'-pun notes into me hand, an', as I live to be bread, they was the same two identical notes you pushed at

me the second evenin' o' Listowel Races. An' there you are, back
where you started.

Thomasheen James sighed deeply and was so long silent that I
ventured to prompt him.

"So you married your Peg Kate?"

"I had no bad intintions agin her that way. She was a dacent bit
of a girl—an' strong as whalebone. I won't deny that any little things
I might be whisperin' in her ear at the butt of a sally bush could be
half-true—at the time—an' sure a man can ha' fancies o' his own.
But, on the other hand, when a man comes face to face with bein'
tied an' tethered an' bound to a female woman over the budget or
before the altar rails it is time for him to stand off an' consider the
jurisdiction of the whole affair. It was that time with me, an' whin
I got me sinses agin I says:

" 'Good enough, Peg Kate! But they's an obligement on me with
a gintleman up in Dub—Belfast,' I says, 'an' I must see him
first.'

"She tightened her hould on me an' began to ullagone.

" 'Tommy, would you fool me? If I let you out o' me sight now
I'll never see you agin, an' I'll be goin' the roads o' Ireland with a
double-barrel gun full o' buckshot to blow your stony heart into
the dust o' the road.'

"I gev her a hug an' a wallop at the same time, an' the wallop
was meant.

" 'Me honor is concerned in this,' says I. 'You wouldn't have me
wrong a gintleman that is like a brother to me?' meanin' yourself.

"But still she cried—as the song says.

" 'Look, Tommy! They's honest blood in me the same as yourself—me father's blood—an' I hate this livin' in bands an' stravagin'
through the country for roguery. Let us go off in our own van an'
start our bit of a travelin' shop.'

" 'But there's oul' Matt,' says I weakenin' a bit.

" 'He's good at the bottom,' says she, 'an' odd times we could
park him with his sister an' Mick Andy.'

"An' so we argyfied back an' fore, till she near melted the
heart in me. It was only the thought of you, an' what you'd say, that
held me up to me guns, an' I was softened so much that in the ind
as a token of me faith I caught a grip of her hand an' agin for

the secon' time put the two fives in her palm an' shut her fingers on them.

" 'There!' says I. 'Thim's for our honeymoon. Take good care o' them or I'll belt the hide off of you.'

" 'I'll take care o' them,' says she, 'till they melt in me bosom.'

" 'I'll hold this receipt,' I says, 'an' you stick to the van. P'ison Paddo for me, but nourish the Oul' Wan, for I want to strangulate him to me own specifications.'

"And there I left her," said Thomasheen James, his tone strangely desolate, "an' I have not been near her since. I been wanderin' the roads o' Ireland like a sowl out o' hell wonderin' whether it would be safer for me to go back to her or vinture me tale for your misunderstandin'. Here I am now, me tale told, and you have a rake in your hand."

I was tempted to clout him one. He had indeed escaped matrimony with a tinker girl, but I was not in the least happy about it. I had seen that girl once and the picture she made remained in my mind; and Thomasheen James himself had subconsciously given her an attraction of her own. I was just being romantic. I moved to the other side of the fire out of temptation.

"Where is this poor girl now?" I asked restrainedly.

"Don't take it into your head you can find her," he warned quickly.

"Does she know where to find you?"

"With a double-barrel gun! You mus' take me for the dam'dest fool in the world." He sidled towards me. "You better keep this here docyment, since it contains your sixty solid quid."

He handed me a folded and draggled scrap of paper. I opened it carefully so that it would not fall apart at the creases. It was the neatly written receipt of one "Matew Sherdan X his mark for one hunderd and twenty pounds the price of van, horse, budget, fitings painted green white and yelow as well as the dog paddo sold to Margaret Catherine Coffey and Tommy J. Doran gettin' marrid."

I refolded that document carefully and put it in my pocket; and I had a queer psychic unfinished feeling about the whole thing. I was not vexed, or inclined towards anger; I was just resignedly sorrowful.

"That is the way in real life," I said. "Winter is upon us and the autumn fire is dead."

"They's wan warmin' our shins this minit," said Thomasheen James, not comprehending.

I looked at him with distaste.

"But sometimes, an old tree blossoms again in spring, and you may find that out to your cost."

"Ah! I have you." He cheered up at some thought of his own. "Becripers, you're right! An' I am no old tree neither. You've took a weight off me an' I knew you would. Do you know what we'll do? We'll give spring another chance at me. How long do you think it would take for two fivers to melt in a warm bosom?"

I then hit him with the rake handle.

The Broken-link Handicap

RUDYARD KIPLING

This tale is very characteristic of its author. Kipling always felt that an Anglo-Saxon should stick as closely as possible to a vocabulary which avoided words of Latin origin. There is hardly a three-syllable word in this whole story. The sentences are short, terse, and descriptive without being in the least verbose. The plot is highly original yet, to a horseman, thoroughly possible.

> While the snaffle holds, or the long-neck stings,
> While the beam tilts, or the last bell rings,
> While horses are horses to train and to race,
> Then women and wine take a second place
>   For me—for me—
>   While a short "ten-three"
> Has a field to squander or fence to face!
>   *Song of the G. R.*

There are more ways of running a horse to suit your book than pulling his head off in the straight. Some men forget this. Understand clearly that all racing is rotten—as everything connected with losing money must be. In India, in addition to its inherent rottenness, it has the merit of being two-thirds sham; looking pretty on paper only. Everyone knows everyone else far too well for business purposes. How on earth can you rack and harry and post a man for his losings, when you are fond of his wife, and live in the same Station with him? He says, "On the Monday following," "I can't settle just yet." You say, "All right, old man," and think yourself lucky if you pull off nine hundred out of a two-thousand-rupee debt. Any way you look at it, Indian racing is immoral, and expensively immoral. Which is much worse. If a man wants your money, he ought to ask for it, or send round a subscription-list, instead of juggling about the country, with an Australian larrikin; a "brumby" with as much breed as the boy; a brace of *chumars* in gold-laced caps; three or four *ekka*—ponies with hogged manes, and a switch-tailed demirep of a mare called Arab because she has a kink in her flag. Racing leads to the *shroff* quicker than anything else. But if you have no conscience and no sentiments, and good hands, and some knowledge of pace, and ten years' experience of horses, and several thousand rupees a month, I believe that you can occasionally contrive to pay your shoeing-bills.

Did you ever know Shackles—b.w.g., 15–1⅜—coarse, loose, mule-like ears—barrel as long as a gate-post—tough as a telegraph-wire—and the queerest brute that ever looked through a bridle? He was of no brand, being one of an ear-nicked mob taken into the *Bucephalus* at four pounds, ten shillings a head to make up freight, and sold raw and out of condition at Calcutta Rs 275. People who lost money on him called him a "brumby," but if ever any horse had Harpoon's shoulders and The Gin's temper, Shackles was that horse. Two miles was his own particular distance. He trained himself, ran himself, and rode himself; and, if his jockey insulted him by giving him hints, he shut up at once and bucked the boy off. He objected to distraction. Two or three of his owners did not understand this, and lost money in consequence. At last he was bought by a man who discovered that, if a race was to be won, Shackles, and Shackles only, would win it in his own way, so long as his jockey sat still. This man had a riding boy called Brunt— a lad from Perth, West Australia—and he taught Brunt, with a trainer's whip, the hardest thing a jock can learn—to sit still, to sit still, and to keep on sitting still. When Brunt fairly grasped this truth, Shackles devastated the country. No weight could stop him at his own distance; and the fame of Shackles spread from Ajmir in the South to Chedputter in the North. There was no horse like Shackles, so long as he was allowed to do his work in his own way. But he was beaten in the end; and the story of his fall is enough to make angels weep.

At the lower end of the Chedputter race-course, just before the turn into the straight, the track passes close to a couple of old brick-mounds enclosing a funnel-shaped hollow. The big end of the funnel is not six feet from the railings on the off-side. The astounding peculiarity of the course is that, if you stand at one particular place, about a half a mile away, inside the course and speak at ordinary pitch, your voice just hits the funnel of the brick-mounds and makes a curious whining echo there. A man discovered this one morning by accident while out training with a friend. He marked the place to stand and speak from with a couple of bricks and he kept his knowledge to himself. *Every* peculiarity of a course is worth remembering in a country where rats play the mischief with the elephant-litter, and Stewards build jumps to suit their own stables. This man ran a very fairish country-bred, a long, racking high mare with the temper of a fiend and the paces of an airy wandering seraph—a drifty, glidy stretch. The mare was, as a delicate tribute of Mrs. Reiver, called "The Lady Regula Baddun," or, for short, Regula Baddun.

Shackles' jockey, Brunt, was a quite-well behaved boy, but his nerve had been shaken. He began his career by riding jump-races in Melbourne, where a few Stewards want lynching, and was one of the jockeys who came through the awful butchery—perhaps you will recollect it—of the Maribyrnong Plate. The walls were colonial ramparts—logs of *jarrah* spiked into masonry—with wings as strong as Church buttresses. Once in his stride, a horse had to jump or fall. He couldn't run out. In the Maribyrnong Plate twelve horses were jammed at the second wall. Red Hat, leading, fell this side, and threw out The Gled, and the ruck came up behind, and the space between wing and wing was one struggling, screaming, kicking shambles. Four jocks were taken out dead; three were very badly hurt, and Brunt was among the three. He told the story of the Maribyrnong Plate sometimes; and when he described how Whalley on Red Hat said, as the mare fell under him— "God ha' mercy, I'm done for!" and how, next instant, Sithee There and White Otter had crushed the life out of poor Whalley, and the dust hid a small hell of men and horses, no one marvelled that Brunt had dropped jump-races and Australia together. Regula Baddun's owner knew that story by heart. Brunt never varied in the telling. He had no education.

Shackles came to the Chedputter Autumn races one year, and his owner walked about insulting the sportsmen of Chedputter generally, till they went to the Honorary Secretary in a body and said, "Appoint handicappers, and arrange a race which shall break Shackles and humble the pride of his owner." The Districts rose against Shackles and sent up of their best; Ousel, who was supposed to be able to do his mile in 1–53; Petard, the stud-bred, trained by a cavalry regiment who knew how to train; Gringalet, the ewe lamb of the 75th; Bobolink, the pride of Peshawar; and many others.

They called that race the Broken-link Handicap, because it was to smash Shackles; and the Handicappers piled on the weights, and the Fund gave eight hundred rupees, and the distance was "round the course for all horses." Shackles' owner said, "You can arrange to race with regards to Shackles only. So long as you don't bury him under weight-cloths, I don't mind." Regula Baddun's owner said, "I throw in my mare to fret Ousel. Six furlongs is Regula's distance, and she will then lie down and die. So also will Ousel, for his jockey doesn't understand a waiting race." Now, this was a lie, for Regula had been in work for two months at Dehra, and her chances were good, always supposing that Shackles broke a blood-vessel—or Brunt moved on him.

The plunging in the lotteries was fine. They filled eight-thousand-rupee lotteries on the Broken-link Handicap, and the account in the "Pioneer" said that "favouritism was divided." In plain English, the various contingents were wild on their respective horses; for the Handicappers had done their work well. The Honorary Secretary shouted himself hoarse through the din; and the smoke of the cheroots was like the smoke, and the rattling of the dice-boxes like the rattle, of small-arm fire.

Ten horses started—very level—and Regula Baddun's owner cantered out on his hack to a place inside the circle of the course, where two bricks had been thrown. He faced towards the brick-mounds at the lower end of the course and waited.

The story of the running is in the "Pioneer." At the end of the first mile, Shackles crept out of the ruck, well on the outside, ready to get round the turn, lay hold of the bit and spin up the straight before the others knew he had got away. Brunt was sitting still, perfectly happy, listening to the "drum-drum-drum" of the hoofs behind, and knowing that, in about twenty strides, Shackles would draw one deep breath and go up the last half-mile like the "Flying Dutchman." As Shackles went short to take the turn and come abreast of the brick mound, Brunt heard, above the noise of the wind in his ears, a whining, wailing voice on the off-side, saying—"God ha' mercy, I'm done for!" In one stride, Brunt saw the whole seething smash of the Maribyrnong Plate before him, started in his saddle and gave a yell of terror. The start brought the heels into Shackles' sides, and the scream hurt Shackles' feelings. He couldn't stop dead; but he put out his feet and slid along for fifty yards, and then, very gravely and judicially, bucked Brunt off—a shaking, terror-stricken lump, while Regula Baddun made a neck-and-neck race with Bobolink up the straight, and won by a short head—Petard a bad third. Shackles' owner, in the stand, tried to think that his field-glasses had gone wrong. Regula Baddun's owner, waiting by the two bricks, gave one deep sigh of relief, and cantered back to the Stand. He had won, in lotteries and bets, about fifteen thousand.

It was a Broken-link Handicap with a vengeance. It broke nearly all the men concerned, and nearly broke the heart of Shackles' owner. He went down to interview Brunt. The boy lay, livid and gasping with fright, where he had fallen off. The sin of losing the race never seemed to strike him. All he knew was that Whalley had "called" him, that the "call" was a warning; and, were he cut in two for it, he would never get up again. His nerve had gone altogether, and he only asked his master to give him a good thrashing, and let him go. He was fit for nothing, he said. He got his dismissal, and crept up to the paddock, white as chalk, with blue lips, his knees giving way under him. People said nasty things in the paddock; but Brunt never heeded. He changed into tweeds, took his stick and went down the road, still shaking with fright, and muttering over and over again— "God ha' mercy, I'm done for!" To the best of my knowledge and belief, he spoke the truth.

So now you know how the Broken-link Handicap was run and won. Of course you don't believe it. You would credit anything about Russia's designs on India, or the recommendations of the Currency Commission; but a little bit of sober fact is more than you can stand.

The Race, from *National Velvet*

ENID BAGNOLD

This description of the running of the Grand National in which
Velvet, heroine of the book, rides "The Piebald" arouses some
of the same emotions as the first movement of Beethoven's
"Eroica." Again and again the suspense is built up, until it
is almost unbearable, only to be followed by a few phrases in
pianissimo. *Each climax is stronger than the last, beginning*
with a simple forte *and finishing with four fs. Even the final*
sentence of the stunned Mi has the quality of three final, crash-
ing chords.

At the post the twenty horses were swaying like the sea. Forward . . . No good! Back again. Forward . . . No good! Back again.

The line formed . . . and rebroke. Waves of the sea. Drawing
a breath . . . breaking. Velvet fifth from the rail, between a bay and
a brown. The Starter had long finished his instructions. Nothing
more was said aloud, but low oaths flew, the cursing and grumbling
flashed like a storm. An eye glanced at her with a look of hate. The
breaking of movement was too close to movement to be borne. It
was like water clinging to the tilted rim of the glass, like the sound
of the dreaded explosion after the great shell has fallen. The will
to surge forward overlaid by something delicate and terrible and
strong, human obedience at bursting point, but not broken. Horses'
eyes gleamed openly, men's eyes set like chips of steel. Rough man,
checked in violence, barely master of himself, barely master of
his horse. The Piebald ominously quiet, and nothing coming from
him . . . up went the tape.

The green Course poured in a river before her as she lay forward, and with the plunge of movement sat in the stream.

... "Black slugs" ... said Mi, cursing under his breath, running, dodging, suffocated with the crowd. It was the one thing he had overlooked, that the crowd was too dense ever to allow him to reach Becher's in the time. Away up above him was the truckline, his once-glorious free seat, separated from him by a fence. "God's liver," he mumbled, his throat gone cold, and stumbled into an old fool in a mackintosh. "Are they off?" he yelled at the heavy crowd as he ran, but no one bothered with him.

He was cursed if he was heeded at all. He ran, gauging his position by the cranes on the embankment. Velvet coming over Becher's in a minute and he not there to see her. "They're off." All around him a sea of throats offered up the gasp.

He was opposite Becher's but could see nothing: the crowd thirty deep between him and the Course. All around fell the terrible silence of expectancy. Mi stood like a rock. If he could not see them he must use his ears, hear. Enclosed in the dense, silent, dripping pack he heard the thunder coming. It roared up on the wet turf like the single approach of a multiple-footed animal. There were stifled exclamations, grunts, thuds. Something in the air flashed and descended. The first over Becher's! A roar went up from the crowd, then silence. The things flashing in the air were indistinguishable. The tip of a cap exposed for the briefest of seconds. The race went by like an express train, and was gone. Could Velvet be alive in that?

Sweat ran off Mi's forehead and into his eyes. But it was not sweat that turned the air grey and blotted out the faces before him. The ground on all sides seemed to be smoking. An extraordinary mist, like a low prairie fire was formed in the air. It had dwelt heavily all day behind the Canal, but the whole Course had remained clear till now. And now, before you could turn to look at your neighbour, his face was gone. The mist blew in shreds, drifted, left the crowd clear again but hid the whole of the Canal Corner, fences, stand and horses.

There was a struggle going on at Becher's; a horse had fallen and was being got out with ropes. Mi's legs turned to water and he asked his neighbour gruffly, "Who's fallen?" But the neighbour, straining to the tip of his toes, and glued to his glasses, was deaf as lead.

Suddenly Mi lashed round him in a frenzy. "Who's fallen, I say? Who's hurt!"

"Steady on," said a little man whom he had prodded in the stomach.

"Who's fallen?" said Mi desperately. "I gotta brother in this. . . ."

"It's his brother!" said the crowd all around him. "Let him through."

Mi was pushed and pummelled to the front and remained embedded two from the front line. The horse that had fallen was a black horse, its neck unnaturally stretched by the ropes that were hauling it from the ditch.

There was a shout and a horse, not riderless, but ridden by a

tugging, cursing man, came galloping back through the curling
fumes of the mist, rolled its wild eye at the wrong side of Becher's
and disappeared away out of the Course. An uproar began along
the fringes of the crowd and rolled back to where Mi stood. Two
more horses came back out of the mist, one riderless. The shades of
others could be discerned in the fog. Curses rapped out from unseen
mouths.

"What's happened at the Canal Turn? What's wrong down at
the Turn?"

"The whole field!" shouted a man. The crowd took it up.

"The field's out. The whole field's come back. There's no race!"
It was unearthly. Something a hundred yards down there in the fog
had risen up and destroyed the greatest steeplechase in the world.

Nineteen horses had screamed down to the Canal Turn, and
suddenly, there across the Course, at the boundary of the fog, four
horses appeared beyond Valentines, and among them, fourth, was
The Piebald.

"Yer little lovely, yer little lovely," yelled Mi, wringing his
hands and hitting his knees. "It's her, it's him, it's me brother!"

No one took any notice. The scene immediately before them
occupied all the attention. Horses that had fallen galloped by riderless, stirrups flying from their saddles, jockeys returned on foot,
covered with mud, limping, holding their sides, some running slowly
and miserably over the soggy course, trying to catch and sort the
horses.

"It's 'Yellow Messenger,' " said a jockey savagely, who had just
seized his horse. "Stuck on the fence down there and kicking hell."
And he mounted.

"And wouldn't they jump over him?" called a girl shrilly.

"They didn't wanter hurt the por thing, lady," said the jockey,
grinning through his mud, and rode off.

"Whole lot piled up and refused," said a man who came up the
line. "Get the Course clear now, quick!"

"They're coming again!" yelled Mi, watching the galloping four.
"Get the Course clear! They'll be coming!"

They were out of his vision now, stuck down under Becher's
high fence as he was. Once past Becher's on the second round would

he have time to extricate himself and get back to the post before they were home? He stood indecisively and a minute went by. The Course in front of him was clear. Horses and men had melted. The hush of anticipation began to fall. "They're on the tan again," said a single voice. Mi flashed to a decision. He could not afford the minutes to be at Becher's. He must get back to the finish and it would take him all his time. He backed and plunged and ducked, got cursed afresh. The thunder was coming again as he reached the road and turned to face the far-off Stands. This time he could see nothing at all, not even a cap in the air. "What's leading? What's leading?"

"Big brown. Tantibus, Tantibus. Tantibus leading."

"Where's The Piebald?"

"See that! Leonara coming up. . . ."

They were deaf to his frantic questions. He could not wait, but ran. The mist was ahead of him again, driving in frills and waiting sedgily about. Could Velvet have survived Becher's twice? In any case no good wondering. He couldn't get at her to help her. If she fell he would find her more quickly at the hospital door than struggle through the crowd and be forbidden the now empty Course.

Then a yell. "There's one down!"

"It's the Yank mare!"

The horse ambulance was trundling back with Yellow Messenger from the Canal Turn. Mi leapt for a second on to the turning hub of the wheel, and saw in a flash across the momentarily mist-clear course, the pride of Baltimore in the mud underneath Valentine's. The Piebald lying third. The wheel turned and he could see no more. Five fences from the finish; he would not allow himself to hope, but ran and ran. How far away the Stands in the gaps of the mist he pushed, gasping, through the people. Would she fall now? What had he done, bringing her up here? But would she fall now? He ran and ran.

"They're coming on to the Racecourse . . . coming on to the Racecourse. . . ."

"How many?"

"Rain, rain, can't see a thing."

"How many?"

Down sank the fog again, as a puff of wind blew and gathered it together. There was a steady roaring from the Stands, then silence, then a hub-bub. No one could see the telegraph.

Mi, running, gasped, "Who's won?"

But everyone was asking the same question. Men were running, pushing, running, just as he. He came up to the gates of Melling Road, crossed the road on the fringe of the tan, and suddenly, out of the mist The Piebald galloped riderless, lolloping unsteadily along, reins hanging, stirrups dangling. Mi burst through on to the Course, his heart wrung.

"Get back there!" shouted a policeman. "Loose horse!"

"Hullo Old Pie there!" shouted Mi. The animal, soaked, panting, spent, staggered and slipped and drew up.

"What've you done with 'er?" said Mi weeping, and bent down to lift the hoof back through the rein. "You let 'er down, Pie? What in God's sake?" He led the horse down the Course, running, his breath catching, his heart thumping, tears and rain on his face.

Two men came towards him out of the mist.

"You got him?" shouted one. "Good fer you. Gimme!"

"You want him?" said Mi, in a stupor, giving up the rein.

"Raised an objection. Want him for the enclosure. Chap come queer."

"Chap did? What chap?"

"This here's the winner! Where you bin all day, Percy?"

"Foggy," said Mi. "Very foggy. Oh my God."

The Horse as Friend, Servant, and Sometimes Master

The Old Hunter

LIAM O'FLAHERTY

Put a horse and an Irishman together and you have the ingredients of a good story. Have an Irishman tell the tale and the result will be an unusually tasty and pleasant dish. Liam O'Flaherty, in a simple and direct style, has given us a tale that could only have happened in Ireland, but in that place would not be considered at all out of the way. In more detail he has restated the old proverb, "There is something about the outside of a horse that is good for the inside of a man."

Mr. Stephen Mullen, the horse-dealer of Ballyhaggard, went to an auction one day. He was a tall, slim man with a red face and white eyebrows. Being a very popular man, on account of his dry wit and his good temper, he met many friends in the town where the auction was being held, and the result was that he spent the morning in the hotels drinking. Slightly intoxicated, he arrived at the auction when everything was sold except an old hunter called Morrisey.

Mr. Mullen went up to the auctioneer, a friend of his, and asked him, had he anything left. The auctioneer pointed to the old hunter.

"That's the lot," he said.

"What's that?" said Mr. Mullen, shutting one eye and cocking his head sideways.

"Pooh!" said the auctioneer, "there's enough iron in that old rascal to keep a factory going for a month. Tell you what, these bank-clerks and shopkeepers that are buying horses now with their ill-gotten gains don't know a—"

"Hech, hech," said Mr. Mullen, "let's have a look at him. I might give ye the price of a drink for him."

They walked over to the hunter. He was a finely built animal, but he looked like a man that had just left a nursing home after a serious nervous breakdown. His bones were sticking through his hide, and though he held his head proudly in the air it was obvious that he did so out of respect for his ancestry and not because of any consciousness of his strength. He was of a bay colour, and somebody had fired his left hind leg, so clumsily and in such a cruel manner that it appeared to have been done with a red-hot crowbar. The pelt was quite naked of hair and the flesh was singed in streaks.

"Look at that," said Mr. Mullen, pointing to the leg. "Did ye get him from a tinker, or what?"

"Lord have mercy on yer soul," said the auctioneer, "that fellah has a pedigree as long as yer arm. Come here, I'll show ye."

"Ye needn't bother," said Mr. Mullen. "What good is a pedigree to a dying man? The Master o' the Hounds might give a few bob for him for the pack."

Mr. Mullen wrinkled up his face in a smile and he looked at the auctioneer with his mouth open. He really wanted the horse, because he liked the old fellow's head, but he wanted to get him for next to nothing. The auctioneer also wanted to get rid of him very badly, but still, he wanted to strike a good bargain.

"Now drop the coddin', Mr. Mullen," he said, "and buy the horse if ye want him. Sure I needn't tell you what a horse is, whether he is a horse or a mule. Man alive, sure a few square meals 'ud change that fellah so much ye wouldn't know him. Look at his—"

"Aye," said Mullen coldly, "let's have a look at them, I mean his insides. I bet he's got a smoker's heart and a liver stitched together with the best silk thread. If I buy him, would ye get him carted home for me?"

"I can see it's out for coddin' me ye are," said the auctioneer, turning to go away.

"Very well," said Mr. Mullen, clearing his throat, "I'll make you an offer for him."

"What's that?" said the auctioneer, halting abruptly and turning around to Mr. Mullen.

"I've got thirty bob on me," said Mullen, contracting his white eyebrows. "I'll give ye the lot, though it's good money wasted."

The auctioneer pursed up his lips and stared at Mr. Mullen for a few moments as if he were dumfounded.

"D'ye really mean it?" he said.

Mr. Mullen nodded.

"Take him home, for God's sake," said the auctioneer, waving his hands.

Mr. Mullen paid for the horse and took him home. He led him along beside his own horse, and it was the devil of a job to keep him in hand. My boy, he had his head in the wind and champed along, rearing and trying to break loose.

"Good Lord," thought Mr. Mullen, "that fellah is a corker only for his age."

Mr. Mullen went to a party that night and there was heavy drinking. In his cups he began to boast about the old hunter he had bought for thirty shillings. Everybody made fun of him about it, so Mr. Mullen boasted that he would ride the old horse to the meet of the Ballyhaggard hounds next day.

"Wait till you see," he cried. "I'll leave you all so far behind that I'll have the fox's skin dressed before you arrive."

Next day Mr. Mullen's head was as big as a pot, and when he remembered his boast he was disgusted with himself. But he was a man of his word and he ordered the old hunter to be saddled for him. He drank a considerable amount of raw whiskey and mounted him. Off he went to the meet.

Everybody in the district turns out with the hounds, from Lord Clonmore to Mr. Mulligan, the butcher of Murren. All sorts of ungainly beasts appear. In fact, Mr. Murchison, the new Protestant curate, once joined, mounted on a cart-horse, which a scoundrel called The Tiger of Donnelly sold him as an Irish hunter. Since the war and the revolution all sorts of people have been thrown together in the district, so that, as Mr. Mullen says, "There's no class about anything nowadays." But when Mr. Mullen himself appeared that day on Morrisey, everybody agreed that such an extraordinary animal had never been seen before. It was like a mortally sick man appearing at a wedding, half drunk and insisting on being the most hilarious person present.

"Bravo, Mr. Mullen," said Lord Clonmore. "The dead have arisen. Eh!"

Everybody laughed and Mr. Mullen was mortally insulted, but when the cavalcade set off, by Jove, Morrisey behaved himself marvellously. Like a good thoroughbred of the old school, he showed every ounce that was in him. He cleared the ditches and fences as lightly as those wonderful horses for which the Galway Blazers were famous, fellows that could live for a week on a raw turnip and cross a bog without wetting their fetlocks. Mr. Mullen kept refreshing himself now and again with stimulants, and as a consequence rode even more daringly than was his custom; but the old hunter carried him all day without a single stumble, until at last, just before the finish, he arrived at the drain that flows from the workhouse, about a mile outside the town. There is no more filthy or evil-smelling drain in the world. There is no necessity to describe it.

But when Morrisey arrived at this drain at full speed, he stopped dead. Undoubtedly the animal was too well bred to face it. Mr. Mullen was pitched over the horse's head and he fell headlong into the stinking place. Several people pulled up, but Mr. Mullen crawled out, uninjured. Seeing him, everybody went into hysterics with laughter. He was indescribable, and in fact unrecognizable. Morrisey lowered his head, sniffed at Mr. Mullen and set off back at a mad canter.

"It must have turned his stomach," laughed a red-haired farmer.

"Yer a lot of scoundrels," shouted Mr. Mullen, struggling to his feet and holding out his dripping hands that were as black and sticky as if they had been dipped in tar.

Morrisey was found again and brought back to the stables. Mr. Mullen went home and had a bath, and by that time his anger had worn off and he was able to laugh at the joke. Next morning he went to look at Morrisey. The poor animal was quite stiff with his efforts of the previous day. But he still had his head in the air and he whinnied joyfully when he saw Mr. Mullen. That softened Mr. Mullen's heart toward him.

"Damn it," he said to the stable-boy, "he's a great old horse. I'll take him down to the shore and give him a dip in the salt water to soften his legs."

He rode Morrisey down to the strand. It was a fine day, but there was a rather heavy ground-swell and the waves broke on the sand with a thundering noise. This thundering noise and the menacing aspect of the dark green waves, rising suddenly within a few feet of the shore and falling with a thud, terrified the horse. It was impossible to get him to walk in the tide. At last Mr. Mullen managed to get him near the surf, when the tide had receded for a particularly long distance, as it does now and again, after a certain number of short waves have broken. Then as the horse was stamping about and snorting, trying to get away from the water, an enormous wave rose suddenly and almost enveloped him. Instead of trying to rush backward, he was so confused by the rush of water under his stomach that he plunged out to sea. Mr. Mullen tried to head him off, but it was not use. Presently another equally large wave arose, and passed right over the horse and the rider, so that they both turned a somersault. Mr. Mullen was thrown from the saddle and he became entangled somehow in the horse's legs. When he came to the surface, after having saved himself, the horse was five yards away and Mr. Mullen was in deep water. He swam a few strokes, struck ground and then looked behind him. There was the horse, swimming mightily out toward the open sea.

"God Almighty!" cried Mr. Mullen. "With ten pounds worth of a saddle on him!"

Mr. Mullen dashed up on to the strand and began to call some boatmen that were there. They ran over to him.

"Hey," he cried, "if he drowns, will he sink or float?"

"God save us," they cried, "who are ye talking about?"

"My horse, damn it," cried Mr. Mullen, "he's gone out to sea. Don't ye see him? Look."

"Aw, sakes alive," they said, when they saw the dark object, heaving along sideways, like an unwieldy porpoise.

"He'll float sure enough," said one man, "with the water he'll swallow."

"All right, then," said Mr. Mullen, "get me a boat. I want to save the saddle. The horse isn't worth his keep, but the saddle is worth money. Get a boat for me."

They rushed down a boat and put to sea after the horse. When they had gone out almost half a mile, they met the horse swimming back toward them.

"There he is," cried one boatman.

"He's floatin' sure enough," said Mr. Mullen. "Get alongside him and get the saddle."

"It's not floatin' he is, but swimmin' like a warrior," said the boatman.

"God!" said Mr. Mullen.

They were all amazed and lay on their oars, as Morrisey swept past them toward the beach, going at a terrific pace. They followed him, and when they reached the strand, Morrisey was standing there, shivering and exhausted. Mr. Mullen took off his hat and struck his forehead.

"Well, that horse beats all I ever saw," he said. "Here, I'll buy a bottle of whiskey over this. Come on, men."

After that Mr. Mullen and the horse that went to sea became quite famous in the district. So that Mr. Mullen grew fond of the horse and he kept him all that winter in his stable with plenty of food. But he made no attempt to ride him, and although the fame of the horse spread afar, still nobody made an offer for him. Because even though he was famous for having swum a mile out to sea and then swum back again, he was also famous for having thrown Mr. Mullen into the workhouse drain.

Then in the following April another extraordinary thing happened to the horse. I must say that he had improved considerably during the winter. He had fattened a great deal and his hide was becoming almost glossy. The mark on his hind leg was not so outrageous, and to an ordinary person he seemed a perfectly sound horse. But to a horseman he was still an old crock. One of those game old things, whether they are old colonels who insist on wearing tight waists in their seventieth year, or old horses or old battered fighting cocks that take a step ferociously and then glare, wagging their chaps aggressively as if they were in the prime of their lives—I say he was one of those game old things that make a virtue of looking fit even when they might be excused for drooping their heads and lying down to die. But all the buyers admired him and left him alone. Then Mr. Stanley Edwards came to the town.

Mr. Edwards might be called a crock as well as the old hunter. He spent the greater part of each year in a nursing home. The remainder of the year he spent in the pursuit of extravagant pleasures, not always very well considered. His money was tied up in this country, otherwise it is very probable that he would never spend a week in it. But when he had done a great bout in London, he always had to return to Ireland to get some more money. After one of those bouts and a month in hospital, he engaged a villa in Ballyhaggard to take the sea air. A few days after his arrival in the town he came to Mr. Mullen. Mr. Mullen looked him up and down, rather surprised that such a weakling should come to him for anything.

"Well," he said, "what could I do for you?"

"Look here," said Mr. Edwards, "I have to live for a few months in this ghastly place. I'm sick and I have very little money. I have been here three days and I'm quite fed up with walking up and down the shore and talking to the lunatics around here. I want a horse. Can you get me one?"

"Let me see," said Mr. Mullen, looking at him shrewdly, "you'd want a nice quiet horse, I suppose?"

"I want a horse," said Mr. Edwards pettishly. "It doesn't much matter what he is. If he breaks my neck it might be a jolly good idea."

"I see," said Mr. Mullen. "I think I've got the very thing that'll suit you."

"Oh, look here," said Mr. Edwards rather nervously, "I don't mean I want some—eh—crazy thing. You know—a—oh, well—"

"You leave it to me," said Mr. Mullen. "You can try him out before you buy him."

Morrisey was brought out and Mr. Edwards immediately mounted him and rode off. Mr. Edwards looked a very poor figure on horseback. Some wit said that he was born to be a rag-picker, because his gaunt frame bent like a hollow rod and his nose was so long that he could use it in the same way that an elephant uses the tip of his trunk. But such a light weight suited the old horse, and he went off very gallantly indeed, with that twirl in his right hind leg which is a sign of old age in a horse and which warns off the cunning buyer but which is very attractive, like the smart twirl of the spurred boot which tells the swagger cavalry officer.

Mr. Mullen looked after the horse, scratching his chin and thinking that he would be very glad to accept a five-pound note for him.

After an hour, Mr. Edwards returned, perspiring but looking very happy. A good hour's trotting on a well-bred horse on a fine spring morning would make a corpse almost come to life again.

"Go all right?" said Mr. Mullen, smiling his most engaging smile. "Splendid," said Mr. Edwards, sitting the horse and wiping his forehead, as if he were loath to dismount. "How much do you want for him?"

"I'll take thirty pounds at a pinch," said Mr. Mullen after a moment's apparent thought and looking at Mr. Edwards as if he were going to do him a favour, which, however, gave him a great deal of pain.

"Oh!" said Mr. Edwards, a little surprised.

Then he dismounted and looked curiously at Mr. Mullen.

"It's a lot," he said.

"Oh! Well," said Mr. Mullen, making a gesture with his hands, "a horse isn't a bicycle."

"Quite," said Mr. Edwards. "Now, let me see."

He walked around the horse and passed his hand over the horse's body in various places. Mr. Mullen was very glad to see that he touched the wrong places. Then Mr. Edwards stood at a distance from the horse and looked at him. He seemed very loath to leave him. Mr. Mullen began to feel very comfortable.

"Look here," said Mr. Edwards at length, "I'll come back to-morrow and have another ride, may I?"

"Why, certainly," said Mr. Mullen affably. "You can have a look at his pedigree now if you like."

"Oh, has he got a pedigree?" said Mr. Edwards.

"Lord, yes," said Mr. Mullen, "yards of it."

Here it must be stated, that although Mr. Edwards was a wealthy country gentleman, he kept motor-cars instead of horses and knew nothing about the animals except on race-courses. So that a pedigree seemed to him as good a guarantee of perfection as the maker's name on a Rolls-Royce.

"Let's have a look at it," he said.

Mr. Mullen produced the pedigree and Mr. Edwards inspected it.

"In that case," he said, "I'll buy the horse right away."

"It's like taking milk from a child," thought Mr. Mullen, as Mr. Edwards wrote out the cheque.

Everyone expected Mr. Edwards to break his neck, and some people said that Mr. Mullen played rather a scurvy trick on the poor fellow, but during the whole of that summer the horse was seen on the roads almost every day, trotting along in the pink of condition. And what was more, Mr. Edwards became quite a new man. Whether it was the sea air or the riding that did it, he regained his health to an extraordinary extent. He did not become robust, but he was no longer an invalid and he led a decent healthy life. In fact, just before he went away, he came to Mr. Mullen and said, "Look here, Mr. Mullen, you've saved my life."

"Glad to hear it," said Mr. Mullen, without winking an eye.

In September Mr. Edwards left the district, but instead of going to England, as was his custom, he returned to his property in County Kilkenny. Nothing more was heard of him or of the horse for two years. And then two months ago I met Mr. Mullen in Dublin. We were having a drink together and talking about various things, when he suddenly gripped my arm and said:

"D'ye remember that horse, Morrisey, I had, the fellah that threw me into the drain?"

I nodded.

"Ye remember I sold him to a chap called Edwards from Kilkenny. Well, I've just been down there to a show. Met him there. He's still got the horse, going as strong as a three-year-old and . . . d'ye know what I'm going to tell ye? That horse saved his life, as he said himself. When I asked him about the horse, he said: "I wouldn't part with that horse for a thousand. I haven't left this district since I saw you last, and I can drink two bottles of port now after dinner without turning a hair."

So that, indeed, it seems that there is something in a pedigree.

Carty Carteret's Sister

DAVID GRAY

The inimitable David Gray takes us to a private sale of hunters at a country house outside Washington in days that are "Gone with the Wind." Dialogue may have changed in the intervening years, but both human and equine counterparts of the characters of this story are still to be found and the horseman will have no difficulty in recognizing them.

"Eleanor," said Miss Carteret, "I'd like a trap at half-past eleven. Mr. Bennings and I want to drive over to Captain Forbes's. And you'll come?" she added to Willie Colfax.

He nodded affably, and helped himself to marmalade. Mr. Bennings looked annoyed.

"We're going to buy horses," she continued. "That is, I'm going to buy *one*. Mr. Bennings, I believe, is going to buy a drove."

Mr. Bennings raised his hand in deprecation.

"Aw—I say, not a drove; just a few likely ones," he remarked.

"Polly Carteret," said Mrs. Braybrooke, "you're an extravagant goose! What in the world will you do with a horse?"

"I shall give him sugar," Miss Carteret replied. "That will be one thing."

Mr. James Braybrooke stared at her, gathered up the sporting pages of the newspaper, and left the table.

"You're impossible!" said Mrs. Braybrooke. She went to the window, and looked out. The Braybrookes' breakfast-room commanded a stretch of rolling lawn set with mighty oaks. The Indian-summer sun was streaming down upon it.

"You see, Mr. Bennings," observed Miss Carteret, "this is the way they encourage me to patronize the Oakdale horses. When I was little I didn't care much about horses, and Eleanor used to make me feel my life was a failure. Now I want to buy a horse, and she calls me extravagant."

"It's like getting married," volunteered Willie Colfax. "Don't do it. You lose your nerve and grow economical. One's always thinking about the little ones who have to be educated and set up in life. Please, more coffee, Nell," he added.

Mrs. Braybrooke colored.

"Don't irritate your sister," said Miss Carteret. "I'll pour it."

Mr. Bennings seemed to have something on his mind. He held the marmalade-jar suspended in air.

"But—aw, I say," he observed seriously, "really, now, a *good* nag, you know, is not a bad investment."

Mrs. Braybrooke turned from the window and regarded him with something like a sniff.

"But she doesn't know a good one. Now, I say, if you don't know horses, just be a lady; only don't pretend. And, Polly Carteret, you don't know any more about horses than"—she looked about as if for a comparison, but found none which was adequate—"than THAT!" she exclaimed. "And the way you *talk* is ridiculous."

"Mr. Bennings," said Miss Carteret, mildly, "do you believe her?" Mr. Bennings deemed himself rather discerning about women.

"No, 'pon my word, Mrs. Braybrooke," he replied, "honestly, now, I can't believe that, you know. You misunderstand Miss Carteret; you really do. We had a long conversation last evening, and she impressed me as very well informed—unusually well informed. Perhaps not so keen about racin', you know, but very well up on huntin'-cattle." He set down the marmalade-jar, and glanced at Miss Carteret for a smile of gratitude; and Miss Carteret smiled.

"There!" she said to Mrs. Braybrooke; "I told you I had learned about horses. Don't be so superior."

Mrs. Braybrooke shot a glance at Bennings, and her nostrils quivered.

"When you finish, come into the morning-room," she remarked.

"I want to find Jimmy." She went out, followed by her brother, who was trying to lead her into a discussion of some ideas relative to matrimony.

"I say," said Bennings, when they were alone—he spoke confidently—"you *were* chaffin', don't you know, about buyin' a nag to feed him sugar?"

"I *was* chaffing," replied Miss Carteret. "You 'caught on,' so to speak, very quickly. Seriously, I should never think of buying a horse just to have something to feed sugar to. With so many poor people who can't afford sugar, it wouldn't be ethical."

"That's so," said Bennings; "but at first it *did* sound just a bit odd, you know. It was a capital joke, though," he added, "and I *do* like a joke."

She dropped her eyelids.

"I could see that," she said. "I can't tolerate people who don't like jokes."

"You don't say so!" he exclaimed. "That's very interesting. You know," he continued, "that's the only thing I have against an Englishman. Awfully good sort, but no sense of fun, you know. I've been over there a good deal, but I can't get used to that. I call it a national defect. This chap, you know—Mark Twain—he's noticed the same thing about 'em." This was Bennings' stock conversation on the English people.

"That's very interesting, too," observed Miss Carteret. "Will you be ready at half-past eleven?"

"At your service—always," he exclaimed, jumping up. Then she went out, and left him to his eggs.

P. St. Clair Bennings had arrived at Oakdale the afternoon before. The last time Braybrooke had gone to town he had met him at the club, and they had lunched together. As it was October, they naturally discussed hunting-stables, and Braybrooke asked him down to look over Forbes's string before it went to the Horse Show. Bennings was glad to come, and he was pleased to find Miss Carteret stopping there, because he ranked women only after horses. Miss Carteret had made rather quick work with him. He already considered her a "devilish fine girl," and an inner voice had begun to ask whether it might not be generous to shorten his visit. When Bennings first came into his money he bravely faced the fact that he could not both hunt and marry, so he put the latter out of his mind. He had sojourned long in Great Britain (as unkind persons intimated, to make amends for having been born in a New Jersey manufacturing town), and, moreover, by nature he had been endowed with an earnest rather than an acute intellect. There was not much more to be said about him. He rode fairly well. His clothes were distinctive. His speech was that version of the cockney speech of England which is peculiar to the "American *malgré lui*."

Miss Carteret was a school friend of Mrs. Braybrooke's. Their mothers had been connected in some way. She lived in Washington, but she had been born on the James River, which accounted for a throaty, Southern quality in her voice. She spoke slowly, and in her accent there was a soft echo of colored mammies which was attractive. Overlooking such artificial classifications as by complexion and by morals, girls seem to fall into two categories. The members of the first inspire esteem and nothing more. A woman belongs to the second when men simultaneously pick up her handkerchief and lurk in wait to put the hassocks under her feet. Conversely, a woman's habit of confidently dropping things is also a sign of the type. Miss Carteret was continually shedding her handkerchiefs and other portables, and, as a rule, all the available men were adjacent, and anxious to restore them. She was tall and blonde, with a double allowance of pleasing red hair, and her eyes were of a curious dark-blue color. As she herself had remarked, she was intelligent without being hampered by an education.

The trap which came to the door at half-past eleven was Willie Colfax's tandem. Colfax had suggested this substitution of vehicles to avoid the possibility of being packed in behind, and Miss Carteret had accepted it gracefully. She liked anything which increased the probability of something happening. "I'm sure Mr. Bennings won't mind," she remarked; "and if he does, he won't say so."

She got into the high cart beside Colfax, and looked down pleasantly.

"I do hope, Mr. Bennings," she said, "that you really don't mind sitting in behind with the man, and riding backward. And if you'll get my parasol—I left it on a chair in the hall; and please ask my maid for my field-glasses; they're in my room. You know," she explained to Willie Colfax, "I'm getting near-sighted, and I'm going to look at these horses critically. Besides, the leather case is rather smart."

"Rubbish!" ejaculated Colfax, jerking the wheeler who was restless. "Oh, hurry up, Bennings!" he bawled.

Presently Mr. Bennings appeared, somewhat out of breath, and climbed up behind, with the parasol and glasses.

"Now, if you'll hold them," remarked Miss Carteret, "I guess we're all ready." She waved her hand to Mrs. Braybrooke, and they drove off. "Good-bye, Eleanor!" she called. "I'm going to buy a nice horsey!"

Mrs. Braybrooke surveyed her with disapproval.

"Jimmy dear," she remarked, when the cart was out of sight, "please, like a good boy, have something saddled, and ride over there. That girl will do something idiotic, and make us ridiculous."

"Why don't you muzzle her?" said Braybrooke. "She's your friend." Then he went in, and telephoned the stables.

As the tandem swung into Forbes's smooth driveway, Mr. Bennings caught a fragment of the conversation which was going on behind him. Thus far he had been occupied in keeping in, for the roads were bad, and they had galloped most of the way. "Well, those are my ideas about horses," Miss Carteret was saying. "I believe in judging a horse according to the things you want him for, just as you would judge dogs or furniture. Seriously, don't you?" She laughed a little.

"You'll be the death of me," replied Mr. Colfax. "Brace and don't make a holy show of yourself. You can make Nell and Jimmy as hot as you want, only behave when you're with me. You don't seem to have any reverence." Bishop Cunningham once had made this comment to him, and he remembered it. Mr. Colfax's acquaintance with Miss Carteret dated from the nursery, and warranted a certain freedom. "Great Scott!" he exclaimed, catching a glimpse of the veranda, "there's about a million men there."

"Shall we go back?" inquired Miss Carteret.

"Don't be foolish," he muttered. He made a spectacular turn, and laid his thong over the leader. Bennings caught himself when he was nearly out and twisted around on the seat.

"But it's all right, you know," he remarked. "Forbes is a married man. It will be all right, Miss Carteret."

"Then of course we needn't go back," replied Miss Carteret. "Thank you, Mr. Bennings. I feel much more comfortable. I'm rather glad, now, that they're there. They can help us choose, can't they?"

"Why, of course," he said doubtfully. "They are all the fellows, you know, from the club. They've come over to see 'em led out."

There was a chorus of "Good mornings" as the cart drew up, and a dozen men in tweed breeches and morning-coats lifted their hats and took their smoking-things out of their mouths.

"Glad to see you," said Forbes, coming down the steps. He had been presented to Miss Carteret before. "The show is waiting. How are you, Bennings? You too, Willie?"

"Quite well, dear boy," replied Mr. Colfax. "Send somebody to stand by my leader while Cook gets the reins. I'm going to send 'em to the stable."

Miss Carteret stood up to be helped out, and the dozen men came forward to assist. Miss Carteret could radiate, so to speak, her appreciation of the civil intentions of strangers, and all the while be impassive and good form. People who had studied her said she did it with her eyes, and it may have been so. At any rate, it was a gift which did not lessen her powers of arousing interest.

"The Oakdale Raleigh," observed Varick, nodding towards Chalmers, "will spread his coat over the wheel, and you may descend."

Chalmers blushed, and performed that service. Thereupon Miss Carteret got down altogether successfully. She wore exceptionally good boots, for a woman.

"May I present these fortunate men?" asked Varick. "We shall then suffer Forbes to go ahead with his equine paradox." At this moment a groom appeared, leading a big, raw-boned bay gelding, which he proceeded to trot around the circle of turf in front of the house. A serious silence fell upon the company.

"He's not very much to look at yet," Forbes remarked; "but he's clever, and is going to make a serviceable horse in any kind of going. What do you think of him, Bennings?"

"A bit rough—a bit rough, old chap," Mr. Bennings replied regretfully. "Don't you agree with me, Miss Carteret?"

"Oh, quite," said Miss Carteret. "Positively malicious. I don't like his color, either, and he's too thin."

Colfax suddenly guffawed, and the men regarded him curiously, and asked him whether he was in pain.

"By jove—'*malicious*'!" exclaimed Mr. Bennings. "That's capital! And you *are* correct about his condition. At least, that's my idea," he added, with a deferential glance at the rest of the company. "I must have more flesh at this time of year—ten stone more, at least." Miss Carteret looked at him out of the corner of her eye. "Really, now, Forbes, that fellow wouldn't last a season," he went on. "But his color will assuredly brighten. Oh, yes, his color will brighten."

"Do you think so?" asked Miss Carteret. "I'm very particular about color."

"And quite right—and quite right!" exclaimed Mr. Bennings. "The Duke of Beaufort lays great stress on color. Says you can invariably tell condition by it. Lord Wicke disregards it, but I admit I agree with the duke. It takes a clever eye, though—a devilish clever eye!"

"I'm glad to hear you say that," said Miss Carteret. "You know, people laugh at me for judging horses by their color." She was on the point of saying that she preferred circus horses, with black and white geographical divisions, when Forbes spoke:

"I'll have to tell you that if you take anything, I must reserve the right to show in November. I've got them all entered, you see, and they're being schooled for the green classes."

"Of course that's all right, Captain Forbes," Miss Carteret answered, with a smile. "And you can keep all the prizes, too; only you must give me the blue ribbons. I shall have a glass case made, and pin them up in rows." The men laughed, and Varick remarked that it was a very good way to store blue ribbons, only he had never tried it himself.

"I say," whispered Bennings to Colfax, "she's a tremendous chaffer, ain't she?"

"Is she?" replied Mr. Colfax.

The talk subsided again as a second horse appeared. It was a

big, well-made chestnut with a free, sweeping action, and a showy
way of carrying its head.

"By Jove!" exclaimed Mr. Bennings. "Now, here we are! That's
a rare good one—regular old-country type, isn't it?" He looked
at Miss Carteret.

She hesitated a moment and surveyed the animal.

"Without doubt," she replied. "I suppose," she added gravely,
"they must call him Jenson or Black-letter."

"Yes, of course," said Bennings. He kept his eyes on the horse.
"Now, that one will jump like a buck, I'll wager. Look at his
quarters! And what a pair of breeches!" he ejaculated soulfully.
"Lovely shoulder, too, isn't it?" Miss Carteret nodded approvingly.
"I say, Forbes," he called, "ask your lead lad to move him round
again, will you? What's your price on him?"

"Fifteen hundred," answered Forbes. "He's up to any weight.
Yon can see that yourself. What do you think of him, Miss
Carteret?"

Miss Carteret gasped, but disguised it in a little cough. The
folly of spending several satisfactory gowns on one beast struck
her forcibly.

"Well," she said, "this is a rather more expensive horse than I
want."

"You are right," observed Bennings, as Forbes moved off.
"There is no sense in paying for weight one doesn't need, is there?
What do you ride at?"

Miss Carteret thought earnestly.

"Really," she replied, "I don't know exactly." She was on the
point of adding that she had never ridden at anything, but checked
herself.

Bennings looked at her critically. "I should say about ten stone,"
he observed.

"I dare say that's just it," she answered. "In fact, I know it is. I
remember, now, distinctly."

"I *have* a rather good eye for weight," he remarked. "Hello!
here's Braybrooke. What's up, old chap? Thought you weren't
coming."

"Changed my mind," replied Mr. Braybrooke. "Good lot,
aren't they?" He gave his horse to a groom.

"They've only begun," said Bennings. "I fancy this chestnut, though. He must be better than three quarters bred, and excellent bone, too. By the way, if you'll pardon me, you know, Mrs. Braybrooke certainly *was* mistaken this morning. That girl, you know, has a capital eye, and by Jove, understands color uncommonly well. She called it on a rangy bay that ought to be fleshed for six months. And you know, old chap, that's a deucedly fine point." Braybrooke glanced apprehensively toward the group of men, and fell to studying a cow in the field beyond. "But of course she ought to be a keen one," added Mr. Bennings. "She's Carty Carteret's sister. You know, I was with Carty at Melton last winter, when he went through thirty minutes with a broken shoulder-blade."

"Really!" observed Braybrooke. He was still considering the cow.

As the next horse was led out, he caught Miss Carteret's eye, and beckoned her aside. "Have you bought anything yet?" he inquired.

She shook her head.

"Well, as a personal favor, I wish you wouldn't. You see, we've got a stable full that you can ride whenever you want, and you'd only pay twelve or fifteen hundred for something that would be very likely to be too much for you when you got him. If you must own something, pick up a cheap pony to hack about."

"All right," said the girl, "you're really a very nice boy, Jimmy, and I don't like to tease you. But you needn't say anything to Captain Forbes."

Just then Forbes and Varick came up.

"What do you think of this one?" inquired Forbes, nodding toward a well-turned little black mare.

"Perfectly sweet," Miss Carteret answered. "But I think I'll watch the rest from the veranda. It's too hot here." She turned to Varick. "Will you come up and tell me all about them?" she asked.

He looked at her curiously.

"I dare say you know a great deal more about such things than I do," he said. He dragged a steamer-chair into position. "You see, I'm only an amateur, a dilettante"—he noted the way she was turned out—"and you—well, you're Carty Carteret's sister."

She threw back her head and laughed.

"Two weeks ago," she said, "I read six pages of a book called

'The Anatomy of the Horse.' That's all I know. You see," she went
on confidentially, "Eleanor and Carty have made my life a burden.
The more they talked horse, the more I despised the whole thing.
But you *are* out of it here if you don't like horses, so when Nell
asked me down I thought I'd try a new tack. You see, I've suspected
all along that they didn't understand half the things they said. They
just mumble gibberish, like that unfortunate Mr. Bennings,—now,
don't they?"

"I must decline to answer," replied Varick. "It might incrimi-
nate me."

"There, I knew it!" she exclaimed triumphantly. "I just decided
to cram up a little, and look knowing; and then I got all these
clothes. I knew I could fool them. I can't take in Nell and Willie, of
course; so I practise on them, and when they tell me I'm foolish I
know enough not to say *that* again. It's really been amusing. Mr.
Bennings thoroughly believes me." She stopped and watched the
little knots of men in the roadway. "Are all those grown men honestly poring over that horse?" she asked.

"They are," said Varick. "An occasion like this is a sacrament
to them."

"How funny it is, when you think about it!" she exclaimed. "And
do they really find out all sorts of things when they feel his legs and
look at his teeth?"

"They really do," said Varick. "In a rudimentary way I can do
it myself."

"Well," she sighed, "it's beyond me. It's like a telegraph tick-
ing. I hear it, but I can't understand what it means. I know a white
horse from a brown one, and I have a preference for long tails,
which I consider sensible. You see, when you are driving, it's the
tail you see most of, isn't it? A system of judging horses by their
tails would appeal to me. But what difference does it make whether
a horse has fluted colonial legs, or smooth round ones? Absolutely
none!"

"Please, a little lower," suggested Varick. "Somebody might
hear."

She laughed.

"But seriously," she continued, "I *should* like to get a horse with
a long tail. My father insists on having his horses docked, and I'm
sick of them. They didn't use to do it. My grandfather used to take

me driving with a pair of thoroughbreds that had tails that touched the ground, and they could trot—I don't know how fast!—in a minute, I think."

"Do you remember," said Varick, artlessly, "that there was a time—you must remember it—when your mother wore very tight sleeves?"

"Thank you," she replied. "I've got trunks full of them myself. But people are the only animals silly enough to have fashions. It's wicked to put horses on the same basis."

She looked down the lawn toward the gateway, where something passing behind the shrubbery attracted her attention. In a moment a fat, undersized gray horse jogged into view drawing a shabby Hempstead cart. Presently he subsided into a sober walk. From his rough coat and fetlocks he seemed to be of Percheron origin. As he drew nearer, a fly attacked him, and he switched a superb tail.

"There!" exclaimed Miss Carteret. "That is the kind of horse I really want. Just look at that tail!"

"Good heavens," cried Varick, "but you mustn't!"

She seemed not to hear him.

"Do you think," she went on, "that no one would take me seriously if I bought that horse?" Varick chuckled. "I have a little plan," she added, and went down the steps.

"Glad to see you are going to join us again," said Mr. Bennings, bowing profusely.

"Mr. Bennings," said Miss Carteret, "if I buy a horse will you ride him home?"

"My dear Miss Carteret," he cried, *"anything.* Anywhere!"

"Thank you so much," she said sweetly. She turned away and went over to Forbes and Galloway.

"Captain Forbes," she said, "Mr. Bennings has promised to ride my horse home. He's been very nice to me, and I really think he would like to do it. Besides, he is a good horseman, and I feel I can trust him. I want to buy that gray horse in the cart."

Forbes and Galloway looked at each other and then at Mr. Bennings. They showed symptoms of exploding.

"Please be very serious," she said. "What's his name and how much is he?"

"His name," replied Forbes, gravely, "is Birdofreedom, and he does my marketing. I have never considered offering him for sale. He is worth about fifty dollars to me, though that may be extortionate."

"It is," said Galloway; "say ten."

"No," replied Miss Carteret; "I'm not going to bargain with you. I'll send you a check to-morrow for fifty dollars. Will you have him saddled and brought down when the cart comes? I don't want to keep Mr. Bennings waiting. No," she replied to Forbes's invitation; "we can't stop to lunch. We promised Mrs. Braybrooke we'd be back. Besides, I want her to see my horse. You know, she thinks I don't know anything about horses."

"I say," gasped Galloway, his sides shaking, "Bennings will never get over this!"

"Get over what?" said Miss Carteret, innocently. She nodded at

Varick, and he joined her. "I've bought him," she said, "and Mr. Bennings is going to ride him home. You won't tell about our talk, will you?"

Varick replied with difficulty.

"No," he said; "I am your dumb slave. Hello, there's your trap."

Willie Colfax drove up to the old-fashioned horse-block and stopped.

"Better hurry up!" he called. "We're late now. Good-bye, Forbes, sorry we can't stop."

"Sorry too," said Forbes. He turned to Miss Carteret and helped her up. "They're getting your horse out as fast as possible. Bennings won't mind waiting. We'll give him something to drink."

"Very well," said Miss Carteret. "Perhaps I would just as soon *not* see Mr. Bennings start off. You won't mind waiting a minute?" she called to him. "You can overtake us, you know, and Jimmy will wait too. Good-bye."

"What was all that?" demanded Willie Colfax. He swung his thong and the horses went away at a gallop.

Miss Carteret explained. What she said was accurate, as far as it went. She considered it unnecessary, however, to dwell upon her own feelings towards Birdofreedom.

"Well," said Mr. Colfax, "you're a peach!"

"And you'll wait and let them catch up?" she asked.

"We certainly must give Nell the procession effect," he observed. Instead of waiting, however, he tore around a two-mile loop, which brought them to the Braybrookes' gateway just as Braybrooke and Mr. Bennings were arriving.

Mrs. Braybrooke was on the steps as they drove up. They were late.

"What's that Mr. Bennings is riding?" she demanded.

"That," said Miss Carteret proudly, "is my horse."

Birdofreedom approached and Mrs. Braybrooke studied him.

"Polly Carteret!" she exclaimed—it was almost a scream—"what on earth do you mean?—Jimmy!"

"He's virtually sound," said Braybrooke.

His wife turned and stalked into the house.

"There, now, Mr. Bennings," said Miss Carteret, mournfully, "you see how a horse will separate friends!"

"Aw—certainly," said Mr. Bennings. "Will you kindly ring for somebody from the stables?"

His manner was stiff. He realized that he had overrated Miss Carteret's eye for horseflesh. "Just fawncy buying such a brute!" he said to himself. "Just fawncy!" The girl was a disappointment. It mortified him to misjudge people, and he went back to town that night.

According to the account which Varick afterward gave Miss Carteret of Forbes's lunch-party, first, "horse" was neglected in a manner without precedent.

"You see," said Varick, "it was unanimously concluded, something more than a dozen times, that you were a bully girl, and had revenged the American people on that ass Bennings. That took up nearly all the time. And besides the absence of 'horse,' there was an interesting display of woman nature. When Mrs. Forbes heard the story, she remarked in her quiet way: 'Well, I don't see how there was any joke on Mr. Bennings. I just think that girl took a fancy to Birdofreedom, and I'm sorry he's sold. He had *such a lovely tail!*' Naturally the laugh was on Mrs. Forbes." Here both Varick and Miss Carteret smiled. "You know, she distinguishes a horse from a cow, and that's about all. She devotes her life to six children. When we had got through enjoying the joke, Forbes said reproachfully (it mortifies him to have his wife display her ignorance): 'perhaps you don't know, my dear, that she's Carty Carteret's sister. If you think best, I'll explain about Bennings later.' "

When Varick had finished this recital Miss Carteret extended her hand and let him hold it longer than was really necessary. She was a very honorable girl about recognizing her obligations.

"I shall keep away from Mrs. Forbes," she said.

Miss Carteret was much interested in what Varick had told her. It explained certain things which had puzzled her, and she disliked being puzzled. When they had sat down to their own lunch on the day of Birdofreedom's purchase, Braybrooke had been severe and dismal. He made her feel that she had disgraced the family. But in the middle of the meal he had been called to the telephone, and had come back affable—more than affable, he was talkative, and called her a "bad girl." She knew that something had come over the

wire which reinstated her. The fact was that Galloway had telephoned from Forbes's an invitation to dinner which he had forgotten
to deliver; and before he rang off he added:

"I say, Brooky, the Carteret girl's a queen. I'd give my jumping
cow to get as good a one on that beast Bennings. Forbes and Varick
have let the thing out."

"What thing?" said Braybrooke.

"Why, buying that plug for a joke, you foolish," said Galloway.
"Aren't you 'on' yet? Ta—ta!"

The Horse Looked at Him

MACKINLAY KANTOR

*As in W. H. Hudson's "The Story of a Piebald Horse" which
follows, the equine hero of MacKinlay Kantor's tale is the pivot
around which the plot revolves. Our interest is aroused by this
circumstance rather than by the development of his character
or accomplishments.*

Jameson thought he saw something stirring on the burnt sullenness
of the desert's face. He thought he saw a quiver among slopes of
brown and red.

He opened his dry, cracked mouth; his mouth had been open
for a long time, but he opened it wider. He tried to say, weakly,
"Posse."

It wasn't a posse. Jameson never thought he'd see the day when
he'd be glad to have a posse come smoking up to him; but he reck-
oned that if a man lived long enough, he saw different days from
those he had expected to see.

No quiver in the blue, no twisting and dividing in the brown. . . .
Jameson turned his head and felt the vast, round flame of sky sear-
ing his eyeballs. He managed to lift his hand, and in the scant shade
granted by swollen fingers, he tried to find some buzzards. He
couldn't find any buzzards. Nothing lived on this dry pan of desertion—nothing lived here but Jameson and Poco.

The man twisted the upper part of his body, and sighed. Poco's
head lay against the burning shale a few feet away; when Jameson
stirred, the little horse moved his neck with the agony of a move-

305

ment five hundred times repeated. There were flies eating slowly away at Poco's ears. His ears twitched them off now and again, but the flies came back.

"How you doing?" Jameson wanted to ask his horse.

Poco wasn't doing so well. He had done well, for the five years Jameson had ridden him. He had taken Jameson bustling out of towns, slapping along narrow mountain roads when the bullets squealed around them. And there was that night in Dundee when the wise little horse waited silently beside a dark doorway, aloof from the stampede of pursuing hoofs, and finally carried Jameson away with two bullets in his arm.

There were marks on Poco, too: there was a dark streak along his sorrel shoulder, where lead had branded him with the only brand he wore. There was a knobby place on one hock, and the contour of one inquisitive ear had been misshapen long before the flies ever sat there.

Jameson said to the horse, "Reckon you'd like a drink. So would I."

He stole Poco from the Maxwell ranch, clear over south of the Estella Plata range, when Poco was only a colt. Jameson had raised Poco on a bottle, so to speak—taught him to blow his nose and keep his clothes buttoned. He was the only kid Jameson had ever had.

Now the heat-warped fingers of the man's hand stole down to find his revolver butt, as they had stolen a dozen times before. He thought, Nothing in this country. Nothing for fifty miles. I ought to have known better than try to ride across. But we made it, other times. No water.

His hand trembled as he exposed the cylinder and saw the solitary undented cartridge cap which reposed on the surface of powder-grimed steel. One chamber was vacant; Jameson never kept a shell under his hammer. There were five shiny little wafers looking at him; the rims of four were marred by hammer strokes.

He put the gun back in its holster again, and felt around his cartridge belt. His raw fingers rubbed across empty sockets. Jameson had known men who wore two cartridge belts but he had never worn more than one. He had never expected that posse to cling upon his trail with such wolfish tenacity.

The blue sky came down and struck him across the face. It was a red sky—now it was yellow—now white. "Sky," he wanted to ask, "do you see any posses? I sure would like to see one."

Poco's ears fluttered again, and he tried to whinny. Still there was moisture in his muzzle, and one bubble formed there, and then it went away. It was mighty strange that there could be any moisture in either of them, after the hot day and the cold night, and the day before that.

Jameson said, "One of us went wrong. That was a bad slide. I reckon you might have seen that crack in the rocks, but I ain't blaming you. You seen plenty I've never seen."

His mind went away from him for a while, and came speeding back amid the hearty hoofs of phantom horses. There were men in this fantasy: enemies who came to gather him in, and all the time they laughed at him.

The mystic enemies said, "Why did you do it, Jimmy Jameson? You ain't never killed anyone. Time was when you were mighty charitable with what you took off the road. You're a bad man; but a lot of people like you."

They said, in this parched dream that formed within his mind, "It wouldn't have been hanging. We're the Law. We know. We've burned powder and shoved lead at each other, but you ain't really got a bad name. Maybe you'd have spent a couple years behind bars, but that's all. You shouldn't have tried the Llano Diablo. No water in the Llano Diablo. Nobody goes there."

He thought that the posse circled him, and then dismounted to pat Poco's red-hot flank and to moisten Jameson's own lips with cool, wet salve from a canteen. "You're an awful idiot," said the posse. "Here you are: your horse has got a broken back, and it looks as if both of your legs is busted, too. Can't either of you move. Can't even crawl. Not even coyotes go out on the Llano Diablo."

Now he awoke from his dream, and he had the gun in his hand. Twice he put the muzzle against his own temple, and twice he fought successfully to keep his finger from tightening. His horse watched him with glazing eyes; again it tried to lift its head.

"No," Jameson thought. "By God, I can't! It's hell for me, but I reckon it's double hell for you."

Once more the desert became a pasture, and in it he saw a lush green place where Poco trotted toward him, stiff-legged, knobby-kneed, his eyes young and coltish. "Sugar?" said Jameson to his darling. "You don't get none. I ain't going to ruin your teeth. I got a piece of apple here . . ." and his hands played with the thick, wiry mane. "Reckon some day you'll be a fine horse."

The sky changed from white back into yellow and orange. The shadow of a steep stone ridge grew longer; it went past the two suffering shapes—the swollen mass of living horseflesh—the dry-skinned, crippled man who lay beside it.

"Not another night," said Jameson. "I can't stand it. Pity there ain't two shells. I never realized I didn't have another loading for this gun."

Again the muzzle found his temple, but the horse still looked at him.

Jameson breathed softly. "O.K.," he croaked. He remembered something about the Bible and a merciful man being merciful to his beast, but Jameson would never in this life call Poco a beast.

He inched forward, suffering horrors until he felt the metal barrel sinking against Poco's ear cavity, soft and warm and silky despite all endurances.

"Be seeing you," he said, and pulled the trigger.

The gun jumped loose from his hand. His first thought was that the flies wouldn't be bothering Poco any longer.

He did not know how many dreams possessed him, but not many; the night came closer every second. And then his ears picked out a faint scrambling, a sound of sliding gravel. Hoof rims scraped the burnished gray rocks.

They rode up; they were angels in leather and flannel; they wore guns. They would carry Jimmy Jameson behind the bars, but still they were angels.

The sheriff was on his knees beside him.

"Can't understand it," Jameson whispered. "So late. Nobody comes to Llano Diablo."

The sheriff looked at the dead horse. He shook his head, even while his hands moved to his water bottle.

"One shell," said Jameson. "It was him or me. Poco needed a break."

The brown, lined face of the sheriff bent closer, and there were other faces behind. Water touched Jameson's lips.

"Guess you got a break yourself, that time," the sheriff said. "We hadn't come across your trail, and we agreed to ride back to Dundee. We were just turning our horses, behind that hill, when we heard you shoot."

The Story of a Piebald Horse

W. H. HUDSON

Although the piebald in W. H. Hudson's romance does not appear a great deal, the resolving of the plot depends upon him. We have here a slightly different locale, and a slightly different national flavor from the ordinary western type of tale.

This is all about a piebald. People there are like birds that come down in flocks, hop about chattering, gobble up their seed, then fly away forgetting what they have swallowed. I love not to scatter grain for such as these. With you, friend, it is different. Others may laugh if they like at the old man of many stories, who puts all things into his copper memory. I can laugh, too, knowing that all things are ordered by destiny; otherwise I might sit down and cry.

The things I have seen! There was the piebald that died long ago; I could take you to the very spot where his bones used to lie bleaching in the sun. There is a nettle growing on the spot. I saw it yesterday. What important things are these to remember and talk about! Bones of a dead horse and a nettle; a young bird that falls from its nest in the night and is found dead in the morning; puff-balls blown about by the wind; a little lamb left behind by the flock bleating at night amongst the thorns and thistles, where only the fox or wild dog can hear it! Small matters are these, and our lives, what are they? And the people we have known, the men and women who have spoken to us and touched us with warm hands—the bright eyes and red lips! Can we cast these things like dead leaves on the

fire? Can we lie down full of heaviness because of them, and sleep
and rise in the morning without them? Ah! friend!

Let us to the piebald. There was a cattle-marking at neighbor
Sotelo's estancia, and out of a herd of three thousand head we had
to part all the yearlings to be branded. After that, dinner and a
dance. At sunrise we gathered, about thirty of us; all friends and
neighbors, to do the work. Only with us came one person nobody
knew. He joined us when we were on our way to the cattle; a young
man, slender, well-formed, of pleasing countenance and dressed as
few could dress in those days. His horse also shone with silver trappings. And what an animal! Many horses have I seen in this life, but
never one with such a presence as this stranger's piebald.

Arrived at the herd, we began to separate the young animals, the
men riding in couples through the cattle, so that each calf when
singled out could be driven by two horsemen, one on each side, to
prevent it from doubling back. I happened to be mounted on a
demon with a fiery mouth—there was no making him work, so I had
to leave the parters and stand with little to do, watching the yearlings already parted, to keep them from returning to herd.

Presently neighbor Chapaco rode up to me. He was a good-
hearted man, well-spoken, half Indian and half Christian; but he
also had another half and that was devil.

"What! neighbor Lucero, are you riding on a donkey or a goat,
that you remain here doing boy's work?"

I began telling him about my horse, but he did not listen; he
was looking at the parters. "Who is that young stranger?" he asked.

"I see him today," I replied, "and if I see him again tomorrow
then I shall have seen him twice."

"And in what country of which I have never heard did he learn
cattle-parting?" said he.

"He rides," I answered, "like one presuming on a good horse.
But he is safe, his fellow-worker has all the danger."

"I believe you," said Chapaco. "He charges furiously and hurls
the heifer before his comrade, who has all the work to keep it from
doubling, and all the danger, for at any moment his horse may go
over it and fall. This our young stranger does knowingly, thinking
that no one will resent it. No, Lucero, he is presuming more on his
long knife than on his good horse."

Even while we spoke, the two we were watching rode up to us. Chapaco saluted the young man, taking off his hat, and said— "Will you take me for a partner, friend?"

"Yes, why not?" returned the other; and together the two rode back.

Now I shall watch them, said I to myself, to see what this Indian devil intends doing. Soon they came out of the herd driving a very small animal. Then I knew what was coming. "May your guardian angel be with you to avert a calamity, young stranger!" I exclaimed. Whip and spur those two came towards me like men riding a race and not parting cattle. Chapaco kept close to the calf, so that he had the advantage, for his horse was well trained. At length he got a little ahead, then, quick as lightning, he forced the calf round square before the other. The piebald struck it full in the middle, and fell because it had to fall. But, Saints in Heaven! why did not the rider save himself? Those who were watching saw him throw up his feet to tread the horse's neck and leap away; nevertheless man, horse and calf came down together. They ploughed the ground for some distance, so great had been their speed, and the man was under. When we picked him up he was senseless, the blood flowing from his mouth. Next morning, when the sun rose and God's light fell on the earth, he expired.

Of course there was no dancing that night. Some of the people, after eating, went away; others remained sitting about all night, talking in low tones, waiting for the end. A few of us were at his bedside watching his white face and closed eyes. He breathed and that was all. When the sunlight came over the world he opened his eyes and Sotelo asked him how he did. He took no notice, but presently his lips began to move, though they seemed to utter no sound. Sotelo bent his ear down to listen. "Where does she live?" he asked. He could not answer—he was dead.

"He seemed to be saying many things," Sotelo told us, "but I understood only this— 'Tell her to forgive me . . . I was wrong. She loved him from the first . . . I was jealous and hated him. . . . Tell Elaria not to grieve—Anacleto will be good to her.' Alas! my friends, where shall I find his relations to deliver this dying message to them?"

The Alcalde came that day and made a list of the dead man's

possessions, and bade Sotelo take charge of them till the relations could be found. Then, calling all the people together, he made each person cut on his whip-handle and on the sheath of his knife the mark branded on the flank of the piebald, which was in shape like a horseshoe with a cross inside, so that it might be shown to all strangers, and made known through the country until the dead man's relations should hear of it.

When a year had gone by, the Alcalde told Sotelo that, all inquiries having failed, he could now take the horse and the silver trappings for himself. Sotelo would not listen to this, for he was a devout man and coveted no person's property, dead or alive. The horse and things, however, still remained in his charge.

Three years later I was one afternoon sitting with Sotelo taking maté, when his herd of dun mares were driven up. They came galloping and neighing to the corral and ahead of them, looking like a wild horse, was the piebald, for no person ever mounted him.

"Never do I look on that horse," I remarked, "without remembering the fatal marking, when its master met his death."

"Now you speak of it," said he, "let me inform you that I am about to try a new plan. That noble piebald and all those silver trappings hanging in my room are always reproaching my conscience. Let us not forget the young stranger we put under ground. I have had many masses said for his soul's repose, but that does not quite satisfy me. Somewhere there is a place where he is not forgotten. Hands there are, perhaps, that gather wild flowers to place them with lighted candles before the image of the Blessed Virgin; eyes there are that weep and watch for his coming. You know how many travelers and cattle drovers going to Buenos Aires from the south call for refreshment at the *pulpería*. I intend taking the piebald and tying him every day at the gate there. No person calling will fail to notice the horse, and some day perhaps some traveler will recognize the brand on its flank and be able to tell us what department and what estancia it comes from."

Next morning the piebald was tied up at the gate of the *pulpería* at the road side, only to be released again when night came, and this was repeated every day for a long time. So fine an animal did not fail to attract the attention of all strangers passing that way; still several weeks went by and nothing was discovered. At length one evening, just when the sun was setting, there appeared a troop of cattle driven by eight men. It had come a great distance, for the troop was a large one—about nine hundred head—and they moved slowly, like cattle that had been many days on the road. Some of the men came in for refreshments; then the storekeeper noticed that one remained outside leaning on the gate.

"What is the capatas doing that he remains outside?" said one of the men.

"Evidently he has fallen in love with that piebald," said another, "for he cannot take his eyes off it."

At length the capatas, a young man of good presence, came in and sat down on a bench. The others were talking and laughing about the strange things they had all been doing the day before; for they had been many days and nights on the road, only nodding a little in their saddles, and at length becoming delirious from want of sleep, they had begun to act like men that are half-crazed.

"Enough of the delusions of yesterday," said the capatas, who had been silently listening to them, "but tell me, boys, am I in the same condition today?"

"Surely not!" they replied. "Thanks to those horned devils being so tired and footsore, we all had some sleep last night."

"Very well then," he said, "now you have finished eating and drinking go back to the troop, but before you leave look well at that piebald tied at the gate. He that is not a cattle-drover may ask, 'How can my eyes deceive me?' but I know that a crazy brain makes us see many strange things when the drowsy eyes can only be held open with the fingers."

The men did as they were told, and when they had looked well at the piebald, they all shouted out, "He has the brand of the estancia de Silva on his flank, and no counter-brand—claim the horse, capatas, for he is yours." And after that they rode away to the herd.

"My friend," said the capatas to the storekeeper, "will you explain how you came possessed of this piebald horse?"

Then the other told him everything, even the dying words of the young stranger, for he knew all.

The capatas bent down his head, and covering his face shed tears. Then he said, "And you died thus, Torcuato, amongst strangers! From my heart I have forgiven you the wrong you did me.

Heaven rest your soul, Torcuato; I cannot forget that we were once brothers. I, friend, am that Anecleto of whom he spoke with his last breath."

Sotelo was then sent for, and when he arrived and the *pulpería* was closed for the night, the capatas told his story, which I will give you in his own words, for I was also present to hear him. This is what he told us.

I was born on the southern frontier. My parents died when I was very small, but Heaven had compassion on me and raised up one to shelter me in my orphanhood. Don Loreta Silva took me to his estancia on the Sarandi, a stream half a day's journey from Tandil, toward the setting sun. He treated me like one of his own children, and I took the name of Silva. He had two other children, Torcuato, who was about the same age as myself, and his daughter, Elaria, who was younger. He was a widower when he took charge of me, and died when I was still a youth. After his death we moved to Tandil, where we had a house close to the little town; for we were all minors, and the property had been left to be equally divided between us when we should be of age. For four years we lived happily together; then when we were of age we preferred to keep the property undivided. I proposed that we should go and live on the estancia, but Torcuato would not consent, liking the place where we were living best. Finally, not being able to persuade him, I resolved to go and attend to the estancia myself. He said that I could please myself and that he would stay where he was with Elaria. It was only when I told Elaria of these things that I knew how much I loved her. She wept and implored me not to leave her.

"Why do you shed tears, Elaria?" I said; "is it because you love me? Know then, that I also love you with all my heart, and if you will be mine, nothing can ever make us unhappy. Do not think that my absence at the estancia will deprive me of this feeling which has ever been growing up in me."

"I do love you, Anacleto," she replied, "and I have also known of your love for a long time. But there is something in my heart which I cannot impart to you; only I ask you, for the love you bear me, do not leave me, and do not ask me why I say this to you."

After this appeal I could not leave her, nor did I ask her to tell me her secret. Torcuato and I were friendly, but not as we had been before this difference. I had no evil thoughts of him; I loved him and was with him continually; but from the moment I announced to him that I had changed my mind about going to the estancia and was silent when he demanded the reason, there was a something in him which made it different between us. I could not open my heart to him about Elaria, and sometimes I thought that he also had a secret which he had no intention of sharing with me. This coldness did not, however, distress me very much, so great was the happiness I now experienced, knowing that I possessed Elaria's love. He was much away from the house, being fond of amusements, and he had also begun to gamble. About three months passed in this way, when one morning Torcuato, who was saddling his horse to go out, said, "Will you come with me today, Anacleto?"

"I do not care to go," I answered.

"Look, Anacleto," said he; "once you were always ready to accompany me to a race or dance or cattle-marking. Why have you ceased to care for these things? Are you growing devout before your time, or does my company no longer please you?"

"It is best to tell him everything and have done with secrets," said I to myself, and so replied—

"Since you ask me, Torcuato, I will answer you frankly. It is true that I now take less pleasure than formerly in these pastimes; but you have not guessed the reason."

"What then is this reason of which you speak?"

"Since you cannot guess it," I replied, "know that it is love."

"Love of whom?" he asked quickly and turning very pale.

"Do you need ask? Elaria," I replied.

I had scarcely uttered the name before he turned on me full of rage.

"Elaria!" he exclaimed. "Do you dare tell me of love for Elaria? But you are only a blind fool, and do not know that I am going to marry her myself."

"Are you mad, Torcuato, to talk of marrying your sister?"

"She is no more my sister than you are my brother," he returned. "I," he continued, striking his breast passionately, "am the only child of my father, Loreto Silva. Elaria, whose mother died in giving her birth, was adopted by my parents. And because she is going to be my wife, I am willing that she should have a share of the property; but you, a miserable foundling, why were you lifted up so high? Was it not enough that you were clothed and fed till you came to man's estate? Not a hand's-breadth of the estancia land should be yours, and now you presume to speak of love for Elaria."

My blood was on fire with so many insults, but I remembered all the benefits I had received from his father, and did not raise my hand against him. Without more words he left me. I then hastened to Elaria and told her what had passed.

"This," I said, "is the secret you would not impart to me. Why, when you knew these things, was I kept in ignorance?"

"Have pity on me, Anacleto," she replied, crying. "Did I not see that you two were no longer friends and brothers, and this without knowing of each other's love. I dared not open my lips to you or to him. It is always a woman's part to suffer in silence. God intended us to be poor, Anacleto, for we were both born of poor parents, and had this property never come to us, how happy we might have been!"

"Why do you say such things, Elaria? Since we love each other, we cannot be unhappy, rich or poor."

"Is it a little matter," she replied, "that Torcuato must be our bitter enemy? But you do not know everything. Before Torcuato's father died, he said he wished his son to marry me when we came of age. When he spoke about it we were sitting together by him."

"And what did you say, Elaria?" I asked, full of concern.

"Torcuato promised to marry me. I only covered my face, and was silent, for I loved you best even then, though I was almost a child, and my heart was filled with grief at his words. After we came here, Torcuato reminded me of his father's words. I answered that I did not wish to marry him, that he was only a brother to me. Then he said that we were young and he could wait until I was of another mind. This is all I have to say; but how shall we three live together any longer? I cannot bear to part from you, and every moment I tremble to think what may happen when you two are together."

"Fear nothing," I said. "Tomorrow morning you can go to spend a week at some friend's house in the town; then I will speak to Torcuato, and tell him that since we cannot live in peace together we must separate. Even if he answers with insults I shall do nothing to grieve you, and if he refuses to listen to me, I shall send some person we both respect to arrange all things between us."

This satisfied her, but as evening approached she grew paler, and I knew she feared Torcuato's return. He did not, however, come back that night. Early next morning she was ready to leave. It was an easy walk to the town, but the dew was heavy on the grass, and I saddled a horse for her to ride. I had just lifted her to the saddle when Torcuato appeared. He came at great speed, and throwing himself off his horse, advanced to us. Elaria trembled and seemed ready to sink upon the earth to hide herself like a partridge that has seen the hawk. I prepared myself for insults and perhaps violence. He never looked at me; he spoke only to her.

"Elaria," he said, "something has happened—something that obliges me to leave this house and neighborhood at once. Remember when I am away that my father, who cherished you and enriched you with his bounty and who also cherished and enriched this ingrate, spoke to us from his dying bed and made me promise to marry you. Think what his love was; do not forget that his last wish is sacred, and that Anacleto has acted a base, treacherous part in trying to steal you from me. He was lifted out of the mire to be my brother and equal in everything except this. He has got a third part of my inheritance—let that satisfy him; your own heart, Elaria, will tell you that a marriage with him would be a crime before God and man. Look not for my return tomorrow or for many days. But if you two begin to laugh at my father's dying wishes, look for me, for then I shall not delay to come back to you, Elaria, and to you, Anacleto. I have spoken."

He then mounted his horse and rode away. Very soon we learned the cause of his sudden departure. He had quarrelled over his cards and in a struggle that followed had stabbed his adversary to the heart. He had fled to escape the penalty. We did not believe that he would remain long absent; for Torcuato was very young, well off, and much liked, and this was, moreover, his first offence against the law. But time went on and he did not return, nor did any message from him reach us, and at last we concluded that he had left the country. Only now after four years, have I accidentally discovered his fate through seeing his piebald horse.

After he had been absent from home for over a year, I asked Elaria to become my wife. "We cannot marry till Torcuato returns," she said. "For if we take the property that ought to have been all his, and at the same time disobey his father's dying wish, we shall be doing an evil thing. Let us take care of the property till he returns to receive it all back from us; then, Anacleto, we shall be free to marry."

I consented, for she was more to me than lands and cattle. I put the estancia in order and leaving a trustworthy person in charge of everything I invested my money in fat bullocks to resell in Buenos Aires, and in this business I have been employed ever since. From the estancia I have taken nothing, and now it must all come back to us—his inheritance and ours. This is a bitter thing and will give Elaria great grief.

Thus ended Anacleto's story, and when he had finished speaking and still seemed greatly troubled in his mind, Sotelo said to him, "Friend, let me advise you what to do. You will now shortly be married to the woman you love and probably some day a son will be born to you. Let him be named Torcuato, and let Torcuato's inheritance be kept for him. And if God gives you no son, remember what was done for you and for the girl you are going to marry, when you were orphans and friendless, and look for some unhappy child in the same condition to protect and enrich him as you were enriched."

"You have spoken well," said Anacleto. "I will report your words to Elaria, and what ever she wishes done that will I do."

So ends my story, friend. The cattle drover left us that night and we saw no more of him. Only before going he gave the piebald and the silver trappings to Sotelo. Six months after his visit, Sotelo also received a letter from him to say that his marriage with Elaria had taken place; and the letter was accompanied with a present of seven cream-colored horses with black manes and tails.

Rodney

LEONARD H. NASON

*The horse in this story actually lived, performed as described
and received the official citation. There must be many other
horses over the centuries that have performed such feats
"above and beyond the call of duty" and remained unrecog-
nized. It is nice to know that at least one horse will go down
through the years as the hero that he was.*

In an Army post, by ten o'clock in the morning, the morning's work
is very nearly finished. Reveille at 5:45, breakfast at six, first call for
drill at 6:45, assembly at seven, and then off to the drill field. By
10:30 the troops begin to move slowly back to quarters to groom,
clean equipment and police up generally before dinner.

Upon an October day, when the sun shines golden through the
turning leaves and the mists hang smokily above the Virginia hills,
two officers stood side by side and watched the troops come slowly
home from drill. One of the officers was a colonel in a many-ribboned
blouse, shiny boots, white cuffs and riding crop; the other a captain,
in a campaign hat and O.D. shirt.

A soldier would guess, because the colonel was wearing the
black stripe of General Staff, that he was an inspector, and that the
captain, because he was in working clothes, had been snatched from
his organization to guide the colonel inspecting about, and also to
be pumped genially on the side as to what he thought of his commanding officer and the way the post and garrison were handled in
general. A soldier would also know that the inspector had posted

320

himself there to watch the troops come in; the hour of their going out being rather early for a field officer to be up in the morning.

Two batteries of artillery clattered by, the men dust-covered, the horses sweating, brass hub caps on limbers and caissons glittering. The colonel replied absent-mindedly to the salute of the officer in charge.

"Some lounging in the saddle there!" he commented. "Ought to correct that."

"There are a lot of recruits in that battery," observed the captain. "They're probably suffering from saddle sores."

A squadron of cavalry in full pack went by, machine rifles, field radio and medical detachment complete.

"What's the idea in that, Captain Black?" snapped the inspector.

"I believe they're off next week for a month's practise march. They've been turning out full pack for some time. Gets the men accustomed to making up packs, pitching camp, packing saddles and that sort of thing. Then, they've never made a march with air-cooled machine guns in pack, and they want to see how they ride. We aren't very familiar with the gun."

"Hurump!" granted the inspector. "Well, where is your outfit?"

"The headquarters detachment does not go to drill," said the captain quietly. He seemed to settle himself as a man might that expected a blow.

"Why don't they? Don't they think they need it?"

"Colonel," said the captain, "my detachment furnishes the telephone operators, the orderlies, the chauffeurs, the messengers, the mail carriers, the radio men and the office boys for this entire post and half the city of Washington. I couldn't get them together for drill if I wanted to. Anyway, in time of emergency, they'd do just as they're doing now. A trained telephone operator or radio man wouldn't take the field."

"But who looks after your animals?"

"We only have two, my own mount and a horse that does odd jobs around the post."

"Your own horse is a private mount, of course?" asked the inspector. "The other one a public animal? Where is he? I want to look at him."

Captain Black turned and led the way across the parade ground toward the stables. An escort wagon loaded with hay stood before the last one on the end, and from this wagon, by means of block and tackle, the bales were being hoisted into the loft. At the end of the rope that did the hoisting was a big chestnut horse, well built, sturdy about the back and loins, one that in his day must have been a beautiful wheeler, but that now was so old his muzzle was quite white. At his bridle was a man in stable clothes and a battered campaign hat, decorated with a cord that still held some faint suspicion of its original red.

"That's the horse," said Captain Black, pointing. "His name is Rodney."

The inspector strode clankily toward the group about the wagon, and the men at once came to attention. But the inspector halted before the chestnut horse and his attendant.

"You!" barked the inspector, addressing the man at Rodney's bridle. "Don't you ever shave?"

The soldier in the dilapidated hat was old. The two days' beard that sprouted from his leather cheek was quite white, and his eyes were bloodshot and watery with the perpetual tears of age. But he stood at attention as straight as a ramrod.

"Yes, sir," he replied, "for Saddidy inspeshun."

"What battery are you with?"

The old soldier's eyes wandered to Captain Black.

"Headquarters detachment, sir," he replied.

"How's this, Black?" demanded the inspector, turning. "Don't you have your men shave every day? Don't you ever visit quarters? Your first sergeant ought to do it if you don't!"

"The headquarters detachment have no quarters, sir," said Captain Black. "The men are mostly married, and they are scattered about Washington, so that it was not practical to have them all come back to the post to sleep."

"But this man must sleep somewhere. He lives on the reservation, does he not? Isn't there someone to keep him up to snuff?"

"He lives in the stable shack here with the horse-shoers. Such duties as he has he performs well, and since he has seen so much service, we allow him—I allow him—a little liberty from strict observance of regulations."

"The commanding officer know about this?" asked the colonel coldly.

"I don't know," replied Captain Black. "I never discussed it with him."

"I see the colonel has the Cuban Pacification medal," observed the old soldier, nodding toward the ribbons on the colonel's chest and smiling politely. "Was the colonel at Camp Columbia? I was there. I was outta G Troop of the 'Leventh Cavalry. Terry Mc-Govern won the boxin' championship o' the camp that year. He was our top. G Troop was always a great troop for boxers. I was in China too. In aught seven."

"How much service have you got in?" asked the colonel, bending his brows sternly upon the old soldier.

"I got two more years to go to retire, sir. I'm on my last hitch."

"And what's the highest grade you've held?"

"Well, sir, now, I never paid much attention to grades. They come an' go. I been a private first-class for a good many years. That's good enough for me. I seen too many o' my buddies made noncoms, and then, when they lost their stripes for no reason at all, it about broke their hearts."

"Did you get overseas in the last war?"

"Yes, sir." The old soldier looked with affection at the old horse. "I drove Rodney. Him an' me an' Jefferson was the wheel team of the first piece in A Batt'ry."

The colonel, his attention once more drawn to the horse, walked over and opened Rodney's mouth. He inspected the horse's teeth, lifted his feet, one by one, then finally turned to Captain Black.

"That's a damned old horse," said the colonel. "Well, come, Black. Let's be moving on!"

Captain Black immediately fell in on his superior's left, and they walked away.

"Come on, Benny!" called the driver of the escort wagon as soon as the two officers were out of hearing. "Git Rodney into his collar and let's git to hoistin' in this hay. You know who that old buzzard was? Well, he's here to make economies. Come from the General Staff. His chauffeur's livin' in my squad room, told me about it. Look out he don't sell you an' Rodney for glue!"

"Don't worry about me!" jeered Benny. "I seen inspectors come and inspectors go. . . . Come, Rodney, boy; up goes a bale o' hay! Tchk! Tchk! Huh. You recruit, pull your hand down outta the air! Why, that colonel was just lookin' Rodney over for his fine points. I mind one time on the Border, Black Jack Pershin' judged a horse show we was in. 'Fine horse that, Benny,' sez he. He always called me 'Benny.' I was with him in Jolo, time I done one o' my hitches in the calvary. 'Fine horse, that, Benny.' 'Yes, general!' sye. 'I'm goin' to give him the blue ribbon,' sez he. Next time I see General Pershin' was in Andernach. Army of Occupation. We was havin' a horse show. When it come I win the blue ribbon with Rodney, an orderly comes over and says they want to see me over by the grandstand. General Pershin'. 'Ain't I seen you an' that horse before?' sez he. Sye, 'Yes, sir. El Paso, in 1915.' 'My, my!' sez he, 'There's a lotta wind been blown through the trumpets since then. An' Rodney still collectin' ribbons!' 'Well, General!' sye, 'we all collected a few since those days, but I'd just as soon not go through any more shows like this last one. Some o' them jumps is a little high for a feller my age.' Well, we lifted a cup that afternoon in the battery competition, and when we went by, Black Jack, he waved his hand to me, and Marshal Haig, he was there, he give me a grin, because they'd told him who me an' Rodney was."

"Yeh," observed the driver. "But don't let's talk about liftin' cups right now. Let's see how good Rodney is at liftin' a little hay."

Meanwhile the inspecting colonel and Captain Black were roaming about the outside of one of those long portable buildings that were put up everywhere during the war and that are still housing Army personnel. This particular one had a sign over the door that said Headquarters Detachment, but within all was dark and silent.

"What's this building serve for, Captain Black?" demanded the inspector.

"My orderly room is in one end, sir. That's all it serves for now. In summer, when the reserve officers are here, we have a tailor shop, a store, barber shop, cafeteria and day room. We give out the concessions, you know, and collect 10 percent of the gross for the mess fund."

"What do you do with a mess fund if your company doesn't eat in quarters?"

"They do in summer, sir. Then, anything that's left over, we use to buy the men tailor-made uniforms, or for athletic goods. Basketball, baseball, that sort of thing."

"These old temporary buildings," said the inspector, "are a great source of expense. There is no reason so valid in the Army for anything becoming permanent as that it was only intended to be temporary. The paint and maintenance cost for these pasteboard affairs is terrific. I have orders to condemn them wherever possible."

"Well, colonel," smiled Captain Black. "I don't know what we'd do for quarters for the headquarters detachment. In the summer, when the civilian components of the Army are out here—the reserve officers, the R.O.T.C., the C.M.T.C. and the National Guard—things are pretty congested."

"Perhaps," said the colonel, "that can be arranged."

They went into the orderly room at the back, where, having dismissed the clerk, the inspector sat down and began going through the company records.

"This forage return is a needless expense," said the inspector suddenly, taking off his eyeglasses and thumping the table. "I'm surprised that you should keep on that one useless animal, eating his head off in the stables. Why can't one of the wagon mules be unhitched to hoist hay into the loft, and if that's not practical—and I don't understand why it shouldn't be—why should the one horse that does it be carried on your returns?"

"Well," said Captain Black," I suppose it simplifies paper work somewhere. That was the arrangement I found when I took over the company."

"And that old file that looks after him there? What's his name? What's he done to rate a gravy train like that?"

"His name is Benny Walsh. He's been in the regiment twenty-two years. When he was younger, there wasn't a better soldier in the United States Army. If it hadn't been for one failing, he'd be a sergeant major now, at least."

"Drink, of course?"

"But between pay days," said Captain Black sadly," he certainly performs his duty well."

"I see no reason for coddling him there!" snapped the inspector.

"No, sir, that's not the reason. He was Rodney's driver during the war. Together they pulled off some kind of a gallant deed up there on the lines. The regiment has felt grateful to them ever since."

"And what was that?"

Well, it was quite a story. Captain Black had not seen it. He had not been with the regiment then. The battalion commander at the time had been lieutenant colonel when Black joined, and there had been some old sergeants that remembered it, but they were all gone now, and he had not heard the story for years. He had rather forgotten the details. Something up in the woods. On the Marne. H'm'm. Oh, yes. Rodney had been wheel horse in A Battery then. The battery had been sent up, early in July, direct from training camp, to a position along those hills through which the Marne trailed its slow way like a lazy snake. They were in thick woods. It was all woods up in that part of the country, with isolated stone farmhouses. Woods on this side of the river, woods on that side, where the Germans were, though there was never a sign of them. Never a shot fired, nor a sound, nor the bark of a dog nor the rattle of a wheel to show that there was anyone across the river, and only the wreckage of the shattered bridge below Jaulgonne to hint that war was going on. A Battery was on the crest of a hill, with a field of fire up and down the river, but they saw nothing to fire at. There were Americans in front of them somewhere, but they never saw them. They saw French soldiers once in a while, going about in their shirts, without helmets or gas masks, carrying water or bringing in wood.

The battery grew sick of the place rapidly. This was no way to fight a war. They grew more and more careless about walking on the paths; even the officers took short cuts through the wheat. It was cold at night, even though it was summer, and after the first week of vigilance the cooks used to leave their fires going in the kitchen after dark.

The men of A Battery played baseball one afternoon against a team of the second battalion and would—had it not been too far away—have gone down and had a swim in the Marne to cool off afterward. Then, upon a night of fine rain, when everyone was celebrating France's Independence Day, the scene was suddenly shifted with a roll of thunder. The curtain went up to the accompaniment of full orchestration, peal after peal, and the men, throwing off their blankets and coming out from under the guns, half awake, saw that the wooded heights across the river were crowned with heat lightning that never ceased its flickering for an instant. All those paths the careless men had trodden through the wheat, the kitchen where the fires had burned all night, the shallow dugouts where officers had sat and smoked through the soft summer evening, all went skyward in the first quarter of an hour. The battery, for some strange reason, was unmolested. What was happening to the rest of the regiment was conjecture, for all the telephone wires were out and runners who went into the shell-lit woods did not come back.

At daybreak, the battery commander crawled out with the executive to an open space along the ridge, and there could see what was going on. There was smoke everywhere like brush fires, and men running like startled bugs. On the upper side of the bend there was no smoke, but there was firing farther back in the trees. Black shrapnel, which meant German shells. The river was black with

boats. The Germans had got across there, and that firing back up the slope was their rolling barrage.

"We've got to get out of here!" decided the captain. "They'll go down to Conde-en-Brie and cut us off!"

He did not fire on the boats because he had run out of ammunition. He went back to his guns, where a pale French lieutenant told him that the Germans were at St. Eugene, on the west side of the hill, and that it would be only a matter of minutes before that whole sector would be pinched out. At this moment a tooth-chattering sergeant reported that there was not a surviving horse on the picket line. Yes, said someone else, there was. There was Rodney, and Jefferson, his team mate. Benny Walsh had taken them in to the farm the night before.

"We can't move a battery that requires five horses with only two!" cried the executive.

"We can try!" said the captain. "I'm not going to leave my guns to the krauts in my first engagement!"

There are supposed to be six horses to each gun, and six more to each caisson. They hitched Rodney and Jefferson in and Benny Walsh drove, while the weary gunners, death staring them in the face, shoved on the wheels. They got three guns out—away over the hill to the new support position. But the enemy had balloons up by then, and spotted what was going on.

An airplane, zooming like an angry hornet, descended upon them just as old Benny had started out with the last piece. A fistful of machine-gun bullets scattered the battery, and another struck down Rodney's team mate. But those that fled saw Benny leap from the saddle, draw a knife and hack away at the traces. The airman swung back in a low bank, and fired another yard or so of clip that knocked Benny into a heap beside his off-wheeler. After that, those present went their way, but in the afternoon, still harnessed to the gun, Rodney arrived at the support position. One horse, dragging gun and limber—a load for six—and with old Benny stretched out insensible on his back.

That was the story. Captain Black had heard it many a time from men who had been witnesses. They were mostly all gone now, and the thing was beginning to be forgotten.

"Humph!" commented the colonel. "They should have tried that captain for letting his men give away the position like that. But in wartime, with an army full of civilians—" He finished the sentence with a vague wave of his hand, and went back to his inspection of the records.

The colonel ruffled books, unfolded reports, inspected records and added figures. Finally he closed the correspondence book with a bang.

"Black," said the colonel calmly, "I see no way out of it. We're going to have to disband this headquarters detachment. Too much waste here, unnecessary paper work. This building costs too much in upkeep. We can tear it down. We'll send the men to duty with troops, or transfer them to the Signal Corps or Motor Transport Section of the Q.M. That will take their pay and maintenance off the artillery accounts. That old horse there, I'll have condemned and sold. The man Walsh I'll recommend be discharged for the good of the service."

"Benny?" gasped Captain Black. "Why do you want to discharge Benny?"

"You told me he did nothing but look after the horse, and if the horse is sold he'll have nothing to do."

"But he's only got two years to go to retire."

"That's the point," said the colonel. "We'll save Uncle Sam the cost of his pension all those years. Why, some of those old horned toads live to be a hundred!"

"I know, colonel," protested Captain Black, "but he won't have anywhere to go; he'll be destitute."

"Bah!" said the colonel. "He can go to the Old Soldier's Home, can't he? It'll be good enough for him!"

The news of the disbanding of the headquarters detachment spread rapidly, but aside from its value as an interesting event, and something to talk about, it aroused little interest. The men in it lived in town, their duties kept them away from the post, and, after all, it meant little more to them than changing their collar ornaments.

The other recommendation—that Rodney be condemned and sold, and old Benny discharged—did not come out until later. The sergeant major whispered it to the first sergeant, who told the stable sergeant, who told the saddlers and the horseshoer that lived in the stable shack with Benny.

"What's the matter with you Johns?" demanded Benny angrily one night. "You're too danged polite all of a sudden! You ain't been goin' through my foot locker, because there ain't ary thing in it worth stealin'. You're puttin' some kind of shine on me, though; I c'n tell by the sneakin' guilty look in your eye! . . . Tom Parsons, you leather spoiler, you put cement in my shavin' powder again?"

"No, Benny," said a saddler contritely.

"That reminds me," said Benny thoughtfully, "speakin' o' shavin' powder, I gotta get some new. I'll go over to the exchange after supper. There's a pair o' breeches there I've a mind to buy. The tailor'll sell 'em to me jawbone. They was made for one o' them recruits in the headquarters detachment that's got sent to the Q.M. and he don't want 'em now. Cheap, they be."

"Better wait until next week," advised the horseshoer. "Wait another week, Benny. Be sure you make up your mind first. Maybe next week you won't want 'em."

There was a solemn hush, while Benny looked all around the circle, blinking his watery eyes.

"That's right," said he slowly; "so I won't." Quickly he jerked his head. "Say, is that what's been botherin' you terrapins? About them dischargin' me? Huh? Don't let that bother you. Cap'n Black, he broke the news to me this afternoon. What's in that to look so sad about? Ain't I gettin' outta this madhouse? All my friends is on the outside, anyway. Black Jack, he's been out for years. The army's full o' recruits. I'll be better off out of it."

No one made any remark. Benny's face was calm, his voice steady, and the hand with which he calmly sorted over the things in his foot-locker tray never trembled.

"The only thing," said Benny, "is that you boys gotta take good care o' Rodney."

"Why, didn't you know?" spoke up the blacksmith, without thinking. "He's been condemned. They're goin' to sell him at auction."

Old Benny recoiled as though he had been struck.

"No!" said he. "Straight goods?"

"Yup," nodded the saddler. "They're gonna put the I.C. on him tomorrow."

"Well, well," marvelled Benny, shaking his head from side to side. "Goin' to condemn Rodney. Old Rodney, that never bucked, nor never refused to pull, nor never went in a horse show he didn't win! Overseas with the outfit and back with it! And now they condemn him! Man, I'll tell the horn-tanglin' universe that that's the best one I ever did hear! You Johns listen to me. Since I come in the outfit they've wore five different styles o' putties, and they finished up by putting white collars and cuffs on enlisted men, but I'll tell you this is the biggest surprise I had since the time I thought coneyac was the French word for 'soup'! So me an' Rodney is gettin' condemned! Well, whaddyuh think o' that for curb chains?"

The other men in the stable shack said nothing, and Benny went on with his sorting. But they noticed, now, that he kept taking out the same two pairs of socks, unrolling them, rolling them up, and then putting them back again, and that his hands shook ever so slightly while he did it.

At noontime, some three weeks later, Captain Black went into the officers' club for lunch. Nearly all the former members of his headquarters detachment had gone, and he had nothing to do now but wait for his own orders. He tossed cap, gloves and riding crop into a corner and, going into the reading room, spoke to an officer there that he knew, the post quartermaster.

"They have the auction this morning?" asked the captain.

"Hello, Black!" greeted the quartermaster. "Yes, all over. Sold 'em all off, horses and mules, as well as a flock of condemned shelter halves."

"About Rodney—that old horse from my outfit—do you know —that is, have you any idea who got him?"

"No. Not the slightest."

"I sent my striker over there to bid up to fifty dollars for him," said Captain Black sadly. "I had in mind having him destroyed. I hate to think of that horse pulling a junk cart."

"Well, you didn't get him," said the quartermaster, "because the cheapest a horse went for was seventy dollars. Oh, by the way, I paid off one of your men yesterday. Old Walsh. He drew quite a lot of money on his final settlement. Clothing allowance, savings deposited with the quartermaster—can you imagine the old bum saving money?—a biggish amount. I thought I'd warn you so you could get him off the reservation as soon as possible, before he gets into a crap game and they take it all away from him."

One of the club servants came softly across the room and touched Captain Black's elbow.

"There's a Mr. Walsh would like to see you, sir," said he.

"Mr. Walsh?" repeated Captain Black.

"It's old Benny!" laughed the quartermaster. " 'Mister' is right. He's a civilian now."

Captain Black went out to the hall, where his visitor awaited him. It was old Benny. He was still wearing his "Saddiday inspecshun" breeches, putties and army shoes, but over his olive-drab shirt was a threadbare, cast-off coat, two sizes too large for him, and his gnarled hands twirled a civilian hat. The old soldier. He had taken off his blouse, taken off his cap, someone had given him an old coat, and he was a civilian!

"Good day, captain," greeted Benny. "I'm through now, and I been paid off, and I just wanted to stop by and say good-by to you, sir."

"Well, Benny," said Captain Black, finding words with some difficulty, "you know I'm sorry to see you go. Er—these things happen, you know! These are evil times. Er—have you any plans for the future, Benny—that is—"

"No, sir," said Benny. "I hadn't just give it much thought. But I'll find somethin' to do. There's no hurry. I'll want to take a little vacation fust, from gittin' up at revvely, an' the like o' that!"

"I understand," went on Captain Black, "that you drew quite a lot of savings of one kind or another. That's fine, Benny, to have saved up all that money! How much was it?"

"Hundred and forty dollars, sir. I always tried to save a little. But what with blinds, and equipment I had to pay for now and again, you know it took a long time. I been over twenty-five years savin' that hundred and forty. When I come in first, a private only got twelve dollars a month."

"Well, you want to hang onto it now. Don't go getting into any crap games or red dog with it. Keep it for emergencies."

Old Benny grinned. "It's all gone a'ready," said he.

"What? Did somebody take it away from you? You give me his name and I'll have it back for you, don't fret! Who got it? What did you do with it, Benny?"

"I bought Rodney with it!"

"You bought Rodney?" gasped Captain Black. "You bought Rodney? Rodney the horse? What on earth did you do that for?"

"The cap'n's heard tell, ain't he, about the time that Rodney pulled the guns outta the woods up on the Marne so the battery wouldn't get captured by the Germans? Well, sir, I got hit that day. Bad. But I got up on old Rodney's back again, an' I sez in his ear, 'Rodney, I'm passin' out, but you take care o' me.' I woke up in the hospital. Why should he keep on goin' draggin' that great gun all alone if he hadn't heard me? He got me outta there. I'd been planted if it hadn't been for Rodney! Captain, I don't mean no offence, but a man that's been through one o' them shellin's ain't got no fear o' hell no more, no, sir-ree! Well, anyway, there was my old pal, and I went round to see him to say good-by, and there was some iceman gittin' ready to buy him. An' it come over me that no buddy o' mine was gonna pull no ice cart. An' so I bid for him. An' when it come to a hundred an' forty dollars, this iceman quit, an' Rodney belongs to me."

The post commander, being married, of course, ate in his own quarters, but the adjutant, who, after all, was the commander's right hand, ate at the club, and he, wiping his mouth with his napkin, walked into the card room to meet someone who said he wanted to see him on a matter of utmost urgency.

"Why, Captain Black," began the adjutant with some surprise, for Black was known to be a sober and somewhat cold-blooded officer. "What's the excitement? I thought we were getting a warning for 'M' day at least!"

"No, no," said Captain Black impatiently, "but we've got to work fast here. You know, of course, that my old headquarters detachment had a big mess fund, and it's all been audited and found correct, and since the outfit has been broken up, each organization to which one of my men goes gets his share of the fund. I'm going to turn it over to the Finance this afternoon. Now, you know all the rules and regs! Old Benny Walsh has gone and bought Rodney with his last cent, and how can I get authority to reimburse him out of the mess fund? After all, the horse belonged to the detachment, anyway! A hundred and forty dollars! A dollar less per man's share of the fund!"

"You can't do it!" said the adjutant. "Even if the fund hadn't been audited. That mess fund isn't to buy animals with, it's for extra food and comforts for the men!"

"Pigweed!" snapped Captain Black. "Somebody can give me authority to disburse those funds. Can the Old Man?"

The adjutant laughed. "Not now. Nobody short of the Secretary of War can do it now."

"I'll go see him."

He swung on his heel, but the adjutant seized his arm.

"Captain!" he pleaded. "Here; let's cool down on this matter! You can't go over everybody's head that way. You know that! If you try to see the Secretary, it will mean your commission!"

"I doubt it," said Black calmly. "The Secretary was a cavalryman first. He was through most of that sausage grinding in France, too. I think he'll understand! We'll try it, anyway. Who makes the biggest bet—old Benny with the last cent between him and starvation, or me with a problematical career? I'm off for Washington. Meanwhile, until this is straightened out, I'd like authority to keep Rodney and Benny on the reservation."

"That's simple," said the adjutant, "but you stay out of the State, War and Navy Building."

The rumor that old Benny Walsh had bought Rodney at the auction with his last cent, and that Captain Black had gone to appeal to the Secretary of War, brought Rodney into a prominence he had not enjoyed since the war. There was eager discussion of the affair that afternoon, and when Captain Black returned from Washington, the officers eagerly demanded if he had been able to see the Secretary, and if so, what the Secretary had said.

"I got in," replied Black to all queries, "and he let me talk. When I had finished, he said he'd look into it. He'd look into it, and that I'd hear from him."

"Yeh," murmured the listeners, "you'll hear from him! And how!"

Among the enlisted personnel, there was a sergeant here, and a caisson jack there, and one or two old privates who remembered Rodney when he was the best wheel horse in the Army, and they refreshed their souvenirs for the memory of the recruits. People suddenly realized that that old horse that so faithfully hauled hay every morning was in a class with Traveller, that bore General Lee through the Civil War, and years afterward, and with Comanche, the sole survivor of the Custer fight, that never had a man on his back after Miles Keogh.

Someone dug up the ribbons Rodney had won, and got permission to have them grouped and mounted separately, to be hung in headquarters. Someone else, in A Battery's storeroom, found the old name board with "First Section. Piece. Wheel. Rodney" on it; and this was taken down to the Battery station and put up over his old stall.

Meanwhile, the result of Captain Black's call on the Secretary of War was not known. The officers gloomily remarked that the least he would get would be immediate orders for Fort Forgotten or Camp Cactus, with an old-issue hump-crawling in the bargain, just for the good of the service. Otherwise, every time an organization commander was displeased with higher authority, he would be off to take his case to the Secretary of War, with resultant destruction of good order and military discipline.

But after a week of excitement there arrived a curt order that the sale of Rodney was declared null and void, and that his purchase money should be refunded. Ah! Well, that took care of Benny Walsh. But the old soldiers shook their heads.

"It ain't over yet," said they. "Keep your heads down. Them War Department orders got delayed-action fuses on 'em."

The following afternoon, just before evening parade, Captain Black burst into the stable shack where old Benny had been a guest until his affairs could be arranged.

"Where's Walsh?" demanded the captain.

"Why, sir, we ain't seen him since yesterday," replied the saddler.

"Did he say where he was going, when he was coming back—anything?" demanded the captain. "I've got to get hold of him.

The War Department is retiring Rodney. A formal retirement order and everything! They're going to give him a review, just as if he were an old noncom going out after thirty years or so!"

"Hot dog!" cried the saddler. "I didn't hear anything about it! That's what you get for not standin' formations! If they was to declare war, they'd give us no hint of it! I gotta see this. I'm glad the captain told me!"

"I should have come down before," said Captain Black hurriedly, "but I've been so busy myself. I didn't hear about it until an hour ago. I've been ordered to the Ecole Militaire in Paris for two years! Why, I've put in for that detail since I was a shavetail, with no more idea of getting it than that I'd be made Chief of Staff! And now I've got it with a week to get ready in!"

"The captain must'a kinda acquired a drag with the War Department," grinned the blacksmith.

"Ugh!" replied Captain Black. "I don't know about that. But that's neither here nor there. I want old Benny to see this review! Now, how can I get hold of him?"

"Sir," said the blacksmith, "I don't think it can be done. As quick as he got his hundred and forty dollars back he high-tailed outta here with it, and it's too soon afterward for him to be in any shape to appear in public, assumin' you could find him, anyways."

Captain Black went out and, leaping on his horse, hurried to the parade grounds. Everyone in the post was there, and a lot of people, sensing the unusual, had come in from the surrounding country and even across the river from Washington. The ceremony had begun by the time Captain Black got there, and Rodney, his coat shining in the setting sun, had been led "front and center" to hear his retirement order read.

"By the direction of the President," read the adjutant, "the exceptional record of service of the horse Rodney is brought to the attention of all organizations. Eighteen years in the same battery of field artillery, from the thirst and drought of border stations to the drenching rains and everlasting mud of France, this animal continually performed more than his share of work allotted to his organization. Without complaint, silently, obscurely, without thought of favor or regard, for eighteen years Rodney has ful-

filled every mission assigned to him by his superiors, his only
thought one of steadfast service to the limit of his ability. In consideration of which the President directs that Rodney be, and
hereby is, placed upon the retired list of the United States Army,
with full ration of oats, for the period of his natural life."

When the order was finished, Rodney was led up to his post
beside the commanding officer, the band struck up "When the
Caissons Go Rolling Along," and the entire garrison, horse, foot,
guns and tanks—went by in review. There was more than one
throat that was dry and catchy when the review was over. As for
Captain Black, he turned and rode slowly back toward the stables.
Old Benny would have enjoyed that! But he had not known, and
a hundred and forty dollars in his jeans at once was too much for
him! Poor old sot, he labored, as did Rodney, only to the limit of
his intelligence!

Suddenly, turning the corner by the riding hall, Captain Black
came upon Rodney, preened and shining, being taken back to
the stables. But what was a civilian leading him for?

"Oh, there! You with the horse! Just a minute!" called Captain
Black. He rode up, then suddenly reined in his horse with astonishment. The civilian was Benny Walsh. Benny Walsh, garbed mod-
estly in dark blue, clean-shaven, a derby hat on his head, gloves
on his hands, a large cigar in his mouth.

"Benny!" choked the captain. "In God's name, where did you
get those clothes?"

"How do you do, Cap'n? The cap'n see the review? Now I
thought that was just fine. Rodney enjoyed that. He understood,
sir; don't the cap'n think he didn't. Yes, sir, that was a right nice
thing to do for Rodney . . . Oh, yes, these clothes! I bought 'em,
sir. With some o' my retirement money. I got reimbursed, sir, for
what I spent, so I bought some clothes with it."

"Oh, Benny," cried the captain, clapping his hand to his brow,
"why didn't you come and talk it over with me first? I'd have given
you some clothes. Why didn't you save that money until you got
yourself some kind of job or something?"

"Oh," chuckled Benny, "don't let the cap'n worry about me.
Hoh! I got me a job! I still got some friends. The minute they
found I was outta this John outfit, they got me a job."

"What kind of job have you got?" demanded Captain Black.

"I'm a civilian employee, Quartermaster Corps, salary thurty dollars a week. Purty good, I calls it."

"Civilian employee, Quartermaster Corps, good Lord! And what do you do?"

Old Benny drew a long puff from his cigar and exhaled it before replying.

"Rodney," said he, "has been, by order, placed in the custody of the Quartermaster Corps. My duties is to look after him."

The Seeing Eye

WILL JAMES

Will James is a natural-born storyteller. He writes as he talks, with straightforward simplicity. The reader of this tale feels that he is really listening to it while sitting by a campfire, a very part of the colorful western background described so clearly. Like the American Indians, Will James knows the nature of horses and of what they are capable. His horses are given personalities, but never a personality or a characteristic that is foreign to the animal. He loves his horses and admires them but they are never overdrawn nor sentimentalized. This story may seem impossible to those who do not know horses. One who does, feels not only that it is possible, but that it really happened.

It's worse than tough for anybody to be blind, but I don't think it's as tough for an indoor born and raised person as it is for one whose life is with the all out-of-doors the most of his life from childhood on. The outdoor man misses his freedom to roam over the hills and the sight of 'em ever changing. A canary would die outside his cage but a free-born eagle would dwindle away inside of one.

Dane Gruger was very much of an out-of-door man. He was born on a little ranch along a creek bottom, in the heart of the cow country, growed up with it to be a good cowboy, then, like with his dad, went on in the cow business. A railroad went thru the lower part of the ranch but stations and little towns was over twenty miles away either way.

He had a nice little spread when I went to work for him, was married and had two boys who done some of the riding. I'd been riding for Dane quite a few days before I knew he was blind, not totally blind, but, as his boys told me, he couldn't see any further than his outstretched hand, and that was blurred. He couldn't read, not even the big print, with any kind of glasses so he never wore any.

That's what fooled me, and he could look you "right square in the eye" while talking to you. What was more he'd go straight down to the corral, catch his horse, saddle him and ride away like any man with full sight. The thing I first noticed and wondered at was that he never rode with us, and after the boys told me, I could understand. It was that he'd be of no use out on the range and away from the ranch.

Dane had been blind a few years when I come there and he'd of course got to know every foot of the ten miles which the ranch covered on the creek bottom before that happened. The ranch itself was one to two miles wide in some places and taking in some brakes. The whole of that was fenced and cross-fenced into pastures and hay lands, and Dane knew to within an inch when he came to every fence, gate or creek crossing. He knew how many head of cattle or horses might be in each pasture, how all was faring, when some broke out or some broke in, and where. He could find bogged cattle, cow with young calf needing help, and know everything that went well or wrong with what stock would be held on the ranch.

He of course seldom could do much towards helping whatever stock needed it or fix the holes he found in the fences, but when he'd get back to the ranch house he could easy tell the boys when there was anything wrong, and the exact spot and what all the trouble might be. It would then be up to the boys to set things to rights, and after Dane's description of the spot it was easy found.

During the time I was with that little outfit I got to know Dane pretty well, well enough to see that I don't think he could of lived if he hadn't been able to do what he was doing. He was so full of life and gumption and so appreciating of all around him that he could feel, hear and breathe in. I'd sometimes see him hold his horse to a standstill while he only listened to birds or the faraway bellering of cattle, even to the yapping of prairie dogs which most cowboys would rather not hear the sound of.

To take him away from all that, the open air, the feel of his saddle and horse under him and set him on a chair to do nothing but sit and babble and think, would of brought a quick end to him.

With the riding he done he felt satisfied he was doing something worth doing instead of just plain riding. He wouldn't of cared for that, and fact was he well took the place of an average rider.

But he had mighty good help in the work he was doing, and that was the two horses he used, for they was both as well trained to his wants and care as the dogs that's used nowadays to lead the blind, and which are called "The Seeing Eye."

Dane had the advantage of the man with the dog, for he didn't have to walk and use a cane at every step. He rode, and he had more confidence in his horses' every step than he had in his own, even if he could of seen well. As horses do, they naturally sensed every foot of the earth under 'em without ever looking down at it, during sunlight, darkness or under drifted snow.

Riding into clumps of willows or thickets which the creek bottoms had much of, either of the two horses was careful to pick out a wide enough trail thru so their rider wouldn't get scratched or brushed off. If they come to a place where the brush was too thick and Dane was wanting to go thru that certain thicket, the ponies, regardless of his wants, would turn back for a ways and look for a better opening. Dane never argued with 'em at such times. He would just sort of head 'em where he wanted to go and they'd do the rest to pick out the best way there.

Them horses was still young when I got to that outfit, seven and eight years of age, and would be fit for at least twenty years more with the little riding and good care they was getting. Dane's boys had broke them especially for their dad's use that way and they'd done a fine job of it.

One of the horses, a gray of about a thousand pounds, was called Little Eagle. That little horse never missed a thing in sight or sound. With his training the rustling of the brush close by would make him investigate and learn the cause before leaving that spot. Dane would know by his actions whether it was a newborn calf that had been hid or some cow in distress. It was the same at the boggy places along the creek or alkali swamps. If Little Eagle rode right on around and without stopping, Dane knew that all was well. If he stopped at any certain spot, bowed his neck and snorted low, then Dane knew that some horse or cow was in trouble. Keeping his hand on Little Eagle's neck he'd have him go on, and by the bend of that horse's neck as he went, like pointing, Dane could tell the exact location of where that animal was that was in trouble, or whatever it was that was wrong.

Sometimes, Little Eagle would line out on a trot, of his own accord and as tho there was something needed looking into right away. At times he'd even break into a lope, and then Dane wouldn't know what to expect, whether it was stock breaking thru the fence, milling around an animal that was down, or what. But most always it would be when a bunch of stock, horses or cattle, would be stringing out in single file, maybe going to water or some other part of the pasture.

At such times, Little Eagle would get just close enough to the stock so Dane could count 'em by the sounds of the hoofs going by, a near impossible thing to do for a man that can see, but Dane got so he could do it and get a mighty close count on what stock was in each pasture that way. Close enough so he could tell if any had got out or others got in.

With the horses in the pastures, there was bells on the leaders of every bunch and some on one of every little bunch that sort of held together and separate from the others. Dane knew by the sound of every bell which bunch it was and about how many there would be to each. The boys kept him posted on that every time they'd run a bunch in for some reason or other. Not many horses was ever kept under one fence, but there was quite a few of the purebred cattle for the upbreeding of the outside herds.

At this work of keeping tab on stock, Little Eagle was a cowboy by himself. With his natural intellect so developed as to what was wanted of him, he could near tell of what stock was wanted or not and where they belonged. The proof of that was when he turned a bunch of cattle out of a hayfield one time, and other times, and drove 'em to the gate of the field where they'd broke out of, circled around 'em when the gate was reached and went to it for Dane to open. He then drove the cattle thru, none got away, not from Little Eagle; and Dane would always prepare to ride at such times, for if any did try to break away Little Eagle would be right on their tail to bring 'em back, and for a blind man, not knowing when his horse is going to break into a sudden run, stop or turn, that's kind of hard riding, on a good cowhorse.

About all Dane would have to go by most of the time was the feel of the top muscles on Little Eagle's neck, and he got to know by them about the same as like language to him. With one hand most always on them muscles he felt what the horse seen. Tenseness, wonder, danger, fear, relaxation and about all that a human feels at the sight of different things. Places, dangerous or smooth, trouble or peace.

The top muscles told him more and more plainly than if another rider had been riding constantly alongside of him and telling him right along of what he seen. That was another reason why Dane liked to ride alone. He felt more at ease, no confusion, and wasn't putting anybody out of their way by talking and describing when they maybe wouldn't feel like it.

And them two horses of Dane's, they not only took him wherever he wanted to go but never overlooked any work that needed to be done. They took it onto themselves to look for work which, being they always felt so good, was like play to them. Dane knew it when such times come and he then would let 'em go as they chose.

Neither of the horses would of course go out by themselves without a rider and do that work. They wouldn't of been interested doing that without Dane's company. What's more they couldn't have opened the gates that had to be gone thru, and besides they wasn't wanted to do that. They was to be the company of Dane and with him in whatever he wanted to do.

Dane's other horse was a trim bay about the same size as Little Eagle, and even tho just as good he had different ways about him. He was called Ferret, and a ferret he was for digging up and finding out things, like a cow with a new-born calf or mare with colt, and he was even better than Little Eagle for finding holes in fences or where some was down.

All that came under the special training the boys had given him and Little Eagle, and if it wasn't for automobiles these days, such as them would be mighty valuable companions in the city, even more useful in the streets than the dog is, for the horse would soon know where his rider would want to go after being ridden such places a few times.

Unlike most horses it wasn't these two's nature to keep wanting to turn back to the ranch (home) when Dane would ride 'em away, and they wouldn't turn back until they knew the ride was over and it was time to. Sometimes Dane wouldn't show up for the noon meal, and that was all right with the ponies too, for they seemed as attached to him as any dog could be to his master.

It was the same way with Dane for them, and he had more confidence in their trueness and senses than most humans have in one another.

A mighty good test and surprising outcome of that came one day as a powerful big cloudburst hit above the ranch a ways and left Dane acrost the creek from home. The creek had turned into churning wild waters the size of a big river in a few minutes, half a mile wide in some places and licking up close to the higher land where the ranch buildings and corrals was.

It kept on a-raining hard after the cloudburst had fell and it didn't act like it was going to let up for some time, and the wide river wouldn't be down to creek size or safe to cross, at least not for a day or so.

The noise of the rushing water was a-plenty to let Dane know of the cloudburst. It had come with a sudden roar and without a drop of warning, and Dane's horse, he was riding Little Eagle that day, plainly let him know the danger of the wide stretch of swirling fast waters. It wasn't the danger of the water only but uprooted trees and all kinds of heavy timber speeding along would make the crossing more than dangerous, not only dangerous but it would about mean certain death.

Little Eagle would of tackled the swollen waters or anything Dane would of wanted him to, but Dane knew a whole lot better than to make that wise horse go where he didn't want to, any time.

Dane could tell by the noise, and riding to the edge of the water and the location where he was, how wide the body of wild waters was. He knew that the stock could keep out of reach of it on either side without being jammed against the fences, but he got worried about the ranch, wondering if the waters had got up to the buildings. He worried too about his family worrying about him, and maybe trying to find and get to him.

That worrying got him to figuring on ways of getting back. He sure couldn't stay where he was until the waters went down, not if he could help it. It wouldn't be comfortable being out so long in the heavy rain either, even if he did have his slicker on, and it wouldn't do to try to go to the neighbor's ranch which was some fifteen miles away. He doubted if he could find it anyway, for it was acrost a bunch of rolling hills, nothing to go by, and Little Eagle wouldn't know that *there* would be where Dane would be wanting him to go. Besides there was the thought of his family worrying so about him and maybe risking their lives in trying to find him.

He'd just have to get home, somehow, and it was at the thought of his neighbor's ranch and picturing the distance and country to it in his mind, that he thought of the railroad, for he would of had to cross it to get there. And then, thinking of the railroad, the thought came of the trestle crossing along it and over the creek. Maybe he could make that. That would be sort of a dangerous crossing too, but the more he thought of it the more he figured it worth taking the chances of trying. That was the only way of his getting on the other side of the high waters and back to the ranch.

The railroad and trestle was only about half a mile from where he now was and that made it all the more tempting to try. So, after thinking it over in every way, including the fact that he'd be taking chances with losing his horse also, he finally decided to take the chance, at the risk of both himself and his horse, that is if his horse seen it might be safe enough. He felt it had to be done and it could be done, and there went to show his faith and confidence in that Little Eagle horse of his. And that confidence sure wasn't misplaced, for a cooler-headed, brainier horse never was.

There was two fences to cross to get to the railroad and trestle, and it wasn't necessary to go thru gates to get there, for the swollen waters with jamming timbers had laid the fence down for quite a ways on both sides of the wide river, causing some of the wire strands to break and snap and coil all directions.

A strand of barbed wire, even if flat to the ground, is a mighty dangerous thing to ride over, for a horse might pick it up with a hoof, and, as most horses will scare, draw their hind legs up under 'em and act up, the result might be a wicked sawing wire cut at the joint by the hock, cutting veins and tendons and often crippling a horse for life. In such cases the rider is also very apt to get tangled up in the wire, for that wicked stuff seems to have the ways of the tentacles of a devilfish at such times.

Loose wire laying around on the ground is the cowboy's worst fear, especially so with Dane, for, as he couldn't see it was many times more threatening as he rode most every day from one fenced-in field to the other. But the confidence he had in two cool-headed ponies relieved him of most all his fear of the dangerous barbed wire, and either one of 'em would stop and snort a little at the sight of a broken strand coiled to the ground. Dane knew what that meant and it always brought a chill to his spine. He'd get down off his saddle, feel around carefully in front of his horse, and usually the threatening coil would be found to within a foot or so of his horse's nose. The coil would then be pulled and fastened to the fence, to stay until a ranch hand, who, with team and buckboard, would make the rounds of all fences every few months, done a general fixing of 'em.

It's too bad barbed wire *has* to be used for fences. It has butchered and killed many good horses, and some riders. But barbed wire is about the only kind of fence that will hold cattle, most of the time, and when there has to be many long miles of it, even with the smaller ranches, that's about the only kind of fence that can be afforded or used. Cattle (even the wildest) seldom get a scratch by it, even in breaking thru a four-strand fence of it, or going over it while it's loose and coiled on the ground, for they don't get rattled when in wire as a horse does, and they hold their hind legs straight back when going thru, while with the horse he draws 'em under him instead and goes to tearing around.

Both Little Eagle and Ferret had been well trained against scaring and fighting wire if they ever got into it, also trained not to get into it, and stop whenever coming to some that was loose on the ground. That training had been done with a rope and a piece of smooth wire at one end, and being they was naturally cool-headed they soon learned all the tricks of the wire and how to behave when they come near any of that coiled on the ground.

There was many such coils as the flood waters rampaged along the creek bottom, and as Dane headed Little Eagle towards the railroad and trestle he then let him pick his own way thru and around the two fence entanglements on the way there, along the edge of the rushing water.

Little Eagle done considerable winding around and careful stepping as he come to the fences that had been snapped and washed to scattering, dangerous strands over the field. Dane gave him his time, let him go as he chose, and finally the roar of the waters against the high banks by the trestle came to his ears. It sounded as tho it was near up to the trestle, which he knew was plenty high, and that gave him a good idea of what a cloudburst it had been.

He then got mighty dubious about trying to cross the trestle, for it was a long one, there was no railing of any kind on the sides, and part of it might be under water or even washed away. There was some of the flood water in the ditch alongside the railroad grade and it wasn't so many feet up it to the track level.

Riding between the rails a short ways he come to where the trestle begins and there he stopped Little Eagle. The swirling waters made a mighty roar right there, and how he wished he could of been able to see then, more than any time since his blindness had overtook him.

Getting off Little Eagle there he felt his way along to the first ties to the trestle, of the space between each, which was about five inches, and just right for Little Eagle's small hoofs to slip in between, Dane thought. One such a slip would mean a broken leg, and the horse would have to be shot right there, to lay between the rails. The rider would be mighty likely to go over the side of the trestle, too.

Dane hardly had any fear for himself, but he did have for Little Eagle. Not that he feared he would put a foot between the ties, for that little horse was too wise, cool-headed and careful to do anything like that, Dane knew. What worried him most was if the trestle was still up and above the water all the way acrost. There would be no turning back, for in turning is when Little Eagle would be mighty liable to slip a hoof between the ties. The rain had let up but the wind was blowing hard and the tarred ties was slippery as soaped glass.

It all struck Dane as fool recklessness to try to cross on that long and narrow trestle at such a time but he felt he should try, and to settle his dubiousness he now left it to Little Eagle and his good sense as to whether to tackle it or not.

If he went he would *ride* him across, not try to crawl, feel his way and lead him, for in leading the horse he wouldn't be apt to pay as much attention to his footing and to nosing every dangerous step he made. Besides, Dane kind of felt that if Little Eagle should go over the side he'd go with him.

So, getting into the saddle again, he let Little Eagle stand for a spell, at the same time letting him know that he wanted to cross the trestle, for him to size it up and see if it could be done. It was up to him, and the little gray gelding understood.

It might sound unbelievable, but a good sensible horse and rider have a sort of feel-language which is mighty plain between 'em, and when comes a particular dangerous spot the two can discuss the possibilities of getting over or acrost it as well as two humans can, and even better, for the horse has the instinct which the human lacks. He can tell danger where the human can't, and the same with the safety.

It was that way with Little Eagle and Dane, only even more so, because as Little Eagle, like Ferret, had been trained to realize Dane's affliction, cater and sort of take care of him, they was always watchful. Then with Dane's affection and care for them, talking to 'em and treating 'em like the true pardners they was, there was an understanding and trust between man and horse that's seldom seen between man and man.

Sitting in his saddle with his hand on Little Eagle's neck the two "discussed" the dangerous situation ahead in such a way that the loud roar of the water foaming by and under the trestle didn't interfere any with the decision that was to come.

There was a tenseness in the top muscles of Little Eagle's neck as he looked over the scary, narrow, steel-ribboned trail ahead, nervous at the so careful investigation, that all sure didn't look well.

But he'd now left it all to Little Eagle's judgment, and as Dane had about expected he'd be against trying, Little Eagle still all tense and quivering some, planted one foot on the first tie, and crouching a bit, all nerves and muscles steady, started on the way of the dangerous crossing.

Every step by step from the first seemed like a long minute to Dane. The brave little horse, his nose close to the ties, at the same time looking ahead, was mighty careful how he placed each front foot, and sure that the hind one would come up to the exact same place afterwards, right where that front one had been. He didn't just plank his hoof and go on, but felt for a sure footing on the wet and slippery tarred ties before putting any weight on it and making another step. Something like a mountain climber feeling and making sure of his every hold while going on with his climbing.

The start wasn't the worst of the crossing. That begin to come as they went further along and nearer to the center. There, with the strong wind blowing broadside of 'em, the swift waters churning, sounding like to the level of the slippery ties would seem about scary enough to chill the marrow in any being. But there was more piled onto that, for as they neared the center it begin to tremble and sway as if by earth tremors. This was by the high rushing waters swirling around the tall and now submerged supporting timbers.

Little Eagle's step wasn't so sure then, and as careful as he was there come a few times when he slipped, and a time or two when a hoof went down between the ties, leaving him to stand on three shaking legs until he got his hoof up and on footing again.

With most any other horse it would of been the end of him and his rider right then. As it was, Little Eagle went on like a tightrope walker, with every muscle at work. And Dane, riding mighty light on him, his heart up to his throat at every slip or loss of footing, done his best not to get him off balance but help him that way when he thought he could.

If the shaking, trembling and swaying of the trestle had been steady it would of been less scary and some easier, but along with the strong vibrations of the trestle there'd sometimes come a big uprooted tree to smash into it at a forty-mile speed. There'd be a quiver all along the trestle at the impact. It would sway and bend dangerously, to slip back again as the tree would be washed under and on.

Such goings on would jar Little Eagle's footing to where he'd again slip a hoof between the ties, and Dane would pray, sometimes cuss a little. But the way Little Eagle handled his feet and every part of himself, sometimes on the tip of his toes, the sides of his hoofs and even to his knees, he somehow managed to keep right side up.

Good thing, Dane thought, that the horse wasn't shod, for shoes without sharp calks would have been much worse than none on the slippery ties. As it was, and being his shoes had been pulled off only a couple of days before to ease his feet some between shoeings, his hoofs was sharp at the edges and toe, and that gave him more chance.

The scary and most dangerous part of the trestle was reached, the center, and it was a good thing maybe that Dane couldn't see while Little Eagle sort of juggled himself over that part, for the trestle had been under repair and some of the old had been taken away in a few places, to later be replaced by new ones; but where each tie had been taken away that left an opening of near two feet wide. Mighty scary for Little Eagle too, but he eased over them gaps without Dane knowing.

Dane felt as tho it was long weary miles and took about that much time to finally get past the center and most dangerous part of the five-hundred-yard trestle, for them five hundred yards put more wear on him during that time than five hundred miles would of.

And he was far from near the safe going as yet, for he'd just passed center and the trestle was still doing some tall trembling and dangerous weaving, when, as bad and spooky as things already was, there come the sounds of still worse fear and danger, and Dane's heart stood still. It was a train whistle he'd heard above the roar of the waters. It sounded like the train was coming his way, facing him, and there'd sure be no chance for him to turn and make it back, for he'd crossed over half of the trestle, the worst part, and going back would take a long time.

All the dangers and fears piling together now, instead of excit-ing Dane, seemed to cool and steady him, like having to face the worst and make the best of it. He rode right on towards the coming train.

He knew from memory that the railroad run a straight line to the trestle, that there was no railroad crossing nor other reason for the engineer to blow his whistle, unless it was for him, himself. Then it came to him that the engineer must of seen him on the trestle and would sure stop his train, if he could.

Standing up in his stirrups he raised his big black hat high as he could and waved it from side to side as a signal for the engineer to stop his train. Surely they could see that black hat of his and realize the predicament he was in. That getting off the trestle would mean almost certain death.

But the train sounded like it was coming right on, and at that Dane wondered if maybe it was coming too fast to be able to stop. He got a little panicky then, and for a second he was about to turn Little Eagle off the trestle and swim for it. It would of been a long and risky swim, maybe carried for miles down country before they could of reached either bank, and it would of taken more than luck to've succeeded. But if they'd got bowled over by some tree trunk and went down in the churning waters that would be better, Dane thought, than to have Little Eagle smashed to smithereens by the locomotive. He had no thought for himself.

About the only thing that made him take a bigger chance and ride on some more was that he knew that the whole train and its crew would be doomed before it got halfways on the trestle, and what if it was a passenger train?

At that thought he had no more fear of Little Eagle keeping his footing on the trestle. His fear now went for the many lives there might be on the train, and he sort of went wild and to waving his big black hat all the more trying to warn of the danger.

But he didn't put on no such action as to unbalance the little gray in any way. He still felt and helped with his every step, and then there got to be a prayer with each one, like with the beads of the Rosary.

He rubbed his moist eyes and also prayed he could see, now of all times and if only just for this once, and then the train whistle blew again, so close this time that it sounded like it was on the

trestle, like coming on, and being mighty near him.—Dane had done
his best, and now was his last and only chance to save Little Eagle
and himself, by sliding off the trestle. He wiped his eyes like as tho
to better see, and went to reining Little Eagle off the side of the
trestle. But to his surprise, Little Eagle wouldn't respond to the
rein. It was the first time excepting amongst the thick brush or bad

creek crossings that the horse had ever went against his wishes that way. But this was now very different, and puzzled, he tried him again and again, with no effect, and then, all at once, *he could see.*

Myself and one of Dane's boys had been riding, looking for Dane soon after the cloudburst hit, and seeing the stopped passenger train with the many people gathered by the engine we high-loped towards it, there to get the surprise of seeing Dane on Little Eagle on the trestle and carefully making each and every dangerous step towards us and solid ground.

We seen we sure couldn't be of no use to the little gray nor Dane only maybe a hindrance, and being there was only a little ways more we held our horses and watched. Looking on the length of the trestle we noticed that only the rails and ties showed above the high water, there was quite a bend in it from the swift and powerful pressure and the rails and ties was leaning, like threatening to break loose at any time.

How the little horse and Dane ever made it, with the strong wind, slippery ties and all a-weaving, was beyond us. So was it with the passengers who stood with gaping mouths and tense watching. What if they'd known that the rider had been blind while he made the dangerous crossing?

And as the engineer went on to tell the spellbound passengers how that man and horse on the trestle had saved all their lives, they was more than thankful, for, as the heavy cloudburst had come so sudden and hit in one spot, there'd been no report of it, and, as the engineer said, he might of drove onto the trestle a ways before knowing. Then it would of been too late.

But Little Eagle was the one who played the biggest part in stopping what would have been a terrible happening. He was the one who decided to make the dangerous crossing, the one who had to use his head and hoofs with all his skill and power, also the one who at the last of the stretch would not heed Dane's pull of the reins to slide off the trestle. His first time not to do as he was wanted to. He'd disobeyed and had saved another life. He'd been "The Seeing Eye."

The fuss over with as Dane finally rode up on solid ground and near the engine, we then was the ones due for a big surprise. For

Dane *spotted* us out from the crowd, and smiling, rode straight for us and looked us both "square in the eye."

The shock and fears he lived crossing that trestle, then the puzzling over Little Eagle not wanting to turn at the touch of the rein had done the trick, had brought his sight back.

After that day, Little Eagle and Ferret was sort of neglected, neglected knee deep in clover, amongst good shade and where clear spring water run. The seeing eyes was partly closed in contentment.

The Sheikh and His Mare

M O S H E   S M I L A N S K Y

The great pride of the Arabs, the closeness between themselves and their horses, is well known. Although Arabia is a land of romance and the birthplace not only of the modern horse but of classical horsemanship, stories about the country, its inhabitants and its horses are rare. Here we have a story which brings out in full the pride of the Arab as well as some rather unusual beliefs in the sagacity of the mare.

Sheikh Abu Hatab and his mare were both unhappy.

A few weeks earlier the mare had foaled, giving birth to a female. On the day of the birth there had been great rejoicing in the tents of the Sheikh and his tribe, which for fifty years, ever since its arrival from the south, had been encamped among the sands lying around the Rubin stream. From all the tents the heads of the families came to congratulate the Sheikh, for his mare was famed throughout the district, being unequalled alike for speed and beauty. It was an honour to the entire tribe that such a mare had propagated in their midst. Abu Hatab had received his guests with all courtesy, regaling them with the fine coffee which he had brought from the town specially in honour of the occasion, and had exhibited to them the magnificent mare and the precious she-foal.

But joy did not swell long in the tent of the Sheikh. When about a fortnight had passed he saw that his steed was no longer herself, that she was sad and disconsolate. The Sheikh knew what was amiss with his mare and said to himself, "Her time of longing is come. I

355

must satisfy her desire," and he did not worry. He loved his mare, and that night when he lay down he thought out a plan. "The police inspector of the town has a fine stallion. I shall ride over to him to-morrow, taking him a kid of the flocks for a gift, and get relief for my mare."

So he slept his usual sound sleep and on the morrow rose with the first flush of dawn, took a fat young kid from the pens and mounted his mare with the kid on his knees.

Abu Hatab went to town in high spirits; he returned utterly downcast. The mare had refused. It was doubly annoying to Abu Hatab. He had made himself ridiculous in the eyes of the police inspector, who had twitted him, saying, "Abu Hatab does not understand his mare!" And he was worried about the mare. What ailed her? Surely her mournful eyes and bent head bore witness to her longings. Why, then, should she refuse? Would she conceal her secret from him, from Abu Hatab? He was vexed to death and to crown all he had wasted the kid, the finest of his pens.

Abu Hatab returned to his tent, thoroughly out of temper, but not a word did he say to his household, who trembled at his silence. They knew that mischief was brewing within him, so kept their distance and hid from him, since he could be very cruel when he was angry or vexed. Even when the elders and notables of the tribe came to greet him at evening as he sat over coffee, he replied to them very curtly. They did not know what to make of it. They looked at the mare, for they knew the purpose of his visit to the town; they saw that she was mournful and drooped her head; and they, too, asked wonderingly how was it possible.

Those were hard days for Abu Hatab. He and his mare hammered their feet and hooves weary, visiting every place in the district in which there was a blood stallion, and as they went so they returned, covered with shame and humiliation. The mare brought disgrace on her master. What ailed her?

All men, whether sons of the faith or unbelievers, would stand in wonder and stare at the splendid couple if they met them on the road. Abu Hatab was sixty or more. His hair and beard were growing grey, but he sat his horse like a youth, upright, supple and strong. His feet were set in his broad jackboots, his black abaya hung from his shoulders with its ends dropping on either side of his mount. He was one of the finest riders of the district, and on festivals, at Nebi Rubin or Nebi Saliah, the young men hesitated to compete with him, while he used to taunt them and cry, "Which of you youngsters will have a race with me?"

And in the whole district there had been none like Abu Hatab's mare. He had brought her from the far south only the year before. She was tall, upright, slender, with legs like those of a gazelle, supple and fine. Her head was the head of a dove, her ears were tiny, pointed and erect. She was entirely white, with never a shadow or blotch on her from her very hooves to the tips of her ears.

"How beautiful are the old man and his white mare," the wayfarers would exclaim. But those who had sharper eyes asked themselves in astonishment what ailed the old man and his mare. Both seemed utterly despondent. Where was their glory of motion? What was wrong with them? What ill had befallen them?

Sheikh Abu Hatab was at his wits' end. At last one evening he summoned the oldest Bedouin dwelling in the swamps of the Rubin stream, the negro Abu Ramadan. From that negro naught was hidden of all that befalls in Allah's world. If there was a robbery in the district they would summon him; he would give a good look at the spot where the deed was done and smile a silent smile, for he had found the trail of the thief. Even on the king's highway, where hundreds of feet had passed, he would recognize the tracks he sought and would follow them to the required spot. Sometimes he would meet a man on the road months after a theft, would glance at his trail and say, "Here is the thief!" "A gift of God!" said all who knew him.

Indeed there were no secrets hidden from Ramadan the black. If a man was hated by his wife, he would send for the negro and offer him a gift, and would receive in return a drink from the juice of the bitter roots of the swamp; this the man would give his wife, and her love would return to him. If a woman was barren, Allah having closed her womb, she would send for the negro of the Rubin swamps and offer him a gift, and he would also give her to drink of the juice of the bitter roots of the swamp, and Allah would open her womb. There was naught he could not do.

Abu Ramadan was head and shoulders taller than ordinary

men. His eyes were like two flaming torches, sunk deep in their sockets. Neither beard, moustache, nor any sign whatever of hair was to be seen on his face. Allah had deprived him of hair. It was hard to guess his age. He seemed still youthful, but he was really the oldest man in the district. Despite his age he still retained his strength and could make a seven days' journey on foot without growing weary. On horse or ass he would never ride, nor had he ridden them from his birth. But none knew better than he the heart of the horse, the ass, and every other animal after its kind; and he had a cure for each sickness and every mischance. To be sure, the negro's eye was "evil," and it boded no good if he gazed at a cow during milking or a mare in foaling. Some whispered that he held converse with the demon who dwelt in the swamp, and from him derived his strength and his charms. And truly, who could tell whether his powers were of Allah or of Satan? Therefore, he would be called in only at the very last moment, when the noose was already around the neck, so to speak.

Toward evening the negro came to the Sheikh in answer to his summons. He neither spoke to him nor greeted him, but stood awaiting his words. Such was the black man's custom, never greeting a man, maybe because his ear had caught some of the whispering that went on about him. The Sheikh invited him to sit by him on the mat spread on the ground at the side of the tent. He then leaned over to him and told him in a whisper the evil that had befallen him. Abu Ramadan listened with great attention; obviously the Sheikh's words were deeply interesting him. When Abu Hatab had finished the black man rose and without a word approached the mare, which stood tethered to a peg in the ground near the tent, and turned his piercing gaze upon her.

The Sheikh's heart throbbed within him. Who could say what kind of moment it was in which the negro had turned his gaze upon the mare? Perhaps it was a moment of evil?

For a long while the black man stared at the mare, which was greatly frightened at him, starting back and breathing heavily through her distended nostrils. Then he returned to his place and sat down silently without uttering a word. The Sheikh gazed at him anxiously, without shifting his eyes from him.

"What did you see, what are you looking at so closely?" he asked at last.

"Your mare is of the mares of the tribe of Tigla?"

"Ay, I brought her thence," answered the Sheikh in a nervous tone.

"You went a long way."

"What does that matter?"

"The eyes of the mares of the Tigla are turned to the south. From the north they will not be satisfied."

The Sheikh grew pale. The black man rose to go. Abu Hatab leapt up and blocked his path, fearing that he would vanish, and his last hope with him.

"There is no counsel or remedy?"

"None."

"It is too much even for you?"

The Sheikh was hinting to the other that for the sake of his mare he would join hands even with a demon from Hell.

"Even for me."

The negro stood still, seemed to consider a moment, then said at length in a voice of admonition:

"The matter depends on you. Should you repent of your evil custom and return to the customs of the Holy Bedouins, your ancestors and forefathers, you can deliver your soul and the soul of your mare. But if you refuse and persist in your frowardness—ere the year is out your mare will perish of sorrow and grief."

The negro vanished, leaving Sheikh Abu Hatab standing mournful and with downcast eyes.

Now this was the matter of the evil custom in which the Sheikh persisted.

It is an ancient custom of the sons of Araby that when a man purchases a mare, she does not become altogether his, but her first master from whom she was bought retains a share in her. This is the case with pedigree and blood mares; ordinary mares for labour are sold for good; no one is particular regarding them. The same rule does not apply even to all riding mares. There are pure-bred and pure-bred. Those whose pedigrees do not ascend to the mares of the

Holy Fathers arc sold practically entirely; only one or two of the first offspring of the mare belong to the former master. But it was not so with mares of famous lineage; such were sold only as far as "half the womb"; meaning that one foal would belong to the former master and the second to the present master, and so on till the end of her breeding days. Now this custom was holy even in ancient times, and not a single one of the notables of the sons of Araby ever transgressed it.

In the beginning Abu Hatab had also followed the custom of his forefathers. When he inherited the seat of his father and became the head Sheikh of his tribe, he purchased a mare of finest lineage and half the womb was his and half belonged to the former owner. On this mare he had ridden for many a year, and she won victories for him on many festive occasions. But she did not establish a breed as unluckily she bore only he-foals. The only she-foal that fell to his lot did not live long. Now when this mare grew old the Sheikh decided to purchase a fresh young one in her place. It was then that the evil spirit took possession of him; he wanted a mare that should be all his and in which no stranger should have any share.

Whence came this evil spirit? His friends whispered that it was from the Yahud. He was on friendly terms with the Jews who lived in the Colonies. From the time they had begun to establish their Colonies Abu Hatab had been drawn to them, he being then but a youth. He visited their Colonies, observed their manner of living and watched their work. Everything he saw attracted him. Since he had become Sheikh of the tribe he had entered into still closer relations with the men of the Colonies, doing business with them and acting as a go-between for them and their neighbours. From these dealings with the men of the Colonies he had become wealthy, and now there was none among the Bedouins of the district as rich as he.

Abu Hatab remained steadfast in his determination to purchase a mare which should be all his; and this proved his undoing. His friends and acquaintances shook their heads over him, and some of them said to themselves, "This is the fruit of his friendship with the unbelievers, accurst of the Prophet."

For a long time Abu Hatab sought to purchase a mare entirely for himself, but without success. Which Bedouin with a pure-blooded steed would consent to sell her without retaining his share?

It would have meant making himself a laughing-stock. But Abu Hatab remained obdurate, and at length decided to buy a fleet Kadisha. So he went to the north of the country, purchased a fleet Kadisha mare and brought her to his tent. The tribesmen saw the mare and hung their heads, heartbroken for shame and disgust. To be sure she was a fast runner, but her legs were thick and her ears were long—a Kadisha! When Abu Hatab rode on his speedy new mare all those who met him on the way jeered at him. Some laughed and said:

"Hast done well, Sheikh Abu Hatab. Half the day she will serve thee for riding and half the day for ploughing!"

Others said mockingly:

"Look at the Sheikh's mare, with the body of a horse and the head of a mule."

Abu Hatab would grow crimson for anger and vexation. In vain did he spur his steed and make her fly like an eagle. Even her wonderful gallop did not hide her ugly legs, her head and ears. The long ears seemed to declare that she was a pure Kadisha of Kadisha stock.

At the turn of the year Abu Hatab took his mare to market and sold her to a fellah for half of what she had cost him. She returned to the plough for which nature had meant her.

For a long time Abu Hatab was torn between conflicting impulses; finally he resolved to purchase a blood stallion. It is no great honour for a Sheikh to ride a stallion, even of pure breed, but at any rate the disgrace of the Kadisha was removed from the tribe. If his new mount was not a mare, at least it was a thoroughbred. Its dam had been the mare of the Mufti from Gaza. The blood stallion was very handsome, sorrel from hooves to ears except for a white star on the forehead. It was long and slender, with fine feet, a tiny head and sharp little upright ears, a real thoroughbred. But it could not compare in speed with the swift mares, and Abu Hatab ceased competing with the youths for fear of disgracing himself. The youths perceived this and revenged themselves for his previous taunts by challenging him to race them.

Abu Hatab tried to deceive himself by saying that he was getting old and his racing days were over. The youths, however, saw through the deception and waited their opportunity.

For a number of years Abu Hatab rode his stallion, and his tribesmen became reconciled to the fact that their Sheikh used a stallion and not a mare. After the sorrel, Abu Hatab purchased a grey that was still more beautiful, and gradually he grew so accustomed to it that he forgot it was only a stallion he rode. And once, during Nebi Saliah, when the young men ran races on their swift mares and became full of excitement, their eyes fell on Abu Hatab and they began to taunt him, saying, "Harajah! Aren't you game any more to race us?" Then the heart of Abu Hatab grew hot, a flame leapt up in his blood and he spurred his grey toward the youths. To begin with fortune favoured him. His grey took the lead and got ahead of the mares; but it soon wearied. It was not as light on its feet as the mares which are specially bred, and it began to slow down. Abu Hatab felt the mares drawing near and spurred on his steed, trembling with rage lest he might become a derision in the eyes of the youths. The grey sprang forward in a final effort, and at that very moment it stumbled over a stone, fell and broke its leg, bringing the Sheikh within an inch of his life.

For a long time Abu Hatab went about like a mourner. He could not be consoled for the reproach that had befallen his white hairs. In vain did his friends comfort him, beseeching him morning and evening to repent of his evil thought and purchase himself a thoroughbred mare after the fashion of the country; to wit, half the womb for himself and half for the former master. The Sheikh refused. Either he would acquire a mare in the fashion he desired or else he would cease riding and remain in his tent like the old folk.

The fame of the mares of the Tigla tribe is known throughout the world. Where is the Bedouin who cannot descant on their beauty, their mettle and the purity of their stock? Their pedigree goes all the way back to the mare of the prophet, on which he rode and did battle against the various unbelievers whom he subdued with his holy sword. None of the Sheikhs of the Bedouins of the district possessed a mare from that tribe; they could not afford it. Only Sheikh Abu Hatab could have afforded to purchase one, even the finest of them. His dealings with the Jews had increased his wealth from year to year. But one thing prevented his aspiring to a Tigla mare; they were never sold completely. Nevertheless, from the time he despaired of the local mares and horses he had begun to play with a daring thought; perhaps fortune would favour him. The sons of Tigla are poor, they live mostly on dates; perhaps he would see what he could do with them. Nothing can resist gold, and the gold was his. Allah had prospered his way.

So after much hesitation and doubt he decided to try his fortune. He placed within two girdles a sum of gold which he thought would suffice to dull the conscience of the Sheikhs of Tigla; he set the girdles round his loins, hired one of the mares of the district and set out. Through all the villages of the south he passed, and on the morrow he came to the borders of the Bedouin. From thence onward there was neither hamlet nor town, nothing but open country and sky and the Bedouins. It was a district which he had known and loved from his childhood. The Bedouins of those parts were all his acquaintances who visited him when they crossed the Rubin stream on their way to the markets of the north. Wherever he came he was received with honour and affection, and when the purpose of his journey became known the esteem in which he was held rose still higher. His friends accompanied him to Beersheba. From Beersheba he hired a desert Bedouin who belonged to a tribe that had had a covenant with his father and his father's father, to accompany him on his distant way.

The men of Tigla did not know Abu Hatab, and had not heard of his tribe. They had no dealings with the north, their traffic being with Egypt. True, however, to their ancestral custom they received their guest and his companion with all honour. When they learned his errand their welcome became most effusive, they slew the best of their flocks and prepared a right royal feast. After regaling themselves on the meat and the delicacies the head Sheikh of the Tigla and his guest went out to view and examine the famous mares. Beside a little pool hidden away like some treasure in a lost corner among the sands the mares of the tribe were at grass amid a cluster of tall date palms. Rooted to the spot, Abu Hatab stared with wide open eyes at a sight such as he had never beheld even in dream. The full glory of the south was revealed to him. Nearly a hundred of the finest mares imaginable stood and lay and promenaded in little groups. His eyes sparkled with excitement. He was particularly captivated by a certain white mare which walked like a queen among her comrades. When the Sheikh of the Tigla and his guest and their companions returned to the tent, the Sheikh began to sing the praises of the mares and their ancestry in highly coloured language and with many a tale of their prowess. Abu Hatab drank in his words like nectar. In the course of his remarks, as though casually, the Sheikh fixed the price of each mare. His prices were exorbitant, yet to Abu Hatab this did not matter. The white mare was worth the half of life! When the Sheikh of the Tigla had finished speaking Abu Hatab asked him to dismiss everyone from the tent, and he and his guest remained alone. Then Abu Hatab whispered his desire and besought him to sell the white mare completely and absolutely. The Sheikh of the Tigla was astonished at his words, and began to tremble. Had such a thing even been heard of? Could it be believed were it to be told? Would a Tigla man sell his mare without retaining for himself a share in her? It could not be! From the days of Muhammad until that day such a thing had never been done!

Abu Hatab plied the Sheikh with every kind of persuasion and cajolery. Finally he opened one girdle and emptied all the gold in it on the carpet before the Sheikh, whose eyes grew dark in their sockets, blinded by the gleam of the precious metal. The Sheikh was wise and cunning like a serpent, and when he saw the gold and looked at the face of Aba Hatab, he knew that his heart had gone out to the white mare; and he thought to himself, "The eyes of our mares turn to the south and in the north they will not let themselves be satisfied. So at the turn of the year after she has foaled, the foolish Sheikh will return to us. And then both his money and the half womb will be mine." Abu Hatab saw hesitation in the eyes of his host and his heart trembled for joy.

"Give me thy hand!"

"Nay! Such a thing is not done in our place!"

Then Abu Hatab emptied the gold that was in his second girdle. The Sheikh grew pale.

"Fix me the price of thy white mare."

"Between me and thee, my dear guest, what is the price of the white mare? Take her if thy soul doth so desire!"

And as he spoke the Sheikh grabbed the two heaps of gold and gathered them into his pouch.

On the morrow the Sheikh of the Tigla handed to the Sheikh his guest the reins of the white mare.

"Mabruk!"

"May Allah bless you."

Abu Hatab rode off on his new mare, his face radiant with happiness.

But his happiness did not long endure. An evil which he had little anticipated had now befallen him.

The negro's words sank deep into Abu Hatab's heart. If it was as he had said he was in the hands of the Tigla once again for good or evil. And if they refused him this thing? He suddenly remembered the face of the Sheikh of the Tigla and his cunning smile. He fancied that even then they had dug a pit for his feet. Abu Hatab clenched his fists in anger and grief. If the Sheikh of the Tigla had appeared before him on the way he would have slain him. Were these as ancient times, the days of his forefathers, when there was no fear of the Government, he would have summoned the warriors of his tribe and set forth to do battle with the Tigla for life or death.

For some days he went about with a scowl on his face. Nothing interested him, neither household nor tribal affairs. He could not speak calmly. All day long he raged and stormed and quarrelled without cause. His household crept about like shadows, hiding from him, while the men of his tribe were astonished and perplexed.

One summer morning while it was still dark he saddled his mare, roused his household and bade them look after the foal; and ere the sun rose he was on his way.

This time he did not follow the highway, but kept to the field paths. In his bitterness of spirit he shrank from meeting his acquaintances; for his very expression announced that Sheikh Abu Hatab was going to sue for mercy. He took no thought either for his own comfort or that of his mare. He rode day and night, resting only for brief intervals. He was impatient to learn his fate. What would it be? Would Heaven show mercy on him or not? Even south of Beersheba he sought no guide this time, depending on his memory to recognize the windings of the paths and tracks. His memory served him well, while in the more difficult places the mare was his guide; he would drop the reins and give her her head; she would sniff a few times with her nostrils and then continue on her way with perfect assurance. She knew the goal of her owner, which was likewise her own haven of desire. Child of the desert, she knew the desert and did not hesitate. Her heaviness forsook her. The whole way her head was held erect and her tiny ears were pricked slightly forward as though she strove to catch some sound; a strong and powerful instinct was drawing her forward and southward.

The desert enveloped Sheikh Abu Hatab on every side; dunes on dunes of sand stretching without end or limit, each one resembling all the rest, one mother having borne them all. From time to time the wind would burst in among the dunes and twirl and whirl about as though bewitched, and become a mighty pillar with feet on the ground and head in the sky. Then suddenly it would shoot forward like lightning, catching up in its wings whatever it might meet, mounting with it to the skies and casting it down again in fury. Then with another whirl it would disappear leaving the entire face of the desert changed—the valley exalted, the hill made low and the twisted straight, as though a besom of fury had passed and swept and upset, levelled and raised till it changed the whole surface. Everything seemed to be born anew. Only the sharp eye of the Sheikh, son of the sons of the Desert, and the scent of the mare could save them from losing their way in this world of sand. Seven days after the Sheikh had forsaken his tent by the Rubin stream the mare suddenly whinnied and from a distance from behind the sand dunes answered the trumpeting of a stallion. Sheikh Abu Hatab and his mare had reached their destination.

The mare carried him forward as though on wings, as though there was no sand beneath her feet. The Sheikh was filled with perplexity. Far off could be seen the shadows of a mountain range. What did this portend for him? Before him were sand dunes. The trumpeting of the stallion showed that there were habitations of men behind them. What fortune awaited him there? A prolonged sigh broke from his lips.

It was a burning hot morning. The air had already begun to grow dry and choking at midnight, and when the crimson ball of the sun rose above the earth, Allah's world became a furnace.

Sheikh Abu Hatab riding on his mare emerged from amid the

dunes which hid the tents of the Tigla. It was hard to recognize him. He had aged overnight. From that day forth shame overhung him and his tribe. The sons of Tigla had humiliated him. He, the guest, had gone forth from them empty and in disgrace. They had abused him. Half the womb had they demanded from him for the satisfaction of his mare. As though he had not given them a pile of gold! But he, Abu Hatab, had paid them in their own coin. In the middle of the night he had left the tent of the Sheikh of the Tigla, harnessed his mare, and stayed among the dunes until the morning. Insult for insult. From that day forth there would be deadly enmity throughout all generations, between his tribe and the sons of the Tigla. Blood alone could atone for the shame. Blood alone might wash away the reproach.

The Sheikh fumed and raged, and his mare was sorrowful. Her belly seemed to have shrunk, her head dropped and her legs might have been chained together. The Sheikh spurred his mare. He was impatient. Away from the borders of the men who had brought shame upon him!

But the mare, as though of set purpose, dawdled.

The Sheikh grew angry. He had already chid his steed time and again. Once, twice, three times he had pressed his jackboots against her sides till it hurt her. Yet she took no notice. What possessed her? Was she, too, a partner to the deceit? Had she ceased obeying him? His rage consumed him like fire. For the first time in his life he lifted his hand against a horse and beat her as the fellah thrashes his Kdadisha.

The mare stopped and quivered. Never before in her life had she been beaten. And it was her master, whom she loved, who had brought this shame upon her head. The mare leapt weirdly like a Kadisha when whipped and began to toss her rider. And she continued thus on her way, jumping and jerking all the while.

The strange movements of the horse were the final drop in the bitter cup which the Sheikh had had to drain these last few days. His very mare was mocking him! He ground his teeth and pulled the bridle violently once and again till it hurt her. He wished to compel her to stop her strange caperings and return to her easy canter. Could she not fly like a bird when she wanted?

The mare, however, remained obstinate. The tugging at the

bridle had insulted her even more than the beating. Did her master think her an ass that he tugged at her bridle? She did not alter her gait, and her tossing became even worse than before.

"Wouldst make me a mockery and a laughing-stock in the eyes of the sun?" shouted the Sheikh in fury. He could no longer control himself and he began to rain furious blows upon his mare's back.

The sun flared like a fire. It unsheathed the full force of its heat and flung it at the Sheikh and his mare. The sand was like furnace-ashes and the air was soaked and drenched in flame. Horse and rider were frenzied with the heat, with anger and with resentment. They forgot the past. They forgot their old affection, their faithfulness to each other. Each of them remembered only one thing, the shame. And the shame and the insult took them both out of themselves. The rider beat the mare and the mare shook the rider. They had only one end in view; to pour as much insult on each other as possible.

Suddenly a thing occurred the like of which has not happened since Allah created His world. The mare raised her head and tried to pull the bridle by force out of her rider's hand. Abu Hatab, whether from anger, from weariness or from the heat, could not withstand the attack of the mare and let the bridle go. The mare felt it and openly revolted against her master. She made a violent dash forward, galloped as though in a race and flew along. Abu Hatab was not prepared for this and for a moment swerved to one side, all but tumbling from her back. But he recovered at once, pulled himself together, regained his balance with a rapid and expert movement and once more sat firm on her. He did not succeed in recovering the bridle, for the mare had tossed it over her head, and it had fallen to the ground. The reason was that in the morning in his anger and vexation he had not fixed it properly—something that had never happened to him before in his life. But the mare would not upset him again! That he knew. He had found himself and was again in control of the situation. Though, indeed, who knew what might happen yet? The dire anger of heaven was poured out upon him that day. How had he sinned against heaven?

The mare knew that her trick had not succeeded, but she did not yet give up or submit tamely to her fate. She cast about for fresh devices. While careening at full speed, she suddenly darted to one side. Had her rider been any other than Abu Hatab, she would certainly have flung him to the ground. But it was Abu Hatab who rode her. He was accustomed to such tricks, for it was he who had taught them to her, and he only smiled inwardly at her simplicity. What did she suppose him to be—a tyro?

The mare continued to twirl around. She bucked and raged. She would race forward at full speed and then suddenly swerve and turn. Abu Hatab sat as though nailed to her body, as though they were one flesh. His *keffiyeh* had fallen from his head, his *abaya* had slipped down around his legs. The white lock of hair in the centre of his head, his beard and moustache, all were flying in the wind. His face was scarlet with heat and anger. His eyes gleamed like fire. Then the mare decided on a strange and dreadful act. She turned about and with all her might began to race back along her traces toward the tents of the Tigla.

The Sheikh's heart dropped within him. The evil which now faced him was greater than all that had preceded. The mare would bring him to his foes. She would shame him before them, so that they would say that Abu Hatab could not master his steed. The Sheikh knew he had no way of saving himself from shame. He could not stop the mare nor turn her aside. Better to fall from her and perish than return to the tents of the Tigla. But what could he do? Could he throw himself from the mare? Nay, for she would think that she had thrown him, that she had vanquished him. It could not be. Would that a miracle might happen, that a pit might open before her feet so that both she and her rider might fall into it and perish together!

See! A dreadful sight. A few hundred paces from them the sharp eyes of the Sheikh saw a snake lying across the path.

Behold the miracle. Here was the death for which he had prayed. Here was salvation. Yet how dire a thing it was! The mare had not perceived the snake. In another moment she would reach it. One of two things would happen; either she would notice it at the last moment and would be terrified and leap aside, when both she and her rider would fall from sheer weariness and the sudden bound; or else she would ride the snake down and he bite her. . . . The mare continued her gallop without noticing the peril. Her weariness, her fury and the sacred power which drew her back to the Tigla robbed her of her faculties and senses.

The snake lay full length across the path without moving. Had it not noticed the mare? Or had the heat of the day stupefied it?

Abu Hatab stared straight ahead. The snake perceived the danger and bestirred itself; it did not crawl aside but rose to half its height in the middle of the track, facing the mare which had just come up to it, and opened its fangs.

The mare started back in terror, rising on her hind legs as though she wished to leap back. The snake fell on her. The Sheikh fell backward his full length.

A fortnight later two Tigla Bedouins brought Sheikh Abu Hatab on a camel to his tent beside the Rubin stream. The Sheikh did not feel any pain and had not been injured by his fall, neither in his arms or in his legs. But there was no peace within his body. His breathing was hard and heavy and when he coughed and spat, drops of blood fell from his mouth.

The far-famed mare of Sheikh Abu Hatab was found dead on the spot where she had fallen. They were both dead, she and the snake, which was coiled about her belly. And her belly was very swollen indeed.

Metzengerstein

EDGAR ALLAN POE

*"Metzengerstein" is a typical example of the style which has
made Edgar Allan Poe so famous as the progenitor of the
horror tale. It is interesting to compare this style with the
simple, yet effective writing of Chief Buffalo Child Long Lance
and his story on page 88, "The Ghost Horse."*

Pestis eram vivus—moriens tua mors ero.

MARTIN LUTHER

Horror and fatality have been stalking abroad in all ages. Why then
give a date to the story I have to tell? Let it suffice to say, that at
the period of which I speak, there existed, in the interior of Hungary, a settled although hidden belief in the doctrines of the Metempsychosis. Of the doctrines themselves—that is, of their falsity,
or of their probability—I say nothing. I assert, however, that
much of our incredulity (as La Bruyere says of all our unhappiness)
"vient de ne pouvoir etre seuls." *

But there were some points in the Hungarian superstition which
were fast verging to the absurdity. They—the Hungarians—differed
very essentially from their Eastern authorities. For example. *"The
soul,"* said the former—I give the words of an intelligent Parisian
—"ne demeure qu'un seul fois dans un corps sensible, au reste—

---

* Mercier, in *L'an deux mille quatre cents quarante,* seriously maintains the
doctrines of the Metempsychosis, and J. D'Israeli says that "no system is so
simple and so little repugnant to the understanding." Colonel Ethan Allen, the
"Green Mountain Boy," is also said to have been a serious metempsychosist.

un cheval, un chein, un homme meme, n'est que la ressemblance peu tangible de ces animaux."

The families of Berlifitzing and Metzengerstein had been at variance for centuries. Never before were two houses mutually embittered by hostility so deadly. The origin of this enmity seems to be found, in the words of an ancient prophecy—"A lofty name shall have a fearful fall when, as the rider over his horse, the mortality of Metzengerstein shall triumph over the mortality of Berlifitzing."

To be sure the words themselves had little or no meaning. But more trivial causes have given rise—and that no long while ago —to consequences equally eventful. Besides, the estates, which were contiguous, had long exercised a rival influence in the affairs of a busy government. Moreover, near neighbors are seldom friends; and the inhabitants of Castle Berlifitzing might look, from their lofty buttresses, into the very windows of the Palace Metzengerstein. Least of all had the more than feudal magnificence, thus discovered, a tendency to allay the irritable feelings of the less ancient and less wealthy Berlifitzings. What wonder, then, that the words, however silly, of that prediction, should have succeeded in setting and keeping at variance two families already predisposed to quarrel by every instigation of hereditary jealousy. The prophecy seemed to imply—if it implied anything—a final triumph on the part of the already more powerful house; and was of course remembered with the more bitter animosity by the weaker and less influential.

Wilhelm, Count Berlifitzing, although loftily descended, was at the epoch of this narrative, an infirm and doting old man, remarkable for nothing but an inordinate and inveterate personal antipathy to the family of his rival, and so passionate a love of horses and of hunting, that neither bodily infirmity, great age, nor mental incapacity, prevented his daily participation in the dangers of the chase.

Frederick, Baron Metzengerstein, was, on the other hand, not yet of age. His father, the Minister G——, died young. His mother, the Lady Mary, followed him quickly. Frederick was, at that time, in his eighteenth year. In a city, eighteen years is no long period;

but in a wilderness—in so magnificent a wilderness as that old principality, the pendulum vibrates with a deeper meaning.

From some peculiar circumstances attending the administration of his father, the young Baron, at the decease of the former, entered immediately upon his vast possessions. Such estates were seldom held before by a nobleman of Hungary. His castles were without number. The chief point of splendor and extent was the "Palace Metzengerstein." The boundary line of his dominions were never clearly defined, but his principal park embraced a circuit of fifty miles.

Upon the succession of a proprietor so young, with a character so well known, to a fortune so unparalleled, little speculation was afloat in regard to his probable course of conduct. And, indeed, for the space of three days, the behavior of the heir out-Heroded Herod, and fairly surpassed the expectations of his most enthusiastic admirers. Shameful debaucheries—flagrant treacheries—unheard-of atrocities—gave his trembling vassals quickly to understand that no servile submission on their part—no punctilios of conscience on his own—were thenceforward to prove any security against the remorseless fangs of a petty Caligula. On the night of the fourth day, the stables of Castle Berlifitzing were discovered to be on fire, and the unanimous opinion of the neighborhood added the crime of the incendiary to the already hideous list of the Baron's misdemeanors and enormities.

But during the tumult occasioned by this occurrence, the young nobleman himself sat apparently buried in meditation, in a vast and desolate upper apartment of the family palace of Metzengerstein. The rich although faded tapestry hangings which swung gloomily upon the walls, represented the shadowy and majestic forms of a thousand illustrious ancestors. *Here,* rich-ermined priests, and pontifical dignitaries, familiarly seated with the autocrat and sovereign, put a veto on the wishes of a temporal king, or restrained with the fiat of papal supremacy the rebellious sceptre of the Arch-enemy. *There,* the dark tall statues of the Princes Metzengerstein—their muscular war-coursers plunging over the carcasses of fallen foes—startled the steadiest nerves with their vigorous expression; and *here,* again, the voluptuous and swan-like figures of the dames of days gone by floated away in the mazes of an unreal dance to the strains of imaginary melody.

But as the Baron listened, or affected to listen, to the gradually increasing uproar in the stables of Berlifitzing—or perhaps pondered upon some more novel, some more decided act of audacity—his eyes were turned unwittingly to the figure of an enormous, and unnaturally colored horse, represented in the tapestry as belonging to a Saracen ancestor of the family of his rival. The horse itself, in the foreground of the design, stood motionless and statue-like —while, farther back, its discomfited rider perished by the dagger of a Metzengerstein.

On Frederick's lip arose a fiendish expression, as he became aware of the direction which his glance had, without his consciousness, assumed. Yet he did not remove it. On the contrary, he could by no means account for the overwhelming anxiety which appeared falling like a pall upon his senses. It was with difficulty that he reconciled his dreamy and incoherent feelings with the certainty of being awake. The longer he gazed the more absorbing became the spell—the more impossible did it appear that he could ever withdraw his glance from the fascination of that tapestry. But the tumult without becoming suddenly more violent, with a compulsory exertion he diverted his attention to the glare of ruddy light thrown full by the flaming stables upon the windows of the apartment.

The action, however, was but momentary; his gaze returned mechanically to the wall. To his extreme horror and astonishment, the head of the gigantic steed had, in the meantime, altered its position. The neck of the animal, before arched, as if in compassion, over the prostrate body of its lord, was now extended, at full length, in the direction of the Baron. The eyes, before invisible, now wore an energetic and human expression, while they gleamed with a fiery and unusual red, and the distended lips of the apparently enraged horse left in full view his sepulchral and disgusting teeth.

Stupefied with terror, the young nobleman tottered to the door. As he threw it open, a flash of red light streaming far into the chamber, flung his shadow with a clear outline against the quivering tapestry and he shuddered to perceive that shadow—as he staggered awhile upon the threshold—assuming the exact position, and pre-

cisely filling up the contour, of the relentless and triumphant murderer of the Saracen Berlifitzing.

To lighten the depression of his spirits, the Baron hurried into
the open air. At the principal gate of the palace he encountered
three equerries. With much difficulty, and at the imminent peril of
their lives, they were restraining the convulsive plunges of a gigantic
and fiery-colored horse.

"Whose horse? Where did you get him?" demanded the youth,
in a querulous and husky tone, as he became instantly aware that
the mysterious steed in the tapestried chamber was the very counter-
part of the furious animal before his eyes.

"He is your own property, sire," replied one of the equerries,
"at least he is claimed by no other owner. We caught him flying, all
smoking and foaming with rage, from the burning stables of the
Castle Berlifitzing. Supposing him to have belonged to the old
Count's stud of foreign horses, we led him back as an estray. But
the grooms there disclaim any title to the creature; which is strange,
since he bears evident marks of having made a narrow escape from
the flames."

"The letters W.V.B. are also branded very distinctly on his
forehead," interrupted a second equerry; "I suppose them, of course,
to be the initials of William Von Berlifitzing—but all at the castle
are positive in denying any knowledge of the horse."

"Extremely singular!" said the young Baron, with a musing
air, and apparently unconscious of the meaning of his words. "He
is, as you say, a remarkable horse—a prodigious horse! although,
as you very justly observe, of a suspicious and untractable character;
let him be mine, however," he added after a pause, "perhaps a rider
like Frederick of Metzengerstein, may tame even the devil from the
stables of Berlifitzing."

"You are mistaken, my lord; the horse, as I think we mentioned, is *not* from the stables of the Count. If such had been the
case, we know our duty better than to bring him into the presence
of a noble of your family."

"True!" observed the Baron, drily; at that instant a page of
the bed-chamber came from the palace with a heightened color, and
a precipitate step. He whispered into his master's ear an account

of the sudden disappearance of a small portion of the tapestry, in an apartment which he designated; entering, at the same time, into particulars of a minute and circumstantial character; but from the low tone of voice in which these latter were communicated, nothing escaped to gratify the excited curiosity of the equerries.

The young Frederick, during the conference, seemed agitated by a variety of emotions. He soon, however, recovered his composure, and an expression of determined malignancy settled upon his countenance, as he gave peremptory orders that the apartment in question should be immediately locked up, and the key placed in his own possession.

"Have you heard of the unhappy death of the old hunter Berlifitzing?" said one of his vassals to the Baron, as, after the departure of the page, the huge steed which that nobleman had adopted as his own, plunged and curveted, with redoubled fury, down the long avenue which extended from the palace to the stables of Metzengerstein.

"No!" said the Baron, turning abruptly toward the speaker, "dead! say you?"

"It is indeed true, my lord; and, to the noble of your name, will be, I imagine, no unwelcome intelligence."

A rapid smile shot over the countenance of the listener. "How died he?"

"In his rash exertions to rescue a favorite portion of the hunting stud, he has himself perished miserably in the flames."

"I—n—d—e—e—d—" ejaculated the Baron, as if slowly and deliberately impressed with the truth of some exciting idea.

"Indeed"; repeated the vassal.

"Shocking!" said the youth, calmly, and turned quietly into the palace.

From this date a marked alteration took place in the outward demeanor of the dissolute young Baron Frederick Von Metzengerstein. Indeed, his behavior disappointed every expectation, and proved little in accordance with the views of many a manoeuvring mamma; while his habits and manners, still less than formerly, offered any thing congenial with those of the neighboring aristocracy. He was never to be seen beyond the limits of his own domain, and, in his wide and social world, was utterly companionless—unless, indeed, that unnatural, impetuous, and fiery-colored horse, which he henceforward continually bestrode, had any mysterious right to the title of his friend.

Numerous invitations on the part of the neighborhood for a long time, however, periodically came in. "Will the Baron honor our festivals with his presence?" "Will the Baron join us in a hunting of the bear?"— "Metzengerstein does not hunt"; "Metzengerstein will not attend," were the haughty and laconic answers.

These repeated insults were not to be endured by an imperious nobility. Such invitations became less cordial—less frequent—in time they ceased altogether. The widow of the unfortunate Count Berlifitzing was even heard to express a hope "that the Baron might be at home when he did not wish to be at home, since he disdained the company of his equals; and ride when he did not wish to ride, since he preferred the society of a horse." This to be sure was a very silly explosion of hereditary pique; and merely proved how singularly unmeaning our sayings are apt to become, when we desire to be unusually energetic.

The charitable, nevertheless, attributed the alteration in the conduct of the young nobleman to the natural sorrow of a son for the untimely loss of his parents—forgetting, however, his atrocious and reckless behavior during the short period immediately succeeding the bereavement. Some there were, indeed, who suggested a too haughty idea of self-consequence and dignity. Others again (among whom may be mentioned the family physician) did not hesitate in speaking of morbid melancholy, and hereditary ill-health; while dark hints, of a more equivocal nature, were current among the multitude.

Indeed, the Baron's perverse attachment to his lately-acquired charger—an attachment which seemed to attain new strength from every fresh example of the animal's ferocious and demon-like propensities—at length became, in the eyes of all reasonable men, a hideous and unnatural fervor. In the glare of noon—at the dead hour of night—in sickness or in health—in calm or in tempest—the young Metzengerstein seemed riveted to the saddle of that colossal horse, whose intractable audacities so well accorded with his own spirit.

There were circumstances, moreover, which, coupled with late events, gave an unearthly and portentous character to the mania of the rider, and to the capabilities of the steed. The space passed over in a single leap had been accurately measured, and was found to exceed, by astounding difference, the wildest expectations of the most imaginative. The Baron, besides, had no particular *name* for the animal, although all the rest in his collection were distinguished by characteristic appellations. His stable, too, was appointed at a distance from the rest; and with regard to grooming and other necessary offices, none but the owner in person had ventured to officiate, or even to enter the enclosure of that horse's particular stall. It was also to be observed, that although the three grooms, who had caught the steed as he fled from the conflagration at Berlifitzing, had succeeded in arresting his course by means of a chain-bridle and a noose—yet not one of the three could with any certainty affirm that he had, during that dangerous struggle, or at any period thereafter, actually placed his hand upon the body of the beast. Instances of peculiar intelligence in the demeanor of a noble and high-spirited horse are not to be supposed capable of exciting unreasonable attention, but there were certain circumstances which intruded themselves perforce upon the most skeptical and phlegmatic; and it is said there were times when the animal caused the gaping crowd who stood around to recoil in horror from the deep and impressive meaning of his terrible stamp—times when the young Metzengerstein turned pale and shrunk away from the rapid and searching expression of his human-looking eye.

Among the retinue of the Baron, however, none were found to doubt the ardor of that extraordinary affection which existed on the part of the young nobleman for the fiery qualities of his horse; at least, none but an insignificant and misshapen little page, whose deformities were in everybody's way, and whose opinions were of the least possible importance. He (if his ideas are worth mentioning at all) had the affrontery to assert that his master never vaulted into the saddle without an unaccountable and almost imperceptible shudder; and that, upon his return from every long-continued and habitual ride, an expression of triumphant malignity distorted every muscle of his countenance.

One tempestuous night, Metzengerstein, awaking from a heavy slumber, descended like a maniac from his chamber, and, mounting in hot haste, bounded away into the mazes of the forest. An occurrence so common attracted no particular attention, but his return was looked for with intense anxiety on the part of his domestics, when, after some hours' absence, the stupendous and magnificent battlements of the Palace Metzengerstein were discovered crackling and rocking to their very foundations, under the influence of a dense and livid mass of ungovernable fire.

As the flames, when first seen, had already made so terrible a progress that all efforts to save any portion of the building were evidently futile, the astonished neighborhood stood idly around in silent if not pathetic wonder. But a new and fearful object soon riveted the attention of the multitude and proved how much more intense is the excitement wrought in the feelings of a crowd by the contemplation of human agony, than that brought about by the most appalling spectacles of inanimate matter.

Up the long avenue of aged oaks which led from the forest to the main entrance of the Palace Metzengerstein, a steed, bearing an unbonneted and disordered rider, was seen leaping with an impetuosity which outstripped the very Demon of the Tempest.

The career of the horseman was indisputable, on his own part, uncontrollable. The agony of his countenance, the convulsive struggle of his frame, gave evidence of superhuman exertion, but no sound, save a solitary shriek, escaped from his lacerated lips, which were bitten through and through in the intensity of terror. One instant, and the clattering hoofs resounded sharply and shrilly above the roaring of the flames and the shrieking of the winds—another, and, clearing at a single plunge the gate-way and the moat, the steed bounded far up the tottering staircases of the palace, and, with its rider, disappeared amid the whirlwind of chaotic fire.

The fury of the tempest immediately died away, and a dead calm sullenly succeeded. A white flame still enveloped the building like a shroud, and, streaming far away into the quiet atmosphere, shot forth a glare of preternatural light, while a cloud of smoke settled heavily over the battlements in the distinct colossal figure of—*a horse.*

I Ride a Bucking Horse

MARK TWAIN

*No horseman could have found a better way to describe the
dynamite of an outlaw bronco than did Mark Twain in this
delightful chapter from* Roughing It. *Interesting incidental information lies in the remark that a ton of hay, at that time in
the West, sold for from two hundred and fifty to eight hundred
dollars in gold!*

I resolved to have a horse to ride. I had never seen such wild, free,
magnificent horsemanship outside of a circus as these picturesquely-
clad Mexicans, Californians, and Mexicanized Americans displayed
in Carson streets every day. How they rode! Leaning just gently
forward out of the perpendicular, easy and nonchalant, with broad
slouch-hat brim blown square up in front, and long *riata* swinging
above the head, they swept through the town like the wind! The
next minute they were only a sailing puff of dust on the far desert.
If they trotted, they sat up gallantly and gracefully, and seemed part
of the horse; did not go jiggering up and down after the silly Miss-
Nancy fashion of the riding-schools. I had quickly learned to tell
a horse from a cow, and was full of anxiety to learn more. I was resolved to buy a horse.

While the thought was rankling in my mind, the auctioneer
came scurrying through the plaza on a black beast that had as many
humps and corners on him as a dromedary, and was necessarily
uncomely; but he was "going, going, at twenty-two!—horse, saddle

380

and bridle at twenty-two dollars, gentlemen!" and I could hardly resist.

A man whom I did not know (he turned out to be the auctioneer's brother) noticed the wistful look in my eye, and observed that that was a very remarkable horse to be going at such a price, and added that the saddle alone was worth the money. It was a Spanish saddle, with ponderous *tapidaros* and furnished with the ungainly sole-leather covering with the unspellable name. I said I had half a notion to bid. Then this keen-eyed person appeared to me to be "taking my measure"; but I dismissed suspicion when he spoke, for his manner was full of guileless candor and truthfulness. Said he:

"I know that horse—know him well. You are a stranger, I take it, and so you might think he was an American horse, maybe, but I assure you he is not. He is nothing of the kind; but—excuse my speaking in a low voice, other people being near—he is, without the shadow of a doubt, a Genuine Mexican Plug!"

I did not know what a Genuine Mexican Plug was, but there was something about this man's way of saying it, that made me swear inwardly that I would own a Genuine Mexican Plug, or die.

"Has he any other—er—advantages?" I inquired, suppressing what eagerness I could.

He hooked his forefinger in the pocket of my army-shirt, led me to one side, and breathed in my ear impressively these words:

"He can out-buck anything in America!"

"Twenty-seven!" I shouted, in a frenzy.

"And sold!" said the auctioneer, and passed over the Genuine Mexican Plug to me.

I could scarcely contain my exultation. I paid the money, and put the animal in a neighboring livery-stable to dine and rest himself.

In the afternoon I brought the creature into the plaza, and certain citizens held him by the head, and others by the tail, while I mounted him. As soon as they let go, he placed all his feet in a bunch together, lowered his back, and then suddenly arched it upward, and shot me straight into the air a matter of three or four feet! I came as straight down again, lit in the saddle, went instantly up again, came down almost on the high pommel, shot up again, and came down on the horse's neck—all in the space of three or four seconds. Then he rose and stood almost straight up on his hind feet, and I, clasping his lean neck desperately, slid back into the saddle, and held on. He came down, and immediately hoisted his heels into the air, delivering a vicious kick at the sky, and stood on his fore feet. And then down he came once more, and began the original exercise of shooting me straight up again.

The third time I went up I heard a stranger say: "Oh, *don't* he buck, though!"

While I was up, somebody struck the horse a sounding thwack with a leathern strap, and when I arrived again the Genuine Mexican Plug was not there. A Californian youth chased him up and caught him, and asked if he might have a ride. I granted him that luxury. He mounted the Genuine, got lifted into the air once, but sent his spurs home as he descended, and the horse darted away like a telegram. He soared over three fences like a bird, and disappeared down the road towards the Washoe Valley.

I sat down on a stone with a sigh, and by natural impulse one of my hands sought my forehead, and the other the base of my stomach. I believe I never appreciated, till then, the poverty of human machinery—for I still needed a hand or two to place elsewhere. Pen cannot describe how I was jolted up. Imagination cannot conceive how disjointed I was—how internally, externally and universally I was unsettled, mixed up, and ruptured. There was a sympathetic crowd around me, though.

One elderly-looking comforter said:

"Stranger, you've been taken in. Everybody in this camp knows that horse. Any child, any Injun, could have told you that he'd buck; he is the very worst devil to buck on the continent of America. You hear *me*. I'm Curry. *Old* Curry. Old *Abe* Curry. And moreover, he is a simon-pure, out-and-out genuine d—d Mexican plug, and an uncommon mean one at that, too. Why, you turnip, if you had laid low and kept dark, there's chances to buy an *American* horse for mighty little more than you paid for that bloody old foreign relic."

I gave no sign; but I made up my mind that if the auctioneer's brother's funeral took place while I was in the Territory I would postpone all other recreations and attend it.

After a gallop of sixteen miles, the Californian youth and the Genuine Mexican Plug came tearing into town again, shedding foam-flakes like the spume-spray that drives before a typhoon, and, with one final skip over a wheelbarrow and a Chinaman, cast anchor in front of the "ranch."

Such panting and blowing! Such spreading and contracting of the red equine nostrils, and glaring of the wild equine eye! But was the imperial beast subjugated? Indeed, he was not. His lord-ship the Speaker of the House thought he was, and mounted him to go down to the Capitol; but the first dash the creature made was over a pile of telegraph poles half as high as a church; and his time to the Capitol—one mile and three-quarters—remains unbeaten to this day. But then he took an advantage—he left out the mile, and only did the three-quarters. That is to say, he made a straight cut across lots, preferring fences and ditches to a crooked road; and when the Speaker got to the Capitol he said he had been in the air so much he felt as if he had made the trip on a comet.

In the evening the Speaker came home afoot for exercise, and got the Genuine towed back behind a quartz wagon. The next day I loaned the animal to the Clerk of the House to go down to the Dana silver mine, six miles, and he walked back for exercise, and got the horse towed. Everybody I loaned him to always walked back; they never could get enough exercise any other way. Still, I continued to loan him to anybody who was willing to borrow him, my idea being to get him crippled, and throw him on the borrower's hands, or killed, and make the borrower pay for him. But somehow nothing ever happened to him. He took chances that no other horse ever took and survived, he always came out safe. It was his daily habit to try experiments that had always before been considered im-possible, but he always got through. Sometimes he miscalculated a little, and did not get his rider through intact, but *he* always got through himself. Of course I had tried to sell him; but that was a stretch of simplicity which met with little sympathy. The auctioneer stormed up and down the streets on him for four days, dispersing the populace, interrupting business and destroying children, and never got a bid—at least never any but the eighteen-dollar one he hired a notoriously substanceless bummer to make. The people only smiled pleasantly, and restrained their desire to buy, if they had any. Then the auctioneer brought in his bill, and I withdrew the horse from the market. We tried to trade him off at private vendue next, offering him at a sacrifice for second-hand tombstones, old iron, temperance tracts—any kind of property. But holders were stiff, and we retired from the market again. I never tried to ride the horse any more. Walking was good enough exercise for a man like me, that had nothing the matter with him except ruptures, internal injuries, and such things. Finally I tried to *give* him away. But it was a failure. Parties said earthquakes were handy enough on the Pacific coast—they did not wish to own one. As a last resort I offered him to the Governor for the use of the "Brigade." His face lit up eagerly at first, but toned down again, and he said the thing would be too palpable.

Just then the livery stable man brought in his bill for six weeks' keeping—stall-room for the horse, fifteen dollars; hay for the horse, two hundred and fifty! The Genuine Mexican Plug had eaten a ton of the article, and the man said he would have eaten a hundred if he had let him.

I will remark here, in all seriousness, that the regular price of hay during that year and a part of the next was really two hundred and fifty dollars a ton. During a part of the previous year it had sold at five hundred a ton, in gold, and during the winter before that there was such a scarcity of the article that in several instances small quantities had brought eight hundred dollars a ton in coin! The consequence might be guessed without my telling it: people turned their stock loose to starve, and before the spring arrived Carson and Eagle Valleys were almost literally carpeted with their carcasses! Any old settler there will verify these statements.

I managed to pay the livery bill, and that same day I gave the Genuine Mexican Plug to a passing Arkansas emigrant whom fortune delivered into my hand. If this ever meets his eye, he will doubtless remember the donation.

Now whoever has the luck to ride a real Mexican plug will recognize the animal depicted in this chapter, and hardly consider him exaggerated—but the uninitiated will feel justified in regarding his portrait as a fancy sketch, perhaps.

About the Author

Margaret Cabell Self is known and loved as an outstanding author on equestrian subjects. In the present volume, she combines her love of literature and good reading with her knowledge of horses and horsemanship, to make a book to delight readers of every age. Among her previous books which have received such high acclaim and readership are: *Horseman's Encyclopedia, A Treasury of Horse Stories, Horsemastership, Horses: Their Selection, Care and Handling; Riding Simplified, Riding with Mariles.*

Born in the hunting country of Virginia, Mrs. Self settled in Connecticut after marriage, and there developed a riding academy, during the Depression, which is still a major interest and activity. She also enjoys the companionship of grandchildren and is currently embarked on a variety of projects, among them learning Russian.

Date Due